The Geological Society of America
Memoir 25

EVOLUTION OF
THE HORSE BRAIN

BY

TILLY EDINGER
Museum of Comparative Zoölogy
Harvard College, Cambridge, Mass.

FEBRUARY 16, 1948

Made in United States of America

WAVERLY PRESS, INC.
BALTIMORE, MD.

CONTENTS

ILLUSTRATIONS

PLATES
(At end of paper)

FIGURES

TABLES

ABBREVIATIONS USED IN ILLUSTRATIONS

A.c.a.,	arteria cerebri anterior
A.c.m.,	arteria cerebri media
C.al.,	canalis alaris
C.call.,	corpus callosum
C.q.a.,	corpus quadrigeminum anterius (tectum mesencephali)

C.q.p.,	corpus quadrigeminum posterius (tectum mesencephali)
C.tem.,	canalis temporalis
Cbl.,	cerebellum
Cbl.h.,	cerebellar hemisphere = lobus ansoparamedianus + paraflocculus
Cer.,	cerebral hemisphere
Cer.ch.,	posterior pole of forebrain chamber
Chi.,	chiasma nervorum opticorum
D.s.t.,	impression of dorsum sellae turcicae
Eth.,	imprint of ethmoturbinal
F.p.m.,	fissura paramediana
F.p.s.,	fissura parasagittalis
F.po.,	fissura posterior of reptilian cerebellum
F.pr.,	fissura prima cerebelli
F.r.a.,	fissura rhinalis anterior
F.r.p.,	fissura rhinalis posterior
F.s.p.,	fissura suprapyramis
F.sec.,	fissura secunda cerebelli
Floc.,	flocculus, or section through flocculus at entrance into fossa subarcuata
For.l.,	foramen lacerum posterius
For.m.,	foramen occipitale magnum
Hyp.,	corpus pituitare
L. ant.,	lobus anterior vermis cerebelli
L. med.,	lobus medius vermis cerebelli
L.p.m.,	paramedian lobe: lobulus ansatus + lobulus paramedianus cerebelli
L. pir.,	lobus piriformis
Lam.c.,	position of lamina cribrosa
Ll.si.,	lobulus simplex
Mes.,	mesencephalon
Obl.,	medulla oblongata
Ol.b.,	bulbus olfactorius
Ol.f.,	fila olfactoria
Ol.g.l.,	gyrus olfactorius lateralis
Ol.p.,	pedunculus olfactorius
Ol.t.,	tuberculum olfactorium (lobus parolfactorius)
Ol.tr.,	tractus olfactorius
Op.ver.,	opercule vermien
Os.o.,	os occipitale
Os.o.c.,	condylus occipitalis
Os.o.p.,	os occipitalis, processus paramastoideus
Os.o.s.,	squama occipitalis
Os.p.,	pars petrosa ossis temporalis
Os.p.i.,	imprint of pars petrosa ossis temporalis
Os.pa.,	os parietale
Os.sp.,	os sphenoidale
Os.v.,	vomer
P. fl.,	paraflocculus
P.g.,	pars glandularis corporis pituitarii
P.int.,	pars intermedia corporis pituitarii
P.n.,	pars neuralis corporis pituitarii
Pacch.,	Pacchonian bodies
Petr.,	impression of petrosal bone
Pons,	pons
S.an.,	sulcus ansatus
S.co.,	sulcus coronalis

S.cr.,	sulcus cruciatus
S.diag.,	sulcus diagonalis
S.e.s.,	sulcus ectosylvius
S.ec.l.,	sulcus ectolateralis
S.en.l.,	sulcus endolateralis
S.i.l.,	sulcus interlateralis dorsalis
S.i.o.,	sulcus intraorbitalis
S.lat.,	sulcus lateralis
S.orb.,	sulcus orbitalis; the orbital sulcus of Marsupials (fig. 5) and insectivores (fig. 4 A) is obviously not homologous with the sulcus so named in the horse (fig. 21 B).
S.po.,	sulcus posticus
S.pr.,	sulcus praesylvius
S.s.l.,	sulcus sagittalis lateralis
S.spl.,	sulcus splenialis
S.su.,	sulcus suprasylvius
S.su.a.,	sulcus suprasylvius, pars anterior
S.su.m.,	sulcus suprasylvius pars media
S.su.p.,	sulcus suprasylvius, pars posterior
S.su.v.,	sulcus suprasylvius, pars media, ramus ventralis
Sin.sag.,	sinus sagittalis superior
Sin.tr.,	sinus transversus
Sy.,	fossa Sylvii
V.i.o.	vena insuloopercularis
V.r.p.,	vena rhinalis posterior
V.s.a.,	vena cerebri superior anterior
V.s.m.,	vena cerebri superior media
Ver.,	vermis cerebelli
*,	casts of irregularities in tabula interna of braincase
I,	nervus olfactorius (fila olfactoria)
II,	nervus opticus
III,	nervus oculomotorius
IV,	nervus trochlearis
V^1,	ramus ophtalmicus nervi trigemini
V^2,	ramus maxillaris nervi trigemini
V^3,	ramus mandibularis nervi trigemini
VI,	nervus abduceus
VII,	nervus facialis
VIII,	nervus acusticus
IX,	nervus glossopharyngeus
X,	nervus vagus
XI,	nervus accessorius
XII,	nervus hypoglossus

ABSTRACT

Endocranial casts of fossil Equidae and the extant horse are described. The series of brain forms from the Lower Eocene *Eohippus* to the Recent *Equus* demonstrates the evolution of the brain in an established ancestry. The outstanding feature is increasing predominance of the cerebrum, with expansion particularly of the neocortex; but in many details the process of phylogenetic evolution during this period of about 55,000,000 years took a course different from that postulated by the current conceptions of mammalian brain evolution which are deduced from the conditions in extant lower and higher mammals. The brain of the earliest representative of this family of the higher mammals was of a type which today is characteristic of the lowest marsupials. The type of brain characterizing ungulates today was not achieved before the late Miocene. In its development, progress was not in every phase linked with either increase in body size or skeleton specialization.

INTRODUCTION

When I was living in Germany I wrote, challenging the American paleontologists: "It would certainly be easy to make an endocranial cast series of the Equidae as complete as the phylogenetic series existing of other parts of the equid body. There simply seems to be a lack of interest in the brains" (translated from T. Edinger, 1929, p. 176).

Now that I am in America, I find that neither of these two sentences is true.

The statement made in the second sentence was refuted by Dr. G. G. Simpson's suggesting, the moment we met, that I investigate the evolution of the horse brain; a grant from the Penrose Bequest of The Geological Society of America for expenses; and the enthusiastic letters I received from the colleagues in charge of the collections which I believed to abound in endocranial casts or complete, undistorted crania of fossil Equidae.

These answers to my confident inquiries invalidated the first sentence quoted above.

So many bones and teeth of fossil Equidae from American soil have been reported in the literature (is there any subject in paleontology on which so much has been written as on the ancestors of the horse?) that outside this country it seemed incomprehensible that the only soft organ accessible to study was practically uninvestigated. Here is the explanation. Several curators of large and famous museums, checking over the collections, found that there was not one specimen suitable for this project. In spite of the splendid willingness of the curators to co-operate, and notwithstanding the large number of crania and endocasts loaned to me, the fact is that it is not possible to bring together a complete series—brains from every stage of the horse lineage—now. I am hoping for the day on which this statement, too, will have become untrue!

At present, no equid brain material is known from the following horizons: Upper Eocene, Lower Oligocene (?), Middle and Upper Pliocene. The two last-named times were not important ones in the evolution of the horse brain. The Lower Oligocene *Mesohippus* brain can be assumed to have been not very different from the brain of the Middle Oligocene *Mesohippus*, which is well known. But our com-

1

plete ignorance of the state of the equid brain in the Upper Eocene severely restricts the value of the entire study, because a considerable transformation of the brain took place between *Orohippus* and *Mesohippus*.

Many of the endocasts studied portray only parts of the brain. Such specimens became of value only through comparisons, particularly with preceding and following phases of equid brain evolution. This applies to all the material representing the Middle Eocene, Upper Oligocene, and Lower Miocene stages.

Genera which existed through several divisions of geological periods are not, or not well, represented by specimens from every stage of their history. This is particularly deplorable in the case of *Parahippus;* when more and better brain material than is now at hand can be studied, it may be discovered that in this form certain features were acquired which now appear to have evolved in *Merychippus*.

Variations in the body size of equid genera were correlated, at least from the early Miocene onward, with variations in cerebral fissuration. One consequently feels that a picture of the state of the brain which would at all approach completeness could be given in a Miocene or post-Miocene genus only on the basis of several endocranial casts of different sizes. In our material, only the *Merychippus* record (and, of course, the horse[1]) comes near fulfilling this requirement. Brain formation presumably did not vary much during the earlier periods; yet the great difference in body size between *Eohippus validus* (whose brain was studied) and *Eohippus resartus* makes one desire to know a brain of the latter species also.

Another deficiency in the material used for study resulted from the circumstance that no brain collection was at hand for comparisons with the endocasts. This will explain my many quotations from the morphological literature on brains of living mammals. It certainly was a handicap that the only brains I studied at first hand were those of opossum, sheep, and horse. On the other hand, the extensive study thus necessitated of the literature on brains of living ungulates made me realize the variability of virtually every detail in those modern brains—a fact very rarely taken into account in the literature, neoneurological or paleoneurological.

In the literature on mammalian brains different names are in use for sulci generally believed to be homologous, and the same name may be used to designate sulci which are certainly not homologous. To give one example of the latter case—an example which the reader will come upon in the present study—: "sulcus orbitalis" is the name (1) of an oblique sulcus on the dorsal convexity of the marsupial neopallium, (2) of a transverse sulcus on the anterior facies of ungulate and other cerebra, (3), for some authors, of what most authors call presylvian sulcus, a sulcus dorsal and lateral to the orbital in the horse brain. As concerns the sulci, therefore, this introduction cannot make the usual comfortable statement: the terminology is the current one. . . . There is no agreed nomenclature of sulci. I have adopted those names which appeared to be used by the majority of authors, and I have on occasion listed synonyms.

In earlier paleoneurological papers I took little interest in sulci. In our present state of knowledge the bewildering and irritating attempt to identify and name every furrow in a single fossil brain will hardly produce results of enough general

---

[1] Only the Recent, the living, the modern equid *Equus caballus* is called a horse in this paper.

importance to make it worth the effort. The matter is altogether different in the case of material such as that of the present study. This phyletic series of brains shows (or, rather, would show if the material were complete) each sulcus in its first appearance in equid phylogeny, and its further development.

Neurological discussion about sulcus homologies has been going on for decades. It is hoped that, when an international nomenclature of brain sulci is being worked out, the nomenclators will take into consideration that all sulci of the horse brain evolved after the Equidae had separated from the primitive, unspecialized mammal stock. The evidence of paleoneurology suggests that there is as much reason for discriminating by different names certain similar sulci of the various mammalian orders as there is in the current distinction between primate and non-primate sulci. However, the decision does not rest with those who know only the position of a sulcus on the brain surface and possibly its evolutionary history. According to present conceptions of fissuration, this task would devolve upon the neoneurologists, who can establish the relations of the sulci to cytoarchitectonic areas.

Only through the data brought together by the neoneurologists can the inorganic masses, the plaster or stones which the paleoneurologists call brains, be seen and interpreted as brains. On the other hand, only paleoneurology can—as has now been done—trace the history of a brain through the ages. A recent publication of a well-known theorist on brain evolution, entitled *On the significance of cranial vault height in phylogenetic brain growth*, is based on conditions in the skulls of three Recent squirrels of different sizes. Current conceptions of brain evolution in mammals rest, necessarily, on comparisons among forms as unrelated as guinea pig, pig, and man.

Paleoneurology, too, in its early stages used mammals not linked in ancestry for evolutionary studies. It happens to be the brain of the horse to which leads Marsh's "development of the brain from the early Tertiary to the present time," illustrated by endocranial casts of *Dinoceras*, *Brontotherium*, and *Equus*. By now, brains from different geological periods of closely related and even of genetically linked mammals are known in quite a number of groups. For example, in the primate suborder Lemuroidea the brains of Pleistocene and living forms have been studied together with the brain of an ancestor of late Eocene age; but there are no neurological data on any of the intermediate stages. The most complete records we had previous to the one presented in this paper are either those of families with a shorter time range than the Equidae, or of orders in which the ancestral sequence is not clear, whereas that of the equid genera is well established. Brain material is known from the whole life span of the primate family Hominidae (Pleistocene-Recent) and of the ruminant family Merycoidodontidae (Upper Eocene-Miocene). Of the different branches of the South-American extinct order Notoungulata, a number of brains have been studied which are from different periods, including the Lower Eocene on the one hand and the Pleistocene on the other hand. Similarly, brains were brought together of Old World Sirenian genera from Middle and Upper Eocene, Middle Oligocene, Lower and Middle Miocene, and Recent times. These genera form (with those of the intermediate horizons) a geological and structurally progressive sequence, but apparently not a genetic series as do the equid genera discussed in the present paper. Further, in the relatively static Sirenia there has been little evolutionary progress of the brain since the Middle Eocene; the living sea-cows have enlarged, but otherwise little changed, Middle Eocene brains—whereas during the same span of time the brain of the Equidae underwent great evolutionary changes. Another difference between the material of previous studies in brain evolution (Notoungulata excepted) and the present one of the Equidae is that the latter includes the Lower Eocene form. The Lower Eocene *Eohippus* was the first animal to have a skeleton with equid characters.

The chief skeletal and odontological characters of each equid genus are briefly noted in paragraphs introductory to the chapters of this paper's Part I. This was done for several reasons. Brain anatomists unfamiliar with paleontology had to be introduced to the fossil forms. From the comparative anatomy of the living mammals it is known that relations exist between brain formation and the evolutionary stages of other parts of the body, and with body size; relevant anatomical data therefore are important for an understanding of brain evolution and had to be included in this paper as far as available. While the evolutionary stages of the equid genera have been and continue to be extensively discussed, published data on the body size of the extinct forms are few. Occasional statements like "cat size" or "collie size" (of *Eohippus*), or "zebra size" (of *Hipparion*) hardly serve our purpose. Exact data on the body size of individual fossil Equidae are scant because the bulk of the material consists of unassociated parts. We are therefore greatly indebted to Dr. Edwin H. Colbert, who measured the equid skeletons mounted in the American Museum of Natural History and allowed the writer to use the unpublished figures in this paper. Skull lengths culled from the literature had to be used to give an idea of the size variations.

Another purpose of the brief characterizations of the consecutive equid genera is to give the frame of the complete phylogeny to the incomplete picture of brain evolution; to call the blank spaces in the picture to the attention of those who may find specimens apt to fill the gaps.

It is not only from additional material that the writer expects future supplements to this study. Several branches of science are involved in an undertaking of the present kind; one author, with her limited knowledge, cannot exhaust all the possibilities of even the material at hand. Comparative anatomists familiar with real brains will, I hope, add to and correct my descriptions and interpretations of the fossil brains. Two quantitative zoologists have already wished to find co-ordinated into graphs the evolutionary changes in certain relations of and within the brain of the Equidae; however, the writer feels that the few figures assembled would make rather empty graphs which (to her) would not show more than her rows of simple indices. A paleontological colleague wondered whether this brain investigation will change the conception of the genetic links between the equid genera; but I have taken as established, just like the labelling of the specimens by their owner museums, the ancestral connections as set forth in the most recent general paper on this subject. As was to be expected from brains, nothing in my material suggested differences from Stirton's (1940) phylogeny of the horse.

Furthermore, it has been suggested that I give reconstructions of the evolutionary series of fossil brains. This challenge I hope to take up myself in a future paper. Since the actual data of most stages of the series are as yet incomplete, imagination will have to play a role in those restorations. The present paper reports the documentary evidence—the facts as I see them. Under the title, and between the lines of the text, there stand in invisible ink the words "as it appears to the writer from the material at hand."

Following is a list of the collections to which the described specimens belong, with the abbreviations used in the text for their brief designation, and the names of the colleagues in charge. I wish to express my deepest gratitude to these colleagues for their assistance and co-operation.

The American Museum of Natural History, New York, N. Y. (AMNH); Dr. George Gaylord Simpson, Dr. Edwin H. Colbert, Mrs. Rachel H. Nichols.

Amherst College Museum, Amherst, Mass.; Dr. Fred B. Phleger, Jr.

Chicago Natural History Museum, Chicago, Ill. (CNHM); Dr. Paul O. McGrew, Mr. Bryan Patterson.

Museum of Comparative Zoölogy at Harvard College, Cambridge, Mass. (MCZ).

Museum of Vertebrate Paleontology, University of Kansas, Lawrence, Kans.; Dr. Claude W. Hibbard.

Los Angeles County Museum of History, Science and Art, Los Angeles, Cal. (LACM); Dr. Chester Stock.

Department of Geology, Princeton University, Princeton, N. J. (PU); Dr. Glenn L. Jepsen, Dr. W. B. Scott.

The private collection of Dr. Horace Elmer Wood, 2nd, Newark, N. J.

Yale University, Peabody Museum of Natural History, New Haven, Conn. (YPM); Dr. C. O Dunbar, Dr. G. E. Lewis, Dr. R. S. Lull.

The photographs were taken by Mr. Frederick P. Orchard. Mr. Eugene N. Fischer skillfully prepared the drawings of the objects so unfamiliar to him. Some of the figures taken from other publications were redrawn in stipple technique by Mr. Fischer, others by Miss Nelda E. Wright. Miss Wright, furthermore, gave invaluable aid by correcting the text of Part I. My special gratitude is due to Dr. A. S. Romer, whose criticism of the manuscript of Part II went far beyond the requested help with the language. Highly valued advice was also received from Dr. G. G. Simpson, the godfather of the project.

In addition to the grant from the Penrose Bequest of The Geological Society of America, I have received a Grant-in-Aid from the Sigma Xi Research Fund to help complete the illustrations and preparation of the manuscript.

PART 1.   THE BRAINS OF THE EQUIDAE

BRAIN-ENDOCAST-ENDOCRANIUM RELATIONS IN THE EQUIDAE

SIZE

The volume or the weight of the brain of the extinct Equidae is not disclosed by their endocranial casts.

The endocranial capacity of a horse with a brain weight of 587 grams was 626 cc.; therefore Köppel, assuming that 1 cc. of horse brain weighs 1 g., concluded that in *Equus caballus* the brain normally fills only 93.7 per cent of the osseous brain capsule (1898, p. 182).

We lack data concerning differences in the space occupied by meninges, blood vessels, and cerebro-spinal fluid in closely related small and large living mammals. Individual and age variations are no doubt great; this is well known to be the case with man.   In the series of endocranial casts from *Eohippus* to *Equus*, the number of individuals representing each genus is very small.   The series, however, suggests that in the evolution from medium-sized to large forms the circumcerebral space increased, in particular under the skull roof.

In the endocasts of Middle Eocene to Middle Miocene age, the entire surface of the cerebral hemispheres is so distinctly fissured that the bone must have lain very close to the brain.   In the larger *Merychippus* (our specimens III and IV), and in all Pliocene, Pleistocene, and Recent endocranial casts, the relief is blurred medially on the dorsal forebrain surfaces.

The medial area in which sulci are indistinct or absent in the larger Equidae must indeed be a region in which the brain is less close to the bone than in the regions which are better moulded on endocranial casts.   On the vertex of the brain, in particular along the sides of the superior sagittal sinus, subarachnoid tissue forms nodes filled with cerebro-spinal fluid, the Pacchionian granulations, which spread into the dura mater.   The pressure of the larger of these arachnoidal proliferations produces pits (foveae glandulares) in the inner plate of the cranium.   Corresponding round or ovoid hillocks on endocranial casts thus represent large Pacchionian bodies. Their presence on fossil brains indicates that there existed an intradural space in which subarachnoidal proliferations could develop to large sizes.

The MCZ has an endocast of a medio-sagittally sectioned skull of *Equus caballus* (MCZ 1713; our specimen I) and another made from a horse skull so sectioned that the skull roof remained intact (specimen II).   A few Pacchionian bodies in I and a large number in II occupy a median strip 30–35 mm. wide, which extends forward to a line just behind the frontal slope of the cerebrum—that is, over more than the posterior three quarters of the length of the cerebral hemispheres.   The foveae glandulares lie not only in the parietal but also spread forward beyond the posterior border of the frontal bone.   On the endocranial casts, the largest Pacchionian hillocks form two irregular parasagittal chains; these border the unmoulded area.   An endodural cast of the No. II individual shows that about 30 small Pacchionian bodies existed between the parasagittal chains of four large and one smaller, and three large ones, respectively; but neither these median granulations nor the brain sulci over which they spread were sufficiently close to the endocranium to mark it.

On our pony endocranial cast (pl. 4) only two Pacchionian bodies could be identified, and on that of the Pleistocene *Equus occidentalis* (pl. 3, fig. 1) only one—anteriorly situated in the former, posteriorly in the latter. It may be significant that these two endocasts show the brain sulci (except in a mostly narrow dorso-median area) much better than do the endocasts of the two common horses. The pony and *Equus occidentalis* endocrania were more sculptured by the brains; these two individuals apparently had fewer or smaller arachnoidal granulations and a narrower circumcerebral space than those two horses. The endocast of the Pleistocene *Equus scotti* is particularly lacking in brain details; Pacchionian bodies are numerous along the border and within the otherwise smooth median area of the posterior half of the hemispheres. The natural endocast of *Hipparion* does not contain this region, nor is this satisfactorily reproduced in the *Neohipparion* rubber endocast; in the latter, however, there is an unmistakable circular hillock on the summit, somewhat behind the middle, of the right hemisphere. In the *Pliohippus* endocasts too, only one Pacchionian body is readily distinguished in I, posteriorly situated.

It seems that arachnoidal granulations of sufficient size and turgor to erode the skull roof first appeared, in the Equidae, in the Upper Miocene, and that they were at first confined to posterior areas.

The oldest Pacchionian bodies in my material were found in *Merychippus*. Specimen III has a symmetrical pair of large ones far posteriorly, and there is a smaller body more anteriorly on the left hemisphere. In the other Upper Miocene *Merychippus* the corresponding region—viz., the posterior third of the medial area— is not distinctly cast. On the Middle Miocene *Merychippus* endocast I, several very small convexities and a larger one are seen in this posterior region; but other regions of this rubber specimen have rather similar outgrowths. There is no trace of Pacchionian bodies in the Middle Miocene *Merychippus* skull roofs A and B and endocast II, although delicate arachnoidal vessels are excellently moulded just in their preferred area. No Pacchionian bodies were found in our *Parahippus* specimens, but this need not mean that arachnoidal granulations were little developed in this genus; both specimens show only patches of the region in question, and, besides, II is the endocast of a young individual (foveae develop rarely before the eighth year in man—Brême, 1903, p. 437).

The Oligocene genus *Mesohippus* had arachnoidal granulations only of the lesser kind which either do not perforate the inner lamella of the dura at all or find room in the intradural space without pressing outward the periosteal lamella. Several natural endocranial casts of *Mesohippus* even show vessels of the pia mater delicately spun over the forebrain area which in later equid endocranial casts is smooth except for the Pacchionian bodies; yet there is no trace of these in *Mesohippus* (nor in *Eohippus*).

It seems that in the early and small fossil Equidae there was a more intimate brain-bone relation in the region later occupied by the Pacchionian bodies. The intermeningeal space was so negligible that pia vessels were in close proximity with the skull interior. The space in which arachnoidal granulations developed to large size in the later genera did not exist.

Consequently, the volume of the endocranial cast had a different proportion to the volume of the long-vanished brain in one stage of the horse series from that in another. Certain special changes of cerebellar and pituitary endocast regions, discussed below, also suggest that endocranial cast size more closely approaches actual brain size the farther down a genus is in the history of the horses.

Just before this paper went to press I discovered that a comparative study of brain and endo-cranium volumes in mammals of different sizes exists, and that these mammals happen to be Equidae. Mobilio (1915) measured brain volume and endocranial capacity in adult horses, mules, and asses. In all his horse specimens the discrepancy between the two volumes was greater than Köppel assumed (1:1.068; my calculation from Köppel's numbers, 1898). The extremes among Mobilio's horses were 1:1.142 and 1:1.200 (1915, table II). While variation is great in the three forms, their medium discrepancies indicate that among living Equidae, too, some correlation exists between circumcerebral space and body size. Average differences between brain volume and endocranial capacity are, according to Mobilio (1915, p. 303): ass 64 cubic cm., mule 78 cubic cm., horse 107 cubic cm.

The fact that we are barred from detecting the exact volumina of the vanished brains is, however, not the only reason why the present investigation does not concern itself with absolute sizes, nor with size comparisons of whole brains.

We are today no longer interested in such statements as that the brain of *Mesohippus* weighed about one third as much as that of *Equus*, and that consequently the brain of the fossil genus was proportionally heavier (Osborn, 1890, p. 87). To begin with, such a statement is necessarily debatable. Total brain weights from 519.5 to 640 grams have been recorded for *Equus caballus* (Kappers, 1928, footnote p. 67). We never know the body size of the fossil individual whose brain we investigate; no complete *Mesohippus* skeleton would be damaged for endocranial cast preparation. Furthermore, assertions of the above kind today do not impart a contrast between thriving ancestor and poor descendant, with the anthropocentric implications enjoyed by an elder generation of anatomists. It is true that *Hipparion* was considerably smaller than the common horse and that the brain of *Hipparion* was not correspondingly smaller; but does this signify that "*Hipparion* représente par conséquent le genre ayant atteint le maximum de développement du système nerveux central"? One certainly cannot reasonably conclude that "Comparativement aux autres représentants des Equidés d'Europe, *Hipparion* présente une supériorité incontestable au point de vue du développement du cerveau" (Simionescu, 1934, p. 168). *Hipparion* was a genus with a wide range in body size. Within such genera, variations of absolute and of relative brain size are enormous. Bonin's list of body and brain weights contains a *Hippotigris zebra* with a body of 166 kilograms and a brain of 674 grams, and a *Hippotigris boehmi* with 250 kilograms body weight but only 612 grams brain weight (1937, p. 385). Cornevin (1889) weighed representatives of five races of domestic horses before they were killed (5 ♂♂, p. 24–25; 3 ♀♀, p. 28), and he measured each individual's cranial capacity. With body weights between 94 and 1040 kilograms, and cranial capacities between 500 and 805 cubic cm., the amount of cranial capacity to every 100 kilograms body weight varied from 531 cubic cm. in the smallest (Corsican pony ♀) to 77 cubic cm. in the largest specimen (heavy Belgian ♂). That the brains of Tertiary Equidae were larger in relation to body size than they are in domestic horses is just another case of smaller forms having relatively larger brains than their larger congeners. Such differences, of the volume of the brain as a whole, have no meaning, in particular no evolutionary significance. The great, rapid, highly significant brain enlargement in the evolution of man was an enlargement of the cerebral hemispheres.

FORM

In the interior of the ungulate neurocranium, each brain portion which reaches the surface is well delimited. The brain moulds the inner plate of the bones to such a degree that the doubts as to the reliability of interpreting endocranial casts as brain forms, frequently expressed in the literature, never referred to ungulates. Moreover, Black's summary of his comparisons between the brain, the endodural, and the endocranial cast in *Ovis*, *Bos*, and *Sus* (and of carnivores as well) states that "practically all the details in the pattern of the lateral convex surface of the cerebrum were recorded on the endocranial casts. . . . On the adult cerebrum in no cases were small sulci present that did not leave some impression (frequently quite sharply defined) upon the corresponding endocranial surface of the bone" (1920–1921, p. 273–274).

It was planned to demonstrate *ad oculos* this same high quality of brain reproduction in equid endocasts by showing in this paper photos of the brain of a horse alongside photos of the endocast of its neurocranium. A horse (*Equus caballus* II in this paper) was electrocuted—instead of the usual shooting in the brain—at the Brighton, Mass., abattoir. Within a few hours after the death, Mr. R. V. Witter removed the brain. The brain was hardened in frequently changed formaldehyde. Mr. Witter made an endodural cast with Latex rubber. Two Latex and four plaster endocasts were made of the cranial cavity; none of them, however, completely cast the ethmoidal chambers.

The hollow Latex casts, now over 2 years old, have not shrunk. The dimensions of the Latex and plaster endocranial casts are the same. Their differences from those of the endodural casts may be noted here as a supplement to the 6.3 per cent volume difference between the brain (presumably with the pia mater) and the endocranium calculated by Köppel, quoted above. Measurements of the endodural and the endocranial casts are: from anterior extremity of forebrain to posterior end of vermis cerebelli, 150, 158 mm.; lengths of cerebral hemispheres, 124, 129; their breadths, 110, 112; their heights, 85, 89. It follows that in this individual there was some, but no considerable, difference between the maximum diameters of the endocranial cast and the brain with only its two thin meninges, pia and arachnoidea.

The brain of this horse very quickly assumed a shape quite different from the form of its removed capsule.

The pituitary body and the olfactory bulbs had come off during the preparation and were lost. This seems to be a common occurrence. In the world's largest collection of animal brains, there is hardly a specimen with a pituitary body. Sisson's description of the horse brain mentions twice (1917, p. 769, 787) that "it is very difficult to remove the olfactory bulb intact."

In the "hardened" brain, the cerebellum receded from the cerebrum. The cerebral hemispheres became so broad and long that the contour of their chamber, taken from the endocranial cast, instead of being wider, fell short of covering the outline.

What our preparations ultimately showed was, therefore, not that the endocranial cast of a horse shows the form of the brain just as well as the brain, but that it preserves the form considerably better than does the brain itself.

All portions of the best-preserved of several sheep brains were carefully adjusted before the two photos (pl. 1, fig. 2, 3) were taken; yet the olfactory bulbs are longer in the side view, the cerebellum is longer in the dorsal view as it has fallen back, and in both pictures the oblongata is curled up.

Comparisons of several published figures of brains of any one mammalian species at once show that the shape changes even in specimens removed and hardened in laboratories with extensive routine in brain preservation. This may be illustrated by the example of the olfactory bulbs of sheep and horse. Preservation of ungulate olfactory bulbs is particularly handicapped by several special factors. The bulbi not only have to be removed from their own, relatively small ethmoidal chamber, but by the fila olfactoria their convex surface is strongly attached to the cribriform plate so that they are apt to be injured when the brain is removed from the skull. Furthermore, the ventriculus bulbi olfactorii (rhinocoele), an embryonic feature in other mammals, in the ungulates remains a considerable cavity throughout life; its presence causes the walls of the bulbs to collapse toward each other when they are freed from their bony support. Fiske (1913, p. 41; figs. 6–8) describes the olfactory bulbs of the sheep as lying entirely on the under side of the hemispheres; see, however, the dorsal view of our sheep brain, pl. 1, fig. 2. In Burkholder's plates of the sheep brain the bulbi are shown much larger than in the other drawings in the dura-covered brain (1904, pl. III); actually, it is as true of the sheep as of the other mammals which Forster describes in his study of the cribriform plate that "le bulbe olfactif la recouvre en totalité et se trouve en contact immédiat avec elle sur toute son étendue" (1927, p. 27). In *Equus* Flatau and Jacobsohn (1899, p. 407) found the olfactory bulbs so flat as to be invisible in dorsal views of the brain. Sisson's (1917) figures of the horse brain show the olfactory bulbs protruding forward from the anterior poles of the cerebral hemispheres by 4 mm. in the dorsal view (fig. 631), 12 mm. in the basal view (fig. 629), 20 mm. in the lateral view (fig. 632). In the latter figure, a 3-mm. cleft completely separates the olfactory bulbs from the cerebral hemispheres down to the olfactory tract. Thus only this picture takes into account the transverse osseous septum which, varying in thickness, dorsally separates ethmoidal and cerebral chambers. Obviously, as a rule, only skulls and endocranial casts preserve the shape and position of protruding ungulate olfactory bulbs, and reveal their 15–20-mm. projection beyond the cerebral hemispheres in the common horse.

NATURAL AND ARTIFICIAL ENDOCASTS

During the present investigation of a large series of endocasts of crania all belonging to one family, including cases of both natural and artificial casts of one genus, characteristic differences between the two kinds of "fossil brains" were so clearly realized and played such a role in interpretation that they are briefly noted here.

As a rule, the paleoneurologist has no choice. Artificial casts are made of skulls imbedded in soft matrix, skulls cleaned inside—if the owners admit that a sectioned neurocranium plus its endocast is not less valuable than whole. Natural casts are prepared from hard matrix material—if the owners are willing to sacrifice the skull.

This sacrifice need not be total and usually is not, for technical reasons; it is of no advantage for the endocast to remove firmly clinging bone. The sacrifice should never be total in rare species. Marsh left the skull base in place when the natural endocast of *Eohippus* (fig. 2) was prepared, and a plaster cast had been taken of that neurocranium before endocast preparation. After my demonstration of pictures of this endocast at the twenty-fourth annual meeting of the American Society of Mammalogists (1942), Dr. W. K. Gregory doubted that a brain so primitive could have belonged to a mammal so specialized as *Eohippus;* but the plaster cast of the cranium easily convinced him of the identity.

Both natural and artificial endocranial casts share with other fossils the drawbacks of distortion and incompleteness. Incompleteness is more apt to occur and can be a greater handicap for interpretation in a fossil brain than in a fossil bone.

Some endocranium areas are not moulded by the brain itself; some crania were not completely filled when the skull was embedded; in some regions of either closely set nerve foramina (base), or minute brain sculpture (*e.g.*, cerebellum), or cancellate bone surface (*e.g.*, dorsal areas of the occipital bone), matrix and bone may be so interlocked that they cannot be cleanly separated. It is extremely important that such areas be recognized as not representing brain surface. They are irregularly hatched in our figures, in contrast to the stippled brain. (Bone quite irremovable from the endocasts is outlined with little or no shading.) To identify on artificial endocasts areas not shaped by the brain, one may have to investigate the cranium used. In natural endocasts of ungulates, moulded surfaces are so smooth, mostly so similar to real brain surface, that areas rough through accidents in bone removal, or due to matrix surface gaps, are easily distinguished. It is much to be regretted that paleoneurologists (including myself) up to now did not set off such areas in figures of fossil brains. For this reason, *e.g.*, Cope's pictures of a fragmentary but otherwise excellent *Merychippus* brain (Cope and Matthew, 1915) are nothing but a puzzle.

A case in which the absence of original surface was not recognized, and in which the disadvantage of natural casts (skull not preserved) was piled on a disadvantage of plaster casts (smooth and rough surfaces not always easily distinguishable), is that of Tilney (1931) and his *Mesohippus*. Tilney studied a plaster replica of a natural endocast. He described and figured as deep Sylvian fossae bilateral gaps in the original surface. He did not find the suprasylvian sulcus which is well seen on the right hemisphere of the original specimen (our specimen I). He consequently labelled as suprasylvian the ectolateral, so that the presence of the ectolateral sulcus was not recorded. This could have led to wrong conclusions; actually, the presence of both ectolateral and entolateral sulci is a typical character of the perissodactyls, in contrast to artiodactyls (Krueg, 1878, p. 328).

Artificial casting has made great progress since my report (1929, p. 13–16). However, none of the endocasts described in the present paper was made with the excellent methods now practiced in the medical sciences. Paleontology should take notice of Poller's method (extensively described by Economo, 1929 a, pp. 327–330, 341–347) and of metal casting. The tiresome necessity of removing all organic material from the bones would not exist if fossil skulls were used for making such endocasts of cavities as Zinram (1931) produced with Wood's metal, silver, and gold. The artificial endocasts of the equid skulls are either plaster or rubber. Smooth rubber can be an improvement over coarse plaster. It is labor-saving, as direct casts can be made with rubber, whereas plaster specimens are casts of endocasts taken with glue. Unfortunately, the rubber used for some of the equid specimens is black. Black rubber is definitely a setback. The shadows are so indistinct that it is difficult to perceive the shallower brain sulci. Where shallow sulci are not readily traced by the eye, paleoneurologists may make them visible by such primitive methods as, e.g., by advancing along them a loosely held pencil point; this is guided even by the shallowest furrows which then appear on the cast as clear pencil lines (see pl. 4), easily erased from the specimen after study. However, pencil does not draw on black rubber, and wet crayon shows only when applied too firmly to be accurately guided by a shallow sulcus.

Perhaps none of the artificial casts in my material was made by a particularly experienced preparator. In this material, with the exception of the *Equus occidentalis* plaster cast, nature has made the better fossil brains. Details such as delicate vessels, width of foramina, and depth of sulci are reproduced far clearer. Fine-grained sand, which more or less slowly filtered into the cranial cavity of *Equus niobrarensis*, when cemented (pl. 2, fig. 2), preserved some brain areas only, but these areas are casts of a quality superior to the plaster endocasts of *Equus scotti* and the living horses. As said above, the brain of a small living horse (pl. 4) moulds the endocranium more than does the brain of a large horse; yet some posterior convolutions, which appear as low elevations on the pony plaster cast, stand out prominently in the natural *Equus niobrarensis* cast.

On the other hand, the preservation of the endocranium along with its man-made cast proved an asset not only in the interpretation of such protruding parts as ill-moulded nerve foramina, but also in the understanding of intra-cerebral features. No one natural or artificial endocast can reveal the whole downward projection of the tentorium cerebelli, except in a form as primitive as *Eohippus* where the osseous tent obviously did not extend below the brain surface. In the later equid genera, a natural cast shows the whole extent only if a break occurs just along the cerebro-cerebellar border as in *Mesohippus* V (fig. 10B). In whole natural casts, all we see of the tent is a transverse strip of bone sticking in the transverse fissure between cerebellum and forebrain. In artificial casting, however, it is not necessary to make separate casts of cerebellar and forebrain chambers, as the skull may offer sufficient evidence. Judging from the cast *Merychippus* III, the cerebellum would project 5 mm. forward between the forebrain hemispheres; but the respective skull D shows the tentorium osseum projecting farther downward and forward to 12 mm. within the telencephalic area (pl. 2, fig. 1).

SOME BRAIN CAPSULE DETAILS

Cerebellar chamber.—The fact that the cauliflowerlike lobulation of most mam-malian cerebella is never reproduced on endocranial casts has deterred paleoneurol-ogists from interpreting those markings which do appear on cerebellar chamber casts. It seemed unpromising anyway; even in the actual cerebellum of the horse, com-plication was found too great for identification of the innumerable separate lobuli by such an expert of cerebellar morphology as Bolk (1906, p. 64). I myself believed (1929, p. 64) that transverse marks on vermis casts need not be just the principal fissures, and indeed this could not be decided as long as vermis marks were observed in very few fossil brains which belonged to unrelated mammals.

The term "vermis," antiquated in description of living cerebella, cannot be relin-quished in paleoneurology because the paramedian fissures, first cerebellar detail to appear in ontogeny, have prominent counterparts in the skull. On practically all endocasts they set off the vermis from the cerebellar hemispheres. Within the latter, traces of the parasagittal fissure may occur in the earlier Equidae, allowing a distinction between the paraflocculus and the paramedian area. In the paramedian area of the cerebellum, brain nomenclature distinguishes paramedian and ansate lobes; these two are one not only in our endocasts but also in the ungulate brain; they are separate in other mammals (Haller, 1934, p. 87).

Our series has shown that the first vermis fissure to appear in ontogeny—the fissura prima—has a counterpart, a transverse ridge in the endocranium; this is well developed up to *Mesohippus* and in later material was observed in *Neohipparion*. Another of the three principal vermis fissures, f. suprapyramis, is a conspicuous dent in cerebellar casts up to the Miocene; it becomes shallower later. Minor vermis sulci mold the endocranium only in *Orohippus*—that is, before evolutionary increase of lamellae produces a surface pattern too complex to shape the increasingly thicker bone.

Similarly, the relation of the flocculus to the pars petrosa of the temporal bone decreases in intimacy in the evolution of the Equidae. Denker (1899, p. 319) as-serts that *Equus caballus* has no floccular fossa. According to Ciurlo, the arcuate fossa is more or less levelled, reduced to a very shallow depression in all adult perisso-dactyls (1932, p. 716). Sisson (1917), while describing the floccular fossa in other genera, says of the medial surface of the petrosal of the horse only that it is "concave and smooth, but irregular" (p. 62). This is indeed true of Recent horses in general. The endocasts of cerebellar chambers have, on the lateral surfaces, low, very variable hillocks without definite borders. However, in the pony, and in the horse ancestors up to at least *Merychippus*, well-shaped casts of the floccular fossa occur on endo-cranial casts.

More than the successive loss of cerebellar fissuration—in which increasing com-plexity played a role—this reduction of the flocculus in fossil equid brains suggests diminishing plasticity of the capsule bones. Presumably the increasing thickness of the temporal, interparietal, and occipital bones made their inner plate increasingly less responsive to moulding by the brain. It seems that during a certain limited period of horse evolution conditions of the inner plate influenced the shape of the cerebellar chamber.

The cerebellum cast of *Merychippus* I is crowned by a transverse ridge, an upward extension of its perpendicular posterior side (fig. 15, A, *). This crest has an antero-posterior length of 7 mm. medially and rises steeply almost 7 mm. above the rest of the dorsal cerebellar surface; it slopes and tapers laterad, covering about three-fifths of the cerebellar breadth. Corresponding to it the *Merychippus* specimen III has a crest much thinner, less regularly shaped, on the left side only, with an antero-posterior length of 3 mm. at its larger paramedian end, where it is 3 mm. high. Skull D, from which brain III was taken, shows the corresponding irregular, narrow dent in the tabula interna of the occipital bone, while in skull B there corresponds an area in which the inner plate is seemingly unfinished, perforated by a number of small and larger holes into the diploë.

Nothing similar was observed below the *Merychippus* stage; the Eocene and Oligocene cerebellar chambers have no irregularities. The irregularities occurring on post-Miocene cerebella differ from those of *Merychippus*. They are found in more anterior locations, and they are not so extensive as in *Merychippus*. One kind is due to gaps in the tabula interna in the border region of the highly cancellate supraoccipital and interparietal bones; another kind of ostensible excrescences from the cerebellum is the endocast of the temporal canal which only from *Pliohippus* onward became very wide.

Obviously the variable crest across the cerebellum of *Merychippus* endocasts also does not pertain to the brain. Had *Merychippus* developed a particularly prominent cerebellar lobule, this could not have been so extremely different in different in-dividuals. Nor does angiology offer an explanation for the corresponding furrow in the endocranial wall. The venae cerebelli superiores do converge toward the vermis summit, and here enter the dura, but the resulting dural sinuses are neither so prominent nor so extensive.

It seems to me that the posterior evagination of the cerebellar chamber in *Mery-chippus* is one feature, hitherto unnoticed, of the much-discussed reorganization of the equid skull in this stage. It may have occurred also in *Parahippus*, but nothing was observed in the single case investigated (the medio-sagitally sectioned occiput of specimen I) except that the tabula interna is, in the region in question, paper-thin.

Up through the Oligocene, there is little diploë in the equid occiput; muscle at-tachment rugosities are so inconspicuous and indefinite that the planum nuchale appears almost smooth in *Mesohippus*. Not even the depressions for the tendons of the complexus muscles, so conspicuous and rough in the later Equidae, are present; and the transverse nuchal crest of the occipital bone hardly protrudes beyond the nuchal plane.

In *Merychippus*, in correlation with the increased length of the muzzle, and with the weight of the now hypsodont and heavily cemented teeth, all the muscles holding, extending, and flexing the head have become much stronger, and their insertions have conspicuously changed the occipital bone. This contains, from *Parahippus* onward, a large mass of cancellate tissue to mediate dorsally and posteriorly between the conservative wall of the cerebellar chamber and the changing outer plate of the (parietal and) occipital bone. The nuchal plane of *Merychippus* is rugose from the attachment of the ligamentum nuchae and the rectus capitis dorsalis and complexus muscles; and the obliquus capitis anterior and splenius muscles' pull can be imagined to have enlarged the nuchal crest, stretching it backward. The crest is now the structure extending like a balcony backward from the (unchangingly perpendicular) back wall of the cerebellar chamber. In the medio-sagitally sectioned skulls of the young adult *Mesohippus* A and *Merychippus* D, the (oblique) distance from the most dorso-posterior point of the cerebellar chamber inside the occipital to the rim of the nuchal crest is 6 and 20 mm., respectively—a 1:3.3 proportion, against the 1:1.76 proportion of skull length average in the two genera. *Parahippus* II was a larger individual than *Merychippus* D; lengths of these two fragments, from the nuchal crest—strongly developed in both—to the point of greatest cranium constriction between the temporal fossae, are 136 and 127 mm., respectively; yet the above-described diameter of the occipital bone is only 17 mm. in the earlier genus. From *Merychippus* to *Equus* it increased, proportionate to skull length which almost doubled, from 20 to 39 mm.

Evidently, while this urgently needed reconstruction of the occiput took place, the inner plate of the occipital, functionally less important, took its time to adjust itself. During this period, it had no definite shape. Its irregularities appear like evaginations of the cerebellum in endocranial casts of *Merychippus*.

(I find that there is another, quite different, but equally variable feature which first appears in *Merychippus*, occurs in some but not all later Equidae, has disappeared in *Equus*, and is also regarded as "primarily conditioned by certain needs in bracing a progressively enlarging skull" (Matthew, 1926, p. 160). These are fossae in front of the orbit whose origin and function are obscure.)

It is a noteworthy point, bearing on the question as to whether skull shape influences brain shape, that the great change in occiput formation, which in Miocene Equidae involved rebuilding of the tabula interna, never altered the cerebellum. The posterior facies of the vermis has remained perpendicular from *Eohippus* to *Equus*.

The vermis expanded in an upward and forward direction in the evolution of the horse. This tendency is clearly shown in the series of endocasts—, that is, in changes of the cerebellar chamber in the skull. Of course paleoneurology is deprived of the knowledge of medullary and mesencephalic facies of mammalian cerebella. No cranium, only a dissection of a real brain (fig. 21 B), can show that the profile of the horse vermis is almost a circle. Nor can the real extent of the anterior facies of the cerebellum be traced in endocasts even when the entire tentorium osseum is exposed. The tentorium is mainly a membranous fold which cannot fossilize, and it is impossible to know exactly how large a portion of it was the upper, bony, fossilizable part. The degree of ossification varies. I found in sheep even the dorsal facies of the cerebellum covered by membrane only, and Black (1915, p. 338) states that ossification of the tentorium osseum is extremely rare in living artiodactyls.

In the Equidae, however, tentorial ossification is particularly extensive. From the first appearance of a cerebro-cerebellar border, *viz.*, from *Orohippus* onward, the tentorium osseum occupies most of the cleft between the cerebellum and the forebrain. The trend of cerebellar evolution from a dorsal hump (*Eohippus*) to a

deep globe (*Equus*) is well shown in the series of endocasts and crania of horse ancestors by the steadily increasing extent of the forward-downward projection of the
tentorium osseum into the brain chamber.   In the earliest Equidae there is, besides,
a forward move of the bone crest in the fissura prima cerebelli.   These changes in the
cerebellar chamber obviously were brought about by size increase not only of the

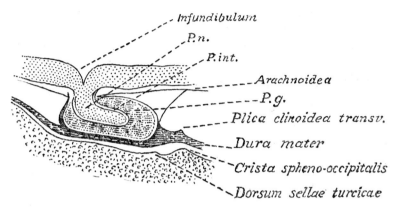

FIGURE 1.—*Equus caballus.   Pituitary body and surroundings*
After Koller. × 1.

cerebellar facies of the cerebral hemispheres but also of the cerebral facies of the
cerebellum through forward expansion.

   Sella turcica.—Horse and ass have no sella turcica.   A shallow groove may occur
in its place, but the region is usually quite flat and even may be slightly convex
(Koller, 1922, p. 190).   There are no clinoid processes, nor is the dorsum sellae
developed.   Rarely, a hardly perceptible ridge marks, on the sphenoid bone, the
posterior side of the pituitary body (Koller, 1922, p. 191; our fig. 1).   A well-de-
limited sella turcica has been reported in only one particularly large horse (Zannini,
in an investigation of 110 horse skulls, 1922, p. 447); but this case must certainly be
regarded as a parallel to the exceptional depth of the sella in human giants.   Consequently, there is no trace of the pituitary body on the endocranial cast of the average
modern horse.

   The flatness of the pituitary region of the *Equus* sphenoid is a secondary condition.
It is first found in the Upper Miocene, for instance in the *Merychippus* skull C.   In
the Middle Miocene endocasts *Merychippus* I and *Parahippus* II, the pituitary
region is somewhat disturbed, but the imprint of the dorsum sellae is marked in both.
The Lower Miocene *Parahippus* I has a low pituitary hillock.   The sphenoid removed from this natural endocast shows the corresponding roundish groove.   This
pituitary groove is limited posteriorly by a distinct, if low, dorsum sellae.   There
may not have been anterior clinoid processes, but the transition from the concavity
to the level sphenoid surface is quite distinct anteriorly too.   The Middle Oligocene
Mesohippus seems to have had a real sella turcica.   In both the specimens whose
brain bases are freed from bone, II and V, the pituitary body is represented by
prominent, well-defined, oval convexities (fig. 11 C).   From their posterior border,

preparation removed a transverse bone ridge: the dorsum sellae. We lack data on the brain base, or the cerebral surface of the cranium base, below the Middle Oligocene; but it is obvious that at least a ventral part of the equid pituitary body originally rested in the sphenoid bone and has gradually come to lie above it.

From the viewpoint of the brain anatomist, the loss of the sella formation in the evolution of the Equidae is surprising, because the pituitary body is usually larger and more prominent in large animals than in their smaller congeners (Edinger, 1942). However, the same osteological progressive reduction can be observed in the phylogeny of the Proboscidea and the Cetacea. The pituitary is prominent on the endocast of the Upper Eocene proboscidean *Moeritherium*, but not modelled on *Elephas* endocasts—no intermediate stages are known. Endocasts of Eocene cetaceans have the pituitary hillock. Among Miocene Odontoceti, *Prosqualodon* (skull length about 460 mm.) has a flat pituitary region, but on several endocasts of *Cyrtodelphis* (skull length 700–800 mm.) dal Piaz observed small or large, low or prominent pituitary convexities (1905, p. 266; for the other literature on nonequid fossil brains, *see* T. Edinger 1929, p. 221–243; 1937, p. 243–251). The cerebral side of the sphenoid is flat in living whales.

In the Equidae, this change in the formation of the pituitary endocast region is another feature in the gradual decrease of intimacy between brain and endocranium. It is another gradual change in which conditions similar to those in the modern horse were attained during the late Miocene.

Cerebral chamber.—In brains with a network of multi-branched neocortical sulci such as the horse brain, many authors found the difficulty of identifying more than the main sulcus trunks too great to take the trouble. As a connection between sulci may be buried under a convolution and detected only when the sulci are opened, and because the principal sulci have somewhat characteristic depths, it is generally believed that those difficulties are insurmountable obstacles in paleoneurology. Paleoneurologists, one believes, have no means to see anything but the surface.

In the present investigation, this limitation was found a considerable handicap only in the case of the Sylvian fossa region. Some neoneurologists—but not all— distinguish between an "original Sylvia" ("pseudosylvian sulcus", "Fissura Sylvia falsa") and the "true Sylvian fossa," a larger and deeper cleft in whose depth lies, operculized, the insula Reilii. Naturally, this distinction cannot accurately be made in fossil brains. But the progress of operculization is traceable in the earlier fossil equid brains. Besides, another shift from the brain convexity to an area invisible in endocasts was observed in the dorso-median area. (*See* "Pronation" in Part II.) Furthermore, it was noticed that also on endocranial casts the sulci have different depths. As Bradley has explored the depths of fissures and sulci of several horse brains in transverse sections (1899, p. 224–225), it was possible to find that the ridges which, between the depressions in the cerebral surface of the bones corresponding to the gyri, project into the sulci (juga cerebralia) are more prominent where they protrude into deep sulci; that is, endocast furrows frequently do allow one to distinguish between deep and shallow sulci of the brain. The equid endocasts usually show that the lateral sulcus (12 mm. deep in the horse brain) is deeper than the ectolateral (7 mm.) and the endolateral (6 mm.). From *Orohippus* onward, the posterior rhinal fissure (11 mm.) is a much deeper furrow than the anterior rhinal fissure; the latter appears on some endocasts more like a line than a furrow (3 mm. deep in the horse brain). The crucial sulcus appears variously deep on fossil equid brains; this corresponds to its varying depth (5–13 mm.) in the horse. Accessory sulci are shallow on the equid endocranial casts.

Incidentally, our equid endocast material also showed the reduction of the juga cerebralia in individual life which is known to occur in man. In the small and simply fissured *Mesohippus* this is negligible; but in Miocene and Pliocene endocranial casts, the neocortical sulci appear definitely deeper in colts (*Parahippus* II, *Pliohippus* I) than in adults (*Parahippus* I, *Pliohippus* II).

When paleoneurology, as in the present paper, traces the evolution of a brain, it is even in a privileged position as regards the identification of sulci. We see the principal sulci come into existence during phylogeny, and in the maze of post-Miocene pallia we recognize in certain undulating lines those straight, unconnected furrows of ancestral brains.

It may well be asked to what purpose paleoneurology pursues sulci investigation, almost entirely abandoned by comparative anatomists working on living brains. Are we compiling insignificant data of surface morphology just because fossil endocrania do not reveal the only significant, the microscopic structure—the cytoarchitectonic areas?

Kappers relates that when forty years ago he became my father's assistant, my father told him "that I was entirely free to work on any subject I liked in comparative neurology, provided I did not deal with gross anatomy and the fissuration of the brain" (1936, p. 61). However, Kappers relates this in a paper on endocranial casts; times have changed. Surface configuration and histological structure have been found to be more closely correlated in the mammalian neocortex than in other organs. "With due account taken of the modifications or variations of certain sulci, it is thought that sulci provide valuable data for the recognition of homologous areas" (Kappers, Huber and Crosby, 1936, p. 1662).

Paleoneurology indeed could extend its indirect investigations to cytoarchitectonics and probably will do so when neurologists will have charted more nonprimate cortices than have been investigated up to now. Recent cytoarchitectonic charts of the sheep brain surface (Rose, 1942, fig. 18, 19) show that the borders of the fields lie in sulci in an ungulate brain. This fact should enable paleoneurologists to draw cytoarchitectonic conclusions from differences between the gyri of a living ungulate and those of its fossil ancestor.

As concerns the Equidae, this is not yet feasible. Only the area striata has been localized in the horse (Alouf, 1929, p. 14–16; text figs. 16, 17; pl. I, fig. 3). This visuo-sensory field of the occipital lobe extends from the splenial sulcus of the median surface (not preserved in fossil brains) over the dorsal surface across the entolateral and lateral sulci to the medial wall of a sulcus on the ectolateral gyrus; that is, the area striata of the horse is bounded by an accessory sulcus between the lateral and ectolateral sulci. This sulcus, incidentally, was not developed in the ancestors of the horse prior to *Parahippus*.

On the other hand, the area striata of the sheep covers the whole suprasplenial, marginal, interlateral, and ectolateral gyri (Rose, 1942, p. 33) so that its distal and anterior borders would be well marked on endocranial casts. Similarly, the ectolateral sulcus forms the lateral boundary of most of the area striata in the one newborn pig investigated by Brodmann (1906, p. 357); but in the one adult pig studied by Alouf (1929, p. 13) the area striata type of cells ended in the lateral sulcus. Such a discrepancy of data, too, shows that the time has not yet come for paleoneurological study of single cytoarchitectonic fields.

It will be shown, however (in the chapter on the neëncephalon in Part II of this paper), that certain form changes of the equid pallium suggest changes in the position and extent of certain cytoarchitectonic fields during the evolution of the horse brain. There exists, furthermore, a manifestation of the relations between sulci and cytoarchitectonics whose study is accessible to paleoneurology. Comparisons of brains of different living members of the mammalian orders have shown that a more complicated fissural pattern is in direct relation not only to larger cell areas, but also to the presence of more specific areas. Consequently, the gradual downward expansion of the neocortex and increase of its fissuration, described in this paper in the evolution of the Equidae, not only reveals the obvious surface increase but also indicates increase in cytoarchitectonic differentiation. Even though our observations rest on the study of brain surfaces only as they are reproduced in endocrania, it suggests, beyond the visible increase in quantity, progress in the cytological quality of the neocortex in the evolution of the horse brain.

LOWER EOCENE (WASATCHIAN): *EOHIPPUS*

STAGE IN PHYLOGENY

Eohippus[2] was very near the root of the Perissodactyla, but it was not the ancestor of any perissodactyls other than the horses. It was an omnivorous equid with four fingers and three toes. Judging from jaws and fragmentary skeletons, Loomis (1926, p. 72–73) and Abel (1928, p. 19) believed that shoulder height varied, within the genus, from less than 250 mm. (*E. index*) to 510 mm. (*E. resartus*).

The mounted skeleton of the best-known species, *E. venticolus*, is 330 mm. high at the shoulder, skull length is 135 mm. (Colbert, M. S.). Greatest height of the back (at the second lumbar vertebra) is 375 mm., and the length of the mounted skeleton is 680 mm. (Simpson, 1932 b, p. 3). "Quite the most primitive species of the genus" (Granger, 1908, p. 236) was *E. validus*, of which until now only a lower jaw fragment and teeth have been published. The p4-m3 tooth series in the *E. validus* type mandible is 31.7 mm.; in Cope's figure of the *E. venticolus* mandible (1884, pl. 49 a, fig. 3) this measurement is 34 mm. In accordance with this slight difference, measurements of the plaster cast of the *E. validus* neurocranium YPM-VP 11694 were found the same as those corresponding in the *E. venticolus* type. The scanty known material of *E. validus* suggests two individuals little, if at all, smaller than *E. venticolus*.

---

[2] This familiar name is used for the form which, according to priority rules, is the American *Hyracotherium*.

MATERIAL

I. *Eohippus* cf. *validus* Marsh, YPM, VP-11694 (fig. 2)

Upper Wasatchian, Almagré zone of Canyon Largo group, San Juan Basin, New Mexico: a plaster cast of a 61-mm.-long neurocranium, and the natural endocranial cast prepared from it, with the base and posterior end of the skull and the right petrosal bone left *in situ*. The anterior end of the specimen is an oblique break across the cast of the olfactory bulb chambers.

I have taken the liberty, for convenience's sake, to drop the "cf." of the label in the discussion of this brain.

II. *Eohippus venticolus* (Cope), AMNH 14810 (fig. 3)

Late Wasatchian, 18 miles up Dry Muddy Creek, Wind River Basin, Wyoming: a muzzle with the 42-mm.-long cheek teeth series (45 mm. in Cope's type specimen). Much of the roof bones is lost; a withered natural cast of the nasal chamber and part of the right olfactory bulb are disclosed. By detaching the endocast of the posterior part of the specimen, the natural cast of the frontal poles of the cerebral hemispheres has been obtained. It ends in a transverse, baso-anteriorly slanting break, and its longest (dorsal) extent is only 10 mm.

III. While all other *Eohippus* skull material examined is too crushed to be of use for the present purpose, one of the (specifically undetermined) skull fragments in the collection of Dr. Horace Elmer Wood, 2nd (No. 32-21) from the San Juan Basin Largo formation is the undistorted roof of the ethmoidal chambers.

Following are the maximum diameters of specimen no. I, with corresponding measurements of specimen no. II in parentheses.

Length: total >62 mm.; cerebrum + mesencephalon + cerebellum 46; cerebellum 15; mesencephalon >8; cerebrum 27; olfactory bulbs >10 (II: 11).

Breadth: medulla oblongata 9; cerebellum 22; mesencephalon 18; palaeopallium 23; neopallium 23; olfactory bulbs >14 (II: 2×10).

Height: medulla oblongata 10; cerebrum 24; olfactory bulbs 16 (II: >13).

DESCRIPTION

Oblongata.—At the posterior end of the No. I specimen, the hind end of the endocast is enclosed by the preserved occipitals. The condyles extend two thirds of their lengths behind the cast. While the medulla oblongata, transversely oval, extended to the sides of the foramen magnum, the notch in the superior border of the foramen and the basal angle between the condyles are osteological features. The length of the post-cerebellar oblongata canal, which is hidden in preserved bone, is probably less than 5 mm.

Cerebellum.—The median portion of the cerebellum seems to have risen perpendicularly from the oblongata. Its posterior facies is at the base hidden by the remnants of the planum nuchale; in the upper part, the cast has an irregularly moulded—that is, partly not the original—surface. There is no indication of the presence of the two transverse fissures characteristic of the posterior cerebellum portions of mammals, the fissurae secunda and suprapyramis. The dorsal vault of the posterior vermis portion is smooth, 5 mm. long, and is separated from the

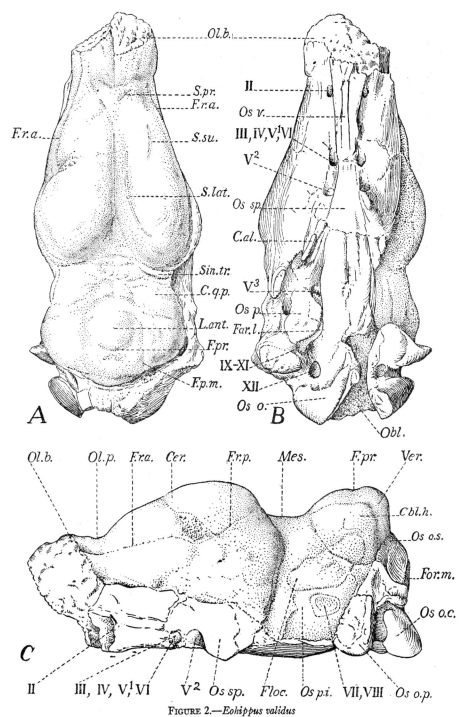

FIGURE 2.—*Eohippus validus*

Natural endocranial cast (specimen no. I). (A) dorsal, (B) ventral, (C) left side view. ×1¾.

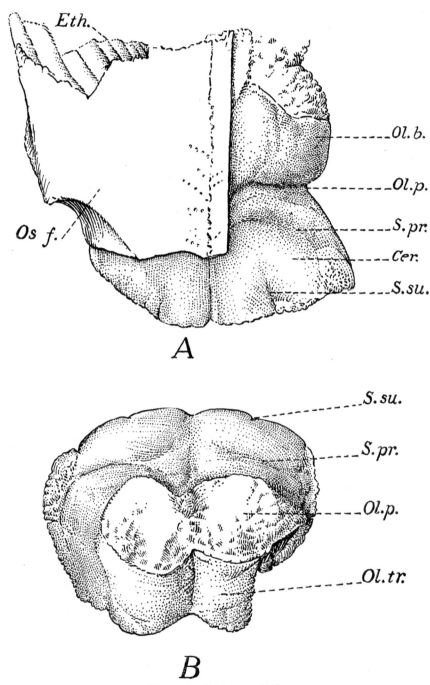

Eth.

Os f.

Ol. b.

Ol. p.

S. pr.

Cer.

S. su.

A

S. su.

S. pr.

Ol. p.

Ol. tr.

B

FIGURE 3.—*Eohippus venticolus*

Natural endocranial cast of anterior part of brain chamber, with left frontal bone *in situ* (specimen no. II).   (A) Dorsal view of whole specimen.   (B) Anterior view of cerebral hemispheres.   × 1.

anterior, somewhat lower, smooth vermis portion by a very distinct transverse furrow. Through its later development this transverse furrow in the oldest equid cerebellum was, in spite of its position so far backward, recognized as the fissura prima (of Elliot Smith; Sulcus primarius of Kuithan), the first cerebellar fissure to appear in mammalian ontogeny.

Paramedian fissures set off the cerebellar hemispheres. On the lateral facies of the left hemisphere there is an area of rough surface—that is, some distal part came off with the removed bone. This area has a distinct outline. It extends antero-basally from over the imprint of the internal acoustic meatus. The rough area is too extensive to represent only the entrance to the subarcuate fossa; this, however, is contained in it. The otherwise irregular lower border of the rough area has an 8-mm.-long horizontal portion; this was the threshold of the fossa subarcuata. Together with the 6 mm. of rough surface above it, it suggests a flocculus 8 mm. long and 6 mm. high. The flocculus cannot have extended far laterally from the preserved endocast surface. On the right side the bone covering this area is preserved, and its outer surface is weathered off without revealing an arcuate fossa endocast.

Mesencephalon.—In front of the cerebellum, a depressed area crosses the entire breadth of the cast. Its antero-posterior breadth is 8 mm., medially between the vermis and the fissura magna cerebri, as well as laterally between the cerebellar hemispheres and the posterior poles of the forebrain hemispheres. This area corresponds to a widely exposed tectum mesencephali. Its surface is rough and irregular on the left side and in the midline. The only midbrain part moulded seems to be the right posterior corpus quadrigeminum, a transverse oval closely adjoining and continuing the anterior slope of the cerebellar hemisphere. In the area of the right anterior corpus quadrigeminum the sinus venosus transversus left its imprint on the cast. As the anterior corpora must have been larger than the posterior, they were possibly anteriorly overlapped by the cerebrum.

Cerebral hemispheres.—The small size, slenderness, and smoothness of the forebrain are readily seen in figure 2. There are no convolutions, and consequently no lobes.

The fissura rhinalis is moulded on the left side. It runs a straight horizontal course except posteriorly where it curves upward. Anteriorly the rhinal fissure continues on the lateral surface of the olfactory peduncle, in a lower position in specimen I than in specimen II. As the base of the No. I cerebrum is hidden in bone, the exact maximum height of the palaeopallium below the rhinal fissure cannot be determined. It is nevertheless clear that the neopallium covered less than half the height of the hemispheres.

The region of the fossa Sylvii is obscured in rough surfaces on both sides. There is an upward dent present such as a Sylvian fossa would cause; but it is in the middle of the antero-posterior length of the left rhinal fissure, while on the right side it divides the forebrain in anterior two-fifths and posterior three-fifths. There also is a furrow extending upward from each dent, but it runs forward on the left side and backward on the right side. Proof that most or all of these markings, ostensibly of the brain surface, are due to accidents of moulding or preparation is provided by the configuration of the Sylvian area in *Orohippus*. *Eohippus* cannot have had more of a Sylvia than an "indication" (Haller, 1934, p. 206: "Die Sylvische Furche scheint, wenigstens in Andeutung, allen Säugetieren zuzukommen.") This is in accordance with the straightness and slenderness of its brain, and with the low degree of its neocortical fissuration.

Markings on the dorsal and lateral surfaces of the *E. validus* cerebrum are few, shallow, different on the two hemispheres, and there are some patches of rough surface which further obscure the tracing of the neopallial sulci.

A shallow, straight, long furrow on the dorsal side of the right but not the left hemisphere is believed to represent the sulcus lateralis, because a similar furrow occurs singly on similar living and fossil brains. In *Lepus timidus*, this dorsal parallel to the rhinal fissure—the only neocortical sulcus—was found long and deep in 39 hemispheres, short and shallow in 18, and nonexistent on one side of 3 of the 30 brains investigated by Rogner (1883, p. 597). The one parasagittal sulcus of the Macrochiroptera is present in one, not in all *Pteropus edulis* hemispheres (Dräseke, 1903, p. 453). There is a corresponding marking on the *Phenacodus* endocast where, as in *Eohippus*, it is "indefinite, and cannot be accepted with much certainty" (Tilney, 1931, p. 455).

One short longitudinal furrow on the right *E. validus* hemisphere is definitely a sulcus, or part of one; imbedded in it are tiny bone particles which must stem from a jugum cerebrale which protruded into this sulcus. It is suprasylvian in position and obviously represents a straight suprasylvian sulcus. The anterior end of this sulcus is well moulded on both sides of the *E. venticolus* forebrain remnant. As in *E. validus*, it runs parallel to the fissura magna at 5–6 mm. distance. It ends at about 5 mm. distance from the frontal pole of the hemispheres, in *E. validus* at 6 mm. distance.

The *E. venticolus* fragment has in front of the suprasylvian an equally distinct transverse sulcus. Situated on a somewhat more ventral level of the dorsal convexity than the suprasylvian, it sets off the anterior poles of the cerebral hemispheres. Medially, it curves upward and backward for about 2 mm. of its course. Laterally, it forms a similar backward curve, and there is no indication in this specimen that this sulcus continued farther back on the lateral surface than it did dorsally. However, it ends laterally just anterior to the posterior end of the specimen which is possibly not a perfect mould. This sulcus was similarly developed in specimen III, in which it is represented by a jugum cerebrale on the small part of the forebrain chamber wall preserved. Light streaks on each hemisphere of specimen I possibly represent the medial parts of corresponding sulci.

Such a lone transverse sulcus in the anterior cerebral regions is recorded, in variable positions, in some marsupials (*see* fig. 4), some but not all Chiroptera, and in insectivores (*see* fig. 3 A). It is variously termed in the descriptions of these different brains, usually sulcus orbitalis. In *Eohippus*, the further evolution of this transverse sulcus makes it clear that it is the presylvian (a sulcus which, incidentally, by some authors is called orbitalis although it is not a homologue of the orbital of the lower orders). As is the case with the lateral and suprasylvian sulci, it appears that only a part of the sulcus praesylvius of the later Equidae was developed in *Eohippus*.

However, with the material at hand it is not possible to decide definitely whether, as it seems, the presylvian sulcus was a short transverse furrow, or whether in *E. venticolus* it continued latero-ventrally toward the Sylvian region—to which condition in later forms it owes its name.

As far as can be judged from the short portion preserved, it appears that the *E. venticolus* forebrain was slightly broader than that of *E. validus*, and perhaps slightly higher. The infinitesimal difference is noted here only because *E. venticolus* is known as a more progressive species. It is not impossible that its cerebrum was somewhat larger, or even otherwise more advanced than the *E. validus* cerebrum. The greatest breadth preserved in II is at the anterior end of the suprasylvian sulcus; here, the right hemisphere was 11 mm. broad, the entire forebrain of I 20 mm. The difference seems even less as regards height. At the fracture, the suprasylvia is 24 mm. above the skull base in II; the corresponding height in I is 23 mm. Just in front of the cerebrum, at the olfactory peduncles, the two braincasts have the same height—14 mm. above the skull base.

Olfactory bulbs.—Both brain specimens show clearly that the olfactory bulbs lay entirely anterior to the cerebral hemispheres, to the degree of having olfactory peduncles. These are seen on the dorsal and lateral sides of both casts as circular furrows, about 1 mm. long. The *E. venticolus* cerebrum is detached in a perpendicular (but slightly oblique) break just across the peduncles so that its anterior view (fig. 3 B) shows the peduncles in cross section and at the same time reveals how high up on the cerebrum the olfactory bulbs were attached. In the base of the (*venticolus*) skull two grooves run steeply up to the peduncles alongside a median crista. The corresponding elevations on the cast are preserved in 5- and 6-mm. breadth—very broad and prominent olfactory tracts.

The anterior and lower surfaces of the olfactory bulbs, and much of the lateral sides, are not revealed. Specimen I shows the dorsal and lateral sides of the passage of the hemispheres into the bulbs (although a thin layer of bone covers the cast here). The latter widen anteriorly. The anterior end of the specimen is a crooked cross section of the bulbs. In II, the right bulb is laid open half way down the lateral side and from above, showing the position of the dorsal rim of the lamina cribrosa. Grooves moulded by the turbinals are seen in right side view (not figured) to radiate antero-basally from the anterior side of the olfactory bulb. (In front of the bone fragment covering the left bulb, the endocast of the nasal chamber likewise is moulded into parallel ridges by the turbinals; see fig. 3 A, Eth.) Specimen III supplements the picture. The oval impressions in the lower surface of this ethmoidal chamber roof suggest olfactory bulbi of 11 mm. length and 10 mm. maximum breadth. These are the dimensions of our *E. venticolus* bulbs. The incomplete *E. validus* cast suggests more slender bulbs, which possibly were somewhat longer.

The three specimens, taken together, show that the ethmoidal chamber of *Eohippus* occupied almost the entire height of the skull. Its roof is dense frontal bone, 2 mm. thick in II, somewhat over 3 mm. thick in III. There is only a 2-mm.-high corpus sphenoidei below the olfactory bulbs in the cross section which forms the anterior end of specimen I.

Cranial nerves.—There are no endocasts of nerve foramina on our specimens, except that of the internal acoustic meatus in I. Of the olfactory nerve entrance, nothing but the position of the upper border of the lamina cribrosa is shown, on the right side of specimen II only. However, the skull base adhering to brain No. I permitted study of the external surface of the nerve foramina. Cope commented but briefly upon these, only suggesting their identity ("I take to be . . .", "It is very probable . . ." 1884, p. 626, p. 632). Cope's basal skull view does not show them, and the base shown is different from ours in that the palate and the complete sphenoid alae are preserved. Our specimen displays the actual brain-case wall. It is criss-crossed by breaks, but careful preparation has ascertained the foramina as shown in figure 2, B and C. The XII to V exits are distributed as in *Equus,* but it is different with the eye group of nerves. The differences, however, are osteological; they do not signify any difference of the nerve roots themselves.

If this basal view of the *Eohippus* cranium is compared only with the outside (not the inside) of the *Equus* skull base, the anteriormost pair of basal foramina of *Eohippus,* next to the midline just behind the front end of the cerebral chamber, will be taken for the ethmoidal—that short transverse canal (shown in our *Equus occidentalis,* pl. 3) through which the ethmoidal branch of V^1 and the ethmoidal artery enter the ethmoidal fossa. There is no other foramen in this region in *Equus.* However, the ethmoidal foramen of *Eohippus* I must have lain in the region where neither bone nor endocast surface are preserved, anterior to and above the foramen in question. Preparation revealed that this foramen is the slitlike opening of a canal running backwards inside the skull base: it is the optic foramen.

Cope searched for this in vain, hence he suggested that the optic nerve entered by the sphenorbital foramen. The position of the optic foramen in *Eohippus* indeed reveals conditions very different from those found in *Equus;* in the horse, the entrance of the optic nerve into the skull lies not in the skull base but laterally, which means higher up.

The topographical relation of the optic foramen to the sphenorbital (eye-muscle nerves) foramen in *Eohippus* resembles the situation in the interior rather than on the outside of the *Equus* skull. The foramina lie one behind the other near the midline, as the nerve roots lie on the brain base. There was an optic canal, conducting the nerve relatively as far forward as in *Equus,* but it was longitudinal in the slender skull base of *Eohippus.* In correspondence with the greater breadth and height of its skull, the horse has 30-mm.-long optic canals diverging antero-dorso-laterally; the outside optic foramina are 55 mm. apart—only 7 mm. in *Eohippus.*

Inside the horse skull, the sphenorbital foramen is 12 mm. behind the optic foramen in the skull base. The outer foramen is immediately below the optic optic foramen—that is, laterally situated, under the postorbital process. The outer sphenorbital foramen in *Eohippus* is 9 mm. straight behind the optic foramen. The typical longitudinal ridge in the braincase wall above and in front of this foramen, preserved on the right side, identifies the exit of the eye-muscle nerves III, V_1, VI, and also IV. There is no sign of a separate trochlear foramen as is sometimes developed in *Equus.* Nor is there evidence of the wall of bone which in the horse leads the eye-muscle nerves forward in a 45-mm.-long canal. Only a low ridge runs forward on the skull base from the distal side of the sphenorbital foramen in this *Eohippus.* It is 5 mm. long and merges into smooth bone almost 5 mm. posterior to the optic foramen. There is no indication that a canal wall is broken off. It conforms with the slender and economic build of the *Eohippus* skull base that, in contrast to *Equus* with its broad sphenoidal sinuses, no sphenorbital canal was developed.

Behind the foramen sphenorbitale, and slightly lower, is the foramen rotundum (V_2). The horizontal bone plate which separates the course of the maxillary nerve from the eye-muscle nerve group for an extent of 27 mm. in *Equus* is 3 to 4 mm. long in *Eohippus;* the intracranial course of the maxillary nerve was short.

While the foramina described above, as well as the lacerum posterius and condyloid foramina, are filled with matrix which yields to the preparing needle, a clot of un-removable crystallized matter nestles in the posterior rim of the foramen rotundum. No bone could be detected between it and the softer matrix, so that at first it seemed to be part of the filling of the V_2 canal. However, the crystals have formed in a wider canal which did not contain a nerve but in which the internal maxillary artery ran outside the braincase proper. In the horse, this alar (alisphenoid) canal perforates the entire length of the pterygoid process of the sphenoid; its wide anterior opening is baso-medial to the foramen rotundum. Cope states that this canal was present in *Eohippus* (1884, p. 626). Our specimen shows its posterior entrance on the right side, as a notch just as in *Equus.* The pterygoid processes themselves however are both broken and chipped. Within that of the left side, part of the canal is seen. It is filled with shiny hard matter, and the course of this fragment points toward the proximal side of the foramen rotundum. The clot in the foramen rotundum of the opposite side therefore marks the anterior entrance of the alar canal. This was 8 mm. long; including the posterior notch it was 10 mm. These lengths are 25 and 36 mm. in *Equus.*

The acoustic foramen shows as a rough oval, 3.5 mm. long and 2.5 mm. high, in the otherwise smooth imprint of the left petrous temporal bone. It contained also the facial nerve root (fig. 2 C, VII–VIII). For comparison with later brain develop-ment, we note that the center of the internal acoustic meatus is 9 mm. posterior to the forebrain.

The foramen lacerum posterius is formed like that of the horse. In the anterior rim of its broad anterior part are the three notches incisura spinosa, ovalis (fig. 2 B, V_3), and carotidis. The narrow posterior part widens only superficially at its pos-tero-lateral end, below the laterally receding petrosal. It is through a slit just like the horse's that the nerves IX–XI and jugular vein left the braincase. The con-dyloid foramen, for nerve XII and condyloid vein, is also as in the horse; it is wide on the surface and narrows as it passes inwards.

COMPARISON

Living mammals.—No living ungulate has a brain similar to the brain of *Eohippus.* Among Recent Mammalia, the smaller have in general the more primitive brains. The smallest living ungulate genus, *Tragulus,* contains species considerably smaller than *Eohippus.* The length of skulls of *Tragulus javanicus* varies around two-thirds that of *Eohippus*. But *Tragulus* brains are miniature deer brains and possess all the principal sulci of the *Cervus elaphus* cerebrum (Kohlbrugge, 1902, p. 346). The brain of the rabbit-sized pygmy antelope *Cephalophus monticola* shows "an exceeding abundance of sulci" (Elliot Smith, 1902, p. 335). The smallest living subungulates are the Hyraces. The data of Elliot Smith (1902, p. 297–300, fig. 168–171), Weber (1928, fig. 262, 263), and Wells (1939) taken together show that *Procavia* skulls are 71–96 mm. long but contain cerebra 32–44 mm. long and 28–35 mm. broad. Cerebral height is 25–28 mm. About five-sixth of the height is neopallium with a "distinctly ungulate, though much simplified" fissuration (Elliot Smith, 1902, p. 297; *see* our fig. 7 B).

Apparently today no placental has a brain in which each part is on so low an evolutionary level as it was in *Eohippus*.

The most primitive brain among living placentals (fig. 4 A) is that of *Centetes*, the Malagasy insectivore which, among other peculiarly primitive characters, has litters of up to 21 young. Le Gros Clark's summary of the outstanding characteristics of the tenrec brain (1932, p. 976) reads like a description of the *Eohippus* brain (which, however, was twice as long): "the enormous olfactory bulbs, the large pyriform lobe and small neopallial development, the simple cerebellum, and the wide exposure of the corpora quadrigemina on the dorsal surface of the brain." Furthermore, *Centetes* too has no fossa Sylvii; it has only one sulcus.

However, the tenrec cerebrum is of a considerably broader (that is, more mammalian) type than that of *Eohippus*, and its posterior poles laterally almost reach the cerebellum. It should be noted that the latter difference between the brains is at once apparent in endocranial cast comparison.

Among the 17 endocranial casts of small mammals of Gervais' (1872, pl. XXI, fig. 8) *Centetes* strikes one as the most primitive, with its smooth cerebral hemispheres, and its large olfactory bulbs quite anteriorly situated. This somewhat artistic picture does not indicate the midbrain exposure at all; so little does this mould the skull that an unobservant draftsman can overlook the phenomenon in *Centetes*. However, the Museum of Comparative Zoölogy possesses a duplicate of the *Centetes* endocast mentioned by Elliot Smith (1909, p. 192). In this 31-mm.-long specimen (our fig. 4 B) there is, between forebrain and cerebellum, a transverse groove of slightly more than 1 mm. antero-posterior length; but, in contrast to the configuration in *Eohippus*, it fades out laterally where, in the brain of *Centetes*, cerebellum and forebrain are almost contiguous. A corresponding structure, a sort of broad tentorial crest is found inside *Centetes* skulls. The retrogressive changes said to take place in the ontogeny of the tenrec cannot account for this shape of the skull inside. If the interior of the skull had retained, or returned to the juvenile form of the brain (Le Gros Clark, 1932, fig. 2), there would have to be an extensive midbrain chamber. The form of the endocast of the adult *Centetes* just emphasizes the fact that even *Centetes* has a more progressive brain than *Eohippus* had. In those bats in which the midbrain is exposed, and the corpora quadrigemina may rise as high as the vermis cerebelli, endocasts show the midbrain; but the chiropteran cerebrum is a formation entirely different from the *Eohippus* forebrain; it has an extensive neopallium and a Sylvian fossa.

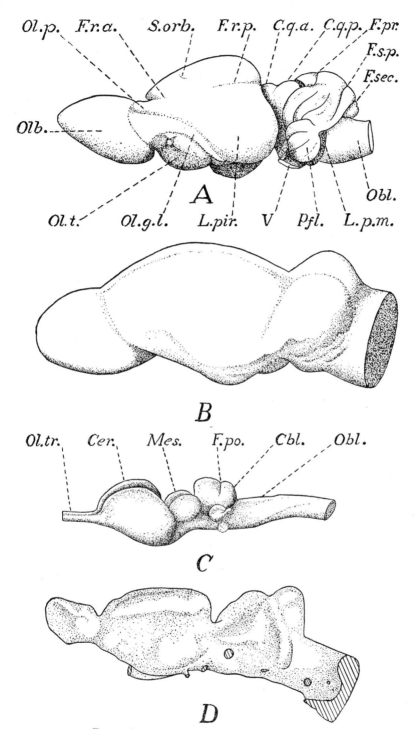

FIGURE 4.—*Centetes, Crocodilus, and Phenacodus*

(A, B) *Centetes ecaudatus* Schreb., brain (after Le Gros Clark) and endocranial cast (MCZ specimen), × 3. (C) *Croco-dilus porosus* Schneid., brain (after de Lange), × 1. (D) *Phenacodus primaevus* Cope, endocranial cast (after Simpson), × 1. Left side views.

29

One naturally looks to the monotremes and marsupials for a Recent brain of the primitive type found in *Eohippus*. The living monotremes, however, are as specialized in their brain forms as in other characters. Their midbrain is overlapped by the cerebrum. This is also the case in many marsupials, even in the otherwise very

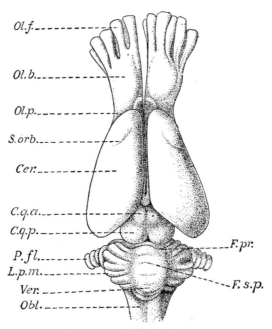

FIGURE 5.—*Didelphis virginiana*
Brain (after Voris and Hoerr), dorsal view. × ⅜.

primitive tiny brains of the miniature South American forms. Yet in that poly-protodont family whose body features make it "in almost every respect ideal ancestors for the whole marsupial group" (Romer, 1933, p. 264), brains occur in *Didelphis* whose form appears like a reconstruction of the brain which the endocranial cast of *Eohippus validus* suggests. Figure 5 shows such a brain; *see also* figure 21 A. In contrast to this specimen, in an opossum which I dissected I found the cerebrum in contact with the cerebellum laterally, and only the posterior corpora quadrigemina exposed. We know the midbrain region only in one individual of a primitive *Eohippus* species; conditions in *Didelphis* suggest that a degree of midbrain overlapping higher than in our specimen could occur within the genus *Eohippus*. On the other hand, we can assume that the following surface features were different from opossums in every *Eohippus*. The opossum has (1) the fissura prima cerebelli in a more anterior position than *Eohippus*, (2) the paraflocculi extending farther laterad, (3) the midbrain more narrow, (4) in a neocortex of similar shape and extent, only one constant sulcus, the orbital; this is an obliquely transverse furrow in a position different from that of the transverse sulcus in *Eohippus*. No longitudinal sulci are developed in *Didelphis*.

These differences of the brain surface appear more or less insignificant with respect to the evolutionary levels of the brain in the two genera. The similarity between the brains of *Eohippus* and *Didelphis* remains striking.

One is tempted to speculate whether the oldest of the Equidae had the mentality of an opossum. But do we know the mentality of the opossum? According to Seton the opossum "has no intelligence . . . is a silly grinning idiot" (1928, p. 882). Yet it can be domesticated and becomes attached to its master (Seton, 1928, p. 887). Its feigning death is an efficient defense. How can man pass judgment on a mammal which, with this brain, thrived during the entire age in which, *e.g.*, the Equidae evolved much higher-developed brains?

Speculative conclusions from the similarities of *Eohippus* and *Didelphis* brains are handicapped, furthermore, by the plain fact that *Eohippus* must have been a placental mammal, whereas *Didelphis* is a marsupial. The opossum brain, in form somewhat more primitive than the lowest developed brain of the other extant mammals, is considerably more primitive than the brains of all Placentalia in structures not seen on the surface. Like the monotremes, all marsupials lack the corpus callosum, the commissure of the placental neopallia. While the cellular structure of the diprotodont neopallium can be regarded as being on an evolutionary level similar to placental neopallia, cytological differentiation is extremely poor in the neopallium of the opossum (Riese, 1943). The opossum is the only mammal known to be born without a cerebral cortex or its primordium (Riese, 1945, p. 151).

Marsupials and placentals have been separate since the Cretaceous. Is it possible that in the early Eocene *Eohippus*, with a skeleton so definitely of placental type, had not developed in its brain (however primitive in form) the placental corpus callosum and neocortex structure? Ignoramus, et ignorabimus.

Reptiles.—The *Eohippus* endocranial cast is quite mammalian, in particular in that it has the form of the brain in contrast to endocasts of reptilian neurocrania. Yet the brain it represents still recalls reptilian brains. Comparison of the endocast of *Eohippus validus* with the modern horse brain on the one hand (fig. 21 B; pl. 2, fig. 3) and, on the other hand, with a brain as typically reptilian as that of a crocodile (fig. 4 C) shows that the *Eohippus* brain was more like the latter than like the former. In one detail there is a surprising conformity; the fissura prima cerebelli of *Eohippus* is located like the fissura posterior of the crocodilian cerebellum.

Jurassic mammals.—Shape and proportions of the brain of *Eohippus validus* appear to have been amazingly similar to those of the oldest mammalian brain we know. From fragments of skull roofs of three *Triconodon* Simpson has reconstructed an almost complete dorsal aspect of the brain (1927, fig. 1, fig. 4 B, p. 260–262). This tiny upper Jurassic brain must have been very much like that of *Eohippus*, except for the neopallium. There were no sulci, nor have any traces of sulci been found on the cerebrum fragments of two other Jurassic mammals studied by Simpson (1927).

Contemporary ungulates.—Endocranial casts are known of two other Wasatchian ungulates, *Coryphodon* and *Phenacodus*. The brains they represent were similar to the *Eohippus* brain in all important features. The only remarkable difference is clearly related to the fact that those animals were larger than *Eohippus*.

The brain of the giant amblypod *Coryphodon* has been studied by several authors (last by Tilney, 1931, and Edinger, 1933b), and a duplicate of the Marsh specimen is here in the MCZ.   Total, medullo-olfactory length is 110 mm.—that is, only about double the brain length of *Eohippus validus*.   However, 33 mm. of this length are post-cerebellar medulla oblongata—at least six times as much as in little *Eohippus*. Oblongatal breadth is stated by Tilney (p. 441) as 36 mm.; but this is the diameter only across the dorsal surface—34 mm. seems more correct to me.   Even so, the oblongata had almost four times the width in *Coryphodon* that it had in *Eohippus*. Oblongatal height (18 mm.) was almost double that of *Eohippus*.

The endocranial casts of *Coryphodon* do not give a clear picture of each brain portion.   In particular, the region between the cerebral and cerebellar vaults is so obscured that an exposed midbrain roof is only suggested.   The better-moulded parts show that other characteristic features of the *Eohippus* brain were similarly developed in this otherwise quite different, bulky beast.   Very large olfactory bulbs lay quite anterior to the cerebral hemispheres.   These were relatively small; definitely less than their dorsal halves was capped by a neopallium which lacks recognizable sulci.

While the 8-feet-long *Coryphodon* was a specialized peak of a peculiar order, the 5½-feet-long condylarth *Phenacodus* was a primitive ungulate, like *Eohippus;* but skeletal differences between these two genera are numerous, and the difference in body size is considerable.

The length of the *Phenacodus primaevus* skull compares to that of *Eohippus venticolus* as 1.75:1.   The brain (last described by Tilney, 1931; Simpson, 1933; *see* our fig. 4 D) naturally was relatively smaller in the larger form; medullo-olfactory length was 75 mm. (Tilney, 1931, p. 455), only 1.11 times the total brain length of *Eohippus validus*.   The heights of the medulla oblongata compare correspondingly, but oblongata breadth and post-cerebellar length of *Phenacodus* are more than twice those of *Eohippus*.   Otherwise there was amazingly little morphological difference between the two brains.

In the cerebellum of *Phenacodus*, the fissure now identified as the fissura prima between the "gently convex anterior lobe" (Simpson, 1933, p. 5; this is as in *Eohippus*) and the "sharp conical posterior lobe" (higher in the larger form), is also considerably behind the middle of the vermis, in contrast to living ungulates.   The lengths of the portions posterior and anterior to it compare as 1:1.7 in *Phenacodus*, 1:2 in *Eohippus*. A large depressed interval between cerebellum and forebrain corresponds to exposed corpora quadrigemina.   The cerebral hemispheres occupied about the same amount of the total brain length, comparing to those of *Eohippus* as 1.1:1.   However, they were considerably broader in *Phenacodus;* breadth was 1½ times the length, while in *Eohippus* it was less than the length.   Yet the degree of fissuration must have been similar in the large and the small animal.   There was only an emargination in the rhinal fissure of *Phenacodus* in place of a Sylvian fossa.   There was one large, definite longitudinal sulcus, the sulcus lateralis.   The presence of one more, the suprasylvian sulcus, stated by Tilney but accepted only as possible by Simpson, has become more probable since this sulcus has been found in the smaller *Eohippus*.   The presylvian sulcus, which was developed at least in two of the three *Eohippus* specimens, is not reported in *Phenacodus*. Yet it may have been developed in this genus. In the *Phenacodus primaevus* endocast, as in that of *Eohippus validus*, neocortical markings are indefinite and are different on the right and left sides. Considering the evolutionary level of the brains which these specimens represent, it seems probable that the indistinctness of the sulci, and the variability of their occurrence in similar brains, are not impressions obtained by our having only the endocranial casts for brain studies; sulcus development and configuration are extremely variable in Recent brains in the initial stage of fissuration, such as rodent, chiropteran, and hyrax brains.

It may be mentioned here that the notoungulate *Notostylops* (Simpson, 1932b; 1933), presumably also of Lower Eocene age, had a brain of the same primitive type as *Coryphodon, Phenacodus* and *Eohippus*. In the *Notostylops* endocranial casts, too, the large olfactory bulbs and the midbrain are fully exposed; the small neopallium had only two, more or less distinct longitudinal sulci and possibly a Sylvian fissure.

SUMMARY

In the brain of *Eohippus*, as portrayed in an almost complete endocranial cast of *E. validus* and an endocast fragment of *E. venticolus*, every portion is in a primitive stage of mammalian brain evolution. No Recent mammalian brain has this combination of primitive features.

The cerebellum was of mammalian type, as cerebellar hemispheres were well developed between the vermis and the flocculi. There is, however, no indication of the lobulation so characteristic of mammalian cerebella. One transverse fissure was developed on the vermis, which thus resembled the vermis of crocodiles rather than that of living mammals. This fissure, the fissura prima cerebelli, was in a more posterior position than in the later Equidae.

The midbrain was apparently not overlapped either by the cerebellum or the cerebrum.

The cerebrum was not higher, and only negligibly broader, than the cerebellum. Neopallium capped somewhat less than the dorsal half of the cerebral hemisphere. A transverse sulcus existed in the anterior region of the neopallium, a short longitudinal sulcus in the middle region, and a longer longitudinal sulcus in the posterior region. Probably not even these three sulci were developed in all *Eohippus* hemispheres.

The olfactory bulbs were anterior to, and almost as high as, the cerebrum.

Whereas the foramina of the posterior cranial nerves were arranged and formed as in *Equus*, the exits and entrances of the anterior cranial nerves were more concentrated in the skull base; foramina sufficed where nerve canals were developed in the larger skulls of the descendants of *Eohippus*.

The outstanding characters of the skeleton place *Eohippus* with the Equidae; the osteologist can see the future horse in this Lower Eocene form. The brain connects *Eohippus* only with the past. The ancestral brain, an unspecialized mammalian brain, was held over in the equid body. No feature of this brain signals the future.

MIDDLE EOCENE (BRIDGERIAN): *OROHIPPUS*

STAGE IN PHYLOGENY

In *Orohippus*, the teeth were slightly advanced over *Eohippus*, and the rudiments of toes I and V had disappeared; but the forefoot still had four functional digits, and body size had not risen above that attained in the genus *Eohippus*. Shoulder height of the only mounted skeleton, *O. osbornianus*, is 330 mm. (Colbert, M.S.), its skull length 140 mm. (Granger, 1908, p. 253; "a medium sized form from the lower horizon," p. 252).

MATERIAL

I. *Orohippus* sp., YPM No. VP-13298 (fig. 6), is from Henry's Fork, Wyoming a locality from which Granger (1908) records remnants of five species of *Orohippus*. Among these, only an *O. osbornianus* skull contains a portion offering comparison with the present specimen—the occipital wings, partly reconstructed, however, in Granger's fig. A, pl. XVII. Occipital breadth is 20 mm. both in that figure and in the Yale specimen. The latter is mainly a cerebellum chamber. The base is missing; the occiput is broken off basally just anterior to the foramen magnum. A part of the skull roof dorso-anteriorly adjoining the cerebellar chamber is preserved; this had been cleaned inside when I received the specimen. We removed all left-side bone, laying half open the cerebellum cast and a median sagittal section of the parieto-occipital skull roof which, between (except for the sagittal crest) thin plates of dense bone, consists of even-sized spongy cellules. The tentorium osseum extends 12 mm. below the outside of the skull roof, whereas the corresponding structure in *Eohippus* must have been but 7 or 8 mm. deep. This difference in the skull corresponds to the change in brain form which had taken place in the evolution from *Eohippus* to *Orohippus*.

II. *Orohippus osbornianus* (Cope), AMNH 12648 (fig. 7), is from Bridger B 1, 6 miles south of Granger, Bridger Basin, Wyoming. In the right side of the neuro-cranium of this mounted skeleton, a gap in the bone wall forms an irregular, roughly pear-shaped window in which is seen the circumsylvian area of the forebrain cast. The exposed area extends from about 27 mm. to about 45 mm. anterior to the (partly preserved) planum nuchale, but basally it is only about 10 mm. long. Its height ranges from 17 to 23 mm. Its lower rim is just above the posterior insertion of the temporal arch. The skull is laterally compressed so that this insertion is only about 6 mm. lateral to, and 32 mm. below, the sagittal crest, while on the left side these numbers are 20 and 22 mm., respectively. Yet within the window, above a small rough area, there is undistorted brain surface. The quality of the mould is demonstrated by the fact that it even reproduces a delicate blood vessel. This vessel rises from a point 6 mm. from the anterior end of the base of the window, becomes thinner, turns more backward in its upward course, and disappears under the bone forming the upper rim of the window, at 3 mm. from the window's posterior border. Just above the middle of its exposed course this vessel gives off anteriorly a slightly thinner branch which runs upward and forward for about 1.5 mm., then turns backward to assume a course almost parallel to the stem. All this corresponds exactly with the upper part and ramification of the median ramus of the arteria carotis cerebralis of the sheep brain injected by Hofmann (1900, pl. IX, fig. 22).

DESCRIPTION

Cerebellum.—As the hind end of specimen I is the planum nuchale, the endocast portion broken away posteriorly represented mainly the free part of the medulla

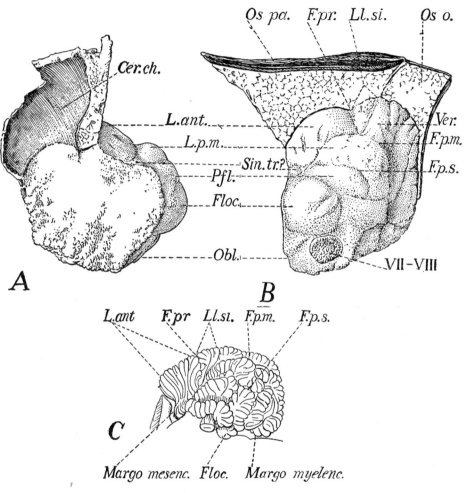

FIGURE 6.—*Orohippus and Equus*

(A, B) *Orohippus* sp., natural endocast of cerebellar chamber with medio-sagitally sectioned roof bones, anterior and left side views. × 1.9. (C) *Equus caballus*, cerebellum, left side view (after Bolk). × 0.6

oblongata. The cerebellar cast is almost complete on the exposed left side. Its antero-posterior length is 19 mm.; its largest lateral circumference is 13 mm. from the median plane; cerebellar width thus was about 26 mm.

The vermis was straight. Its posterior part is more vaulted than in *Eohippus* and has several transverse fissures. It is separated from the almost smooth and lower anterior part by the deepest of the transverse furrows—the fissure which in *Eohippus* is the only one distinctly moulded. In this *Orohippus* specimen, the inner plate of the parietal bone is seen protruding downward into this fissure, forming a

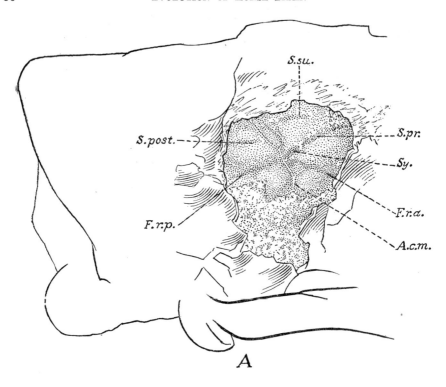

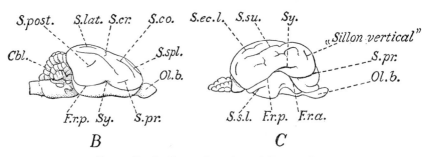

FIGURE 7.—*Orohippus, Procavia, and Equus embryo*

(A) *Orohippus osbornianus* (specimen no. II). Posterior skull region in right lateral view, with window showing circumsylvian brain region. × 2. (B, C) Right lateral views of extant ungulate brains showing certain similarities to *Orohippus*. (B) *Procavia capensis* Pallas (after Elliot Smith), × ⅔. (C) *Equus caballus* L., embryo of 113 mm. head length (after Anthony and Grzybowski), × ⅔.

transverse internal crest like a jugum cerebrale—an osteological demonstration of the depth of the fissure. Just behind this fissure of the vermis the paramedian sulcus is conspicuously shallow; the two lobules of the vermis just posterior to the fissure obviously continued laterally into the paramedian lobe. It is behind the fissura prima that the two lamellae of the lobulus simplex (of Bolk; area lunata of Elliot

Smith) stretch right across the paramedian fissure in various mammals. This fact, together with the relative smoothness of the lobe anterior to it, decide the identity of the fissure. It is the fissura prima, the first vermis fissure appearing in mammalian ontogenesis, and usually the deepest in the adult. It lies farther forward in *Orohippus* than in *Eohippus*, *viz.*, in the middle of the antero-posterior length.

The transverse sulci posterior to the fissura prima cannot be named because probably one or two baso-posterior lamellae of the vermis are not included in the cast, and because there is no indication in the cast of the different depth of the sulci. It is their presence and arrangement which are significant. They show that the vermis of *Orohippus* was like that of small living ungulates. It consisted of anterior and posterior lobes, with relatively few lobules, and a median lobe with narrower lobules.

The paramedian sulcus is well moulded. The lateral lobe is practically smooth in the cast. The parasagittal (parafloccular) sulcus is well recognizable too, setting off the floccular lobe. There is a third parasagittal sulcus on a lower level. This sulcus lies, relatively, on a higher plane than in the modern horse, indicating a relatively larger flocculus. The flocculus set off by this sulcus in *Orohippus* was 8 mm. high and 8 mm. long and protruded laterad by about 1 mm.

Below the flocculus, in the smooth impression of a part of the petrosal bone, a rough subcircle 5 mm. high and 4 mm. long represents the porus acusticus internus (fig. 6, VII, VIII). Its center is in a vertical plane about 7 mm. posterior to the posterior poles of the cerebral hemispheres.

On the dorsal surface a horizontal triangle is inserted anteriorly between floccular lobe and vermis; it probably represents the posterior curve of the transverse venous sinus.

The tentorium osseum tapers basally to a thin transverse crest.

The cross section through the osseous falx cerebri at the anterior end of this specimen (see below) shows that the falx had a concave lower surface. This concavity in the posterior region of the falx, 8 mm. broad, roofed the space which was occupied by the tonguelike anterior extremity of the vermis cerebelli.

There is no possibility to know whether or not anterior to this space a median area of the midbrain was exposed. A more complete *Orohippus* endocast will have to decide about that. Laterally, there was no space between the cerebellar and forebrain chambers; cerebellum and forebrain touched, and overlapped the midbrain.

Cerebral hemispheres.—In the anterior aspect of the specimen I fragment (fig. 6 A), description has to distinguish two portions. The lower portion consists of matrix. This is the endocranial cast of the lower brain at the anterior end of the cerebellum. The original outline is not moulded at the right side, and an unknown quantity is missing at the base. The upper portion consists of bone. Although fragmentary, too, it still reveals certain features of the cerebral hemispheres. Its apex is a break through the parietal crest, immediately anterior to its splitting into the temporal crests. (The left temporal crest is seen, cross-sectioned, in figure 6 A.)

The rough median part of the bone—the cross section through the falx cerebri— is hour-glass-like constricted. The concavities of its outline correspond to the median convexities of the cerebral hemispheres. Smooth bone shells spread laterally (the left is removed). They housed the dorso-posterior forebrain poles. This doubly concave transverse wall is almost perpendicular basally. This means that the occipital cortex projected backward hardly more than 1 mm. in the first 5 mm. of its posterior facies; above these, the profile curves forward. The bone appears completely smooth. An unfissured occipital cortex is suggested, even though some firmly adhering matrix particles may somewhat obscure the internal bone surface.

The greatest forebrain breadth in this occipital region was 25 mm., the same as in *Eohippus validus*. Brain height was more, but presumably not much more than the preserved 30 mm. A similar measurement in *Eohippus*—viz., brain height just posterior to the highest forebrain vault—is about 23 mm. It is much less because it does not really correspond; in *Eohippus*, the mesencephalon lies posterior to this region, while in *Orohippus* it has been overarched by the forebrain. No skull height of *Orohippus* is known, as the only existing skull is badly crushed laterally. The formation of the brain in *Orohippus* definitely suggests that the forebrain chamber had achieved a higher vault than in *Eohippus*, in skulls of similar length. The similarity of the skull lengths on the one hand, and the difference in brain structure on the other hand, permit an estimate of the length of the *Orohippus* cerebrum. We know that the hemispheres did not expand over the olfactory bulbs, because this was not the case in the Oligocene descendants of *Orohippus*. Posteriorly, however, the cerebral hemispheres had expanded and achieved contact with the cerebellum. Their length was, consequently, at least the added lengths of the *Eohippus* forebrain and midbrain; this sum is 34 mm. in the small species *E. validus*.

Specimen II likewise suggests that the exposed 17 mm. represent an area about half the antero-posterior extent of the cerebrum, in the middle of its right side.

From the posterior border of the exposed area a well-moulded fissura rhinalis posterior runs forward, rising slightly. It is continued anteriorly in a very shallow furrow with which it forms a wide angle; this furrow, therefore, is the anterior rhinal fissure.

Above the apex of this angle, there is a 1.5 mm.-long dent in the brain surface, delimited dorsally by a semicircle. This is the only sinuous line on this otherwise straightly fissured cortex; it was the phylogenetical beginning of the Sylvian fossa. An obviously corresponding formation has been described by Elliot Smith (1902, p. 299) in one of his hyrax brains (our fig. 7 B) as a very slight notch in the upper lip of the right rhinal fissure, similar to the Sylvian fossa of some Viverridae, but so faint on the left hemisphere that it seemed "of doubtful significance." Conditions in *Orohippus* permit no doubt. Additional evidence as to the character of the notch above the angle of the rhinals comes from the blood vessel moulded on our specimen. The median ramus of the cerebral carotid ran over the brain surface in *Orohippus* and rose across the posterior side of the Sylvian notch; where a fossa is developed (*e.g.*, in sheep; *Mesohippus*, see fig. 9 B), a corresponding section of this artery is submerged into the fossa.

Separated from the Sylvian dent by a very short and low elevation of the endocast surface, there rises anteriorly a long, distinct furrow whose course is ended, in this specimen, by the antero-dorsal rough area. It represents an apparently long sulcus which rises diagonally over the lateral brain surface, beginning in the immediate vicinity of the Sylvia.   It is difficult to identify a sulcus in this position with any known sulcus of the ungulate brain.   I believe that it is the course, over the lateral surface, of the presylvian sulcus.   The presylvian is not so near the Sylvian fossa in either the living ungulates or the fossil descendants of *Orohippus*.   We must remember, however, (1) that the dorsal leg of the presylvian existed already in *Eohippus* so that a laterad extension was to be expected in the further evolution of the Equidae; (2) that sulci are extremely variable in primitive brains.   For example, on the right side of the hyrax brain which is shown in figure 7 B, the presylvian sulcus is a short furrow, but on the left hemisphere of this specimen it joins the anterior rhinal fissure (Elliot Smith, 1902, p. 299).   In another hyrax brain, the praesylvius is not developed at all (1902, p. 300).   From *Mesohippus* onward, the presylvian sulcus rises more anteriorly than the sulcus of *Orohippus* and joins the anterior rhinal fissure.   Possibly with the evolution of a Sylvian fossa and circumsylvian gyri the ventral extremity of the presylvian was removed from the proximity of the Sylvia, shifted anterad, and thus came into contact with the fissura rhinalis anterior.

The suprasylvian sulcus is developed only as a 4.5-mm.-long, straight, horizontal, shallow but definite furrow.   Another shallow horizontal sulcus—the sulcus posticus —is present posteriorly, at a level 3 mm. below the suprasylvian, 4 mm. above the posterior rhinal fissure.

COMPARISON

Eohippus.—Endocast material of *Orohippus* consists only of half a cerebellum of *O.* sp. and a circumsylvian area of *O. osbornianus*.   This scanty direct evidence, however, together with the interior aspect of the posterior extremity of a forebrain chamber, and the knowledge of the brain of both the ancestor and the descendants of *Orohippus*, convey a fairly reliable picture of the most important features of the *Orohippus* brain.

In striking contrast to bones, teeth, and body size, considerable development had taken place in the brain from *Eohippus* to *Orohippus*.

The cerebellum was higher vaulted, considerably more laminated, and longer. While the vermis of *Eohippus* was as poorly folded as is that of some Insectivora, that of *Orohippus* was definitely that of a small representative of the higher mammalian orders.   It was not, however, twisted, nor was it as complexly fissured as that of a modern horse.   In the floccular lobe, preponderance of flocculus over paraflocculus can be regarded as a primitive evolutionary stage.   This condition, different from that in the horse, is today found in the tapir whose cerebellum is called "exceedingly simple" by Elliot Smith (1902, p. 310).   The expansion in length of the vermis had taken place in a forward direction.   The fissura prima was moved forward to the middle of the vermis, that is, nearer to its position in *Equus*.   The minor part played by the cerebellum in midbrain overlapping had been achieved; the vermis tongue had come to lie between the posterior poles of the forebrain hemispheres.

There is no evidence that the midbrain roof was exposed in *Orohippus*.   The evidence at hand shows cerebellum and forebrain in contact. However, in a narrow median area, our specimens offer no indication of the configuration anterior to the vermis tongue. It is possible that a very small median portion of the midbrain roof was not overlapped (this has been observed in one small living artiodactyl, *Madoqua;* see Beddard, 1909, p. 190).

That the forebrain had considerably expanded posteriorly follows from the fact that its posterior poles are, in *Orohippus*, in contact with the cerebellum, across the midbrain. Besides, the occipital profile of the hemispheres, which was a low forward curve in *Eohippus*, not only had risen to a perpendicular line, but had a slight backward bulge. No sulci were found in the occipital cortex region.

The rhinal fissure was not a straight line as it had been in *Eohippus*, but its anterior and posterior legs formed an angle. It is from conditions in *Mesohippus* rather than from the *Orohippus* specimen at hand that we know that the rhinal fissure was still on a high level of the lateral brain surface. A small depressed area above the apex of the rhinalis angle represents the earliest Sylvian fossa in our series. Fissuration shows definite progress over the *Eohippus* stage. The sulci still were straight furrows without rami. Of the suprasylvian system only the pars media sulci suprasylvi was developed, and this was only slightly longer than it had been in *Eohippus*. An oblique sulcus has developed on the lateral surface of the cerebrum; as this is presumably the lateral leg of the presylvian, this sulcus had come to be in *Orohippus* relatively as long as it is in the later Equidae. Furthermore, a sulcus not developed at all in *Eohippus*, the sulcus posticus, is observed in the small region revealed of the neocortex of *Orohippus*. Its presence suggests that more than this one of the many sulci of the later Equidae may have come into existence in the Middle Eocene.

Procavia.—In the Middle Eocene the equid brain had become comparable to the brains of living mammals of the higher orders. *Orohippus* did not have the brain that would today be found in an ungulate of similar body size; in fact even the tiniest Recent ungulates do not have brains as primitive as the brain of *Orohippus* probably was. However, in several important characters our *Orohippus* brain material resembles the slightly smaller brain of the much smaller hyrax (fig. 7 B). The uncomplicated cerebellum, its relation to the cerebrum, the incipient fossa Sylvii, and the existence of few, widely spaced, simple neocortical sulci are features similarly developed in the Middle Eocene collie-sized perissodactyl and in the living hare-sized subungulate. On the other hand, hyrax brains have progressive features not observed in our *Orohippus* material. Hyraces have a long, arched suprasylvian sulcus; a short ectosylvian sulcus can occur (Wells, 1939, p. 371); the fossa Sylvii is not in all brains an indistinct small groove as in *Orohippus*, but it was developed as a deep sulcus in an undisclosed number of Wells' eight hyrax brains (1939, p. 371) and in one of the seven brains investigated by Elliot Smith (1902, p. 299). It remains a question whether this higher degree of Sylvia development occurred in *Orohippus*. Even though the skull of *Orohippus* is distorted, there can be no doubt that the rhinal fissure delimited the neocortex at a considerably higher level than it does in *Procavia*. Consequently, the neocortical area was considerably smaller in the fossil equid than in the Recent subungulate. Furthermore, the olfactory bulbs of the hyrax are much lower formations than the cerebral hemispheres. Oligocene equid brains reveal that the olfactory bulbs of *Orohippus* must have been almost as high as the *Orohippus* cerebrum; this is another feature more primitive in *Orohippus* than in *Procavia*.

Contemporary perissodactyls.—The brains of several ungulates contemporary with *Orohippus* are known. In none of them was the midbrain exposed on the brain surface; even the queerly primitive brain of the giant Amblypoda had progressed beyond at least this reptilian character. Brains of four genera of Bridgerian perissodactyls have been discussed in the literature (recently: Edinger, 1929, p. 171–172, 178–179; Osborn, 1929, p. 792–796, 881–883; Wood, 1934, p. 273–275). They all belonged to animals far larger than *Orohippus*, but they do not all show the higher degree of forebrain fissuration which among living mammals usually would distinguish larger forms from their smaller congeners.

The skulls of the bulky titanotheres *Palaeosyops leidyi* and *Mesatirhinus petersoni* were three times as long as the *Orohippus* skull. The *Palaeosyops* endocast is a complete one. In Osborn's figures (fig. 713 A dorsal view, fig. 716 A left side view) one notes the large and high olfactory bulbs, a Sylvian fossa, and several arched sulci. Of *Mesatirhinus* there exist two endocasts, neither of them complete with olfactory bulbs. One specimen (Osborn, 1929, fig. 716 C) seems to have, like *Orohippus*, extensive smooth neocortex areas. The other specimen (Edinger, 1929, fig. 161; Osborn, 1929, fig. 716 B) is the smaller of the two but gives the impression of a somewhat higher degree of fissuration; there is a deep fossa Sylvii, and the sulci are longer. This still primitive fissuration was that of cerebral hemispheres 62 mm. long—that is, of a cerebrum approximately double the size of the *Orohippus* cerebrum. It seems, consequently, that, within the Perissodactyla, during Middle Eocene times, body size only gradually began to play its role in the expansion of the neocortex by infolding.

The Bridger Rhinoceridae are another example of this. At least some individuals of these relatively large forms must have had cerebra of *Orohippus* type. The first, Lower Bridgerian rhinoceros, *Hyrachyus*, was still closely related to the Equidae but was the size of a wolf. Estimated skull lengths (Wood, 1934, p. 278, 279) are about $1\frac{3}{4}$ times the *Orohippus* skull length. The brain of *Hyrachyus* is figured only in one of those semidiagrammatical Marshian pictures of endocast in skull, in dorsal view, with no scale given (Marsh, 1884, fig. 71). The three or four sulci which this drawing shows on the dorsal surface of the right hemisphere suggest a stage of fissuration similar to that suggested by our *Orohippus* brain fragment. In the brain of the Upper Bridgerian *Colonoceras* (Marsh, 1884, fig. 70; redrawn by Edinger, 1929, fig. 151) the cerebral hemispheres appear to be a short portion, but they were broad, and they probably were $1\frac{1}{2}$ times as long as those of *Orohippus*. This form had several long and arched neocortical sulci.

SUMMARY

Half a cerebellum with the adjacent wall of the cerebral chamber, and the circumsylvian area of one cerebral hemisphere are all that we know of the brain of *Orohippus*. These regions, however, were significantly different from the corresponding ones in the *Eohippus* brain. While still not like brains of similar-sized living ungulates, the Middle Eocene equid brain had acquired characters similar to those of a small Recent subungulate brain.

The highly vaulted vermis of *Orohippus* was folded into numerous lobuli. The fissura prima cerebelli was in a more anterior position than it had been in the Lower Eocene genus. The midbrain was either completely or almost completely overlapped. The enlarged cerebrum had developed a small but definite Sylvian fossa. At least one more sulcus than in *Eohippus* had appeared in the neopallium of *Orohippus*.

UPPER EOCENE (*UINTAN*)

No skull is known of the Uinta stage of the Equidae; there is no brain material. The dentition of *Epihippus* was close to that of, and the animal presumably was only slightly larger than, *Orohippus*.

Upper Eocene equoid cerebra are known from Europe, namely, a small part of that of *Anchilophus desmaresti* (Weinberg, 1903), and those of *Palaeotherium kleini* (Dietrich, 1936, p. 194, fig. 41, 43) and of *P. medium* (Cuvier, 1822, p. 37–38, pl. LV, fig. 1). These animals' large body size and the advanced character of their hard parts are reflected in their forebrain configuration. *Palaeotherium kleini* was of *Mesohippus* size and in its neocortical fissuration had reached the stage attained by the Equidae in the Oligocene. The forebrain hemispheres of *P. medium* are 3 times as long as those of our *Eohippus validus*, $1\frac{1}{3}$ as long as the average *Mesohippus* cerebra, and as abundantly convoluted as those of Miocene Equidae.

MIDDLE OLIGOCENE (ORELLAN): *MESOHIPPUS*
STAGE IN PHYLOGENY

Mesohippus, three-toed and three-fingered, browsing Chadronian and Orellan genus, had far advanced over the Eocene Equidae in specialization of extremities and teeth. It also was from its start, and increasingly became in time, a much larger form. Shoulder heights of mounted Middle Oligocene *M. bairdii* are 450 mm. (AMNH) and 515 mm. (MCZ), of *M. barbouri* 510 mm. (MCZ); Abel contends that the average was 610 mm. in *M. bairdii* (1928, p. 31). The MCZ skeleton of *M. bairdii* as mounted, with hanging tail, is 920 mm. long. Robb's five skull lengths of *M. bairdii* are 172 (that of the AMNH skeleton) to 190 mm. (1935, p. 43).

MATERIAL

Owing to the abundance of *Mesohippus* in the Middle Oligocene and to the wealth of skulls imbedded in fine-grained undisturbed matrix in American collections, reports of four brains of *Mesohippus* (*M.* sp. and *M. bairdii*) have already been published.

Osborn (1890, p. 87–88, fig. 10) described an excellent natural endocast, Scott (1891, p. 312; reprinted in Scott, 1941, p. 918) another complete one, and Moodie (1922, p. 367–368, fig. 24, 25k) a natural endocast of the forebrain chamber. Moodie's specimen is (as Dr. Claude W. Hibbard kindly informed me) *M. bairdii* from the Lower Brulé Clay, Orellan age, of Custer County, South Dakota. Only Tilney (1931, p. 479–481, fig. 25, 26) gave a thorough description, including fissure identification of a specimen which, however, unfortunately was only a plaster cast of a natural endocranial cast.

The following description is based on seven natural endocasts. It includes those formerly described, except Moodie's fragmentary specimen. Thus it was possible to gain a fairly complete picture of the *Mesohippus* brain as it was in the heyday of the genus, the Middle Oligocene.

I. *Mesohippus* sp., a natural endocranial cast in the Amherst College Museum (fig. 8). A plaster replica of this specimen was described by Tilney as a Lower Oligocene *M. bairdii*—a *contradictio in adjecto*. In Amherst it is listed as from the Middle Oligocene of Indian Creek, Wyoming. Doctor Phleger suggested that I decide its age. This brain is somewhat smaller than the definitely Middle Oligocene specimens, its relative cerebral height is lower, its frontal lobe appears to have been shorter, and its cerebral sulci are generally straighter. This brain may have belonged to an adult individual of a small, and perhaps primitive, kind of *Mesohippus*. However, its geological age cannot be decided from the brain form alone, and this specimen lacks entirely bones and teeth. Tilney's list of its defects, "in the olfactory bulbs, medulla oblongata and lateral lobes of the cerebellum," is not a complete one. Some regions of the lateral cerebral convexity do not represent brain surface but are rough, and two smaller areas are obscured by bone particles. This is not recognizable in the plaster replica. Thus, Tilney's "Deep Sylvian fossa . . . a prominent landmark on the lateral surface" (1932, p. 481) are wide dents caused by destruction of the original surface in both Sylvian areas. A rough band intervenes between the cerebral and cerebellar surfaces; this is a section through the internal occipital protuberance. With removal of the skull base, the brain base has been destroyed, but only anterior to the foramen lacerum posterius so that the basal bulge of the pyriform lobe is preserved. Casts of the olfactory chambers are entirely lacking. Their breaking off provided a good cross section of the dorsal rim of their insertion on the cerebral cast. Ventrally this steeply oblique break slopes into the break which removed the brain base.

II. *Mesohippus* sp., PU 11114 (fig. 11 C). This fragmentary skull from the *Oreodon* beds of South Dakota had a 65 mm.-long series of six functioning teeth: P^1; DP^2–DP^4 (worn); M^1; and the M^2 quite unworn. The M^2 erupts at 2 years in the horse. Germs were discovered of P^2, which in the horse erupts at the age of $2\frac{1}{2}$ years, and of the very unfinished crown of M^3 whose average period of eruption is at $3\frac{1}{2}$ to 4 years in the horse (Sisson, 1917, p. 403). Thus, the age of this individual corresponded to an *Equus caballus* between 2 and $2\frac{1}{2}$ years old. (Incidentally, this is an age between Matthew's (1924, p. 163) stages 2 and 3 of *Merychippus* from the Stonehouse Draw quarry where intermediates are not found, as entombment occurred only at one definite season each year). The distance from the lateral notch of the foramen magnum to the anterior border of P^1 is 130 mm. Removal of all detachable bone from the endocast revealed a well-moulded brain surface except along the forebrain vault; it seems that the matrix had not filled the cavity up to the roof.

III. *Mesohippus bairdii*, MCZ 18111 (fig. 11 A), the skull from Nebraska whose endocast was described by Osborn.

I believe this specimen is also mentioned in a publication of a quite different nature—Marcou's biography of Louis Agassiz. As this book is not readily obtainable,
I shall insert here the whole paragraph which, in my opinion, refers to our *Mesohippus* III. It is one of those fascinating illustrations of the force which built the
Museum of Comparative Zoölogy, the irresistible charm of its founder.

"Among the few specimens I had kept from my numerous geological explorations was the head
of a mammifer of the Miocene of Nebraska, showing the brain, with even a little reddish colour of
the animal's blood on it. Agassiz tried two or three times to get it for the Museum. I resisted,
wishing to keep it as a memento of my excursion in Nebraska in 1863. When on the point of leaving
for a long sojourn in Europe in 1864, Agassiz gave a large dinner party in my honour; and as soon as
we were all seated at table, in a loud voice, with an imploring tone and in the most friendly way, he
begged for that specimen so hard that it would have seemed cruel to deny his request. In fact,
that day he acted like a spoiled child who wanted a long-desired toy. Of course he got it" (Marcou,
1896, vol. II, p. 227).

The skull base and muzzle are left *in situ*. The teeth are very worn; this was a
small old individual. In addition to the upper side of the olfactory bulbs, the upper
and lateral sides of the cerebrum, and some features of the cerebellum, this specimen
exhibits much of the endocast of the nasal chamber.

IV. *Mesohippus bairdii*, AMNH 9768 (fig. 11 B), from the Lower *Oreodon* beds
of the White River Group, Spring Draw Basin, South Dakota. This specimen is
preserved similar to III, but the posterior half of the right forebrain hemisphere and
the cerebellum with most of the foramen magnum are destroyed. The age of this
animal corresponded to a horse just over 4 years old; in the 69 mm.-long P²-M³
series, only M¹ shows slight signs of wear. (This stage, too, does not occur among
the Stonehouse Draw Merychippi but is between their stages 3 and 4. As Matthew
found a more rapid development in *Merychippus* than in *Equus* (1924, p. 164),
Mesohippus IV was presumably not 4 but 3 years old.)

V. *Mesohippus bairdii*, AMNH 39408 (fig. 10)—Orellan, White River group,
Cedar Draw, South Dakota: a natural cast of the forebrain chamber so excellently
moulded that one sees delicate vessels spreading all over the dorsal brain surface.
All sides of the cerebrum can be studied, but baso-anteriorly breaks have removed
the olfactory tract region and the lower side of the olfactory bulbs. Only the dorsal
surface of the proximal part of the bulbs is preserved. Their attachment to the
anterior poles of the hemispheres is obscured by adhering bone substance. A mass
of spongiosa has remained medially at the posterior forebrain poles, hiding about
three-fifths of their breadth. A fortunate break behind the forebrain has removed
the matrix just along the posterior surface of the tentorium. It laid open a feature
not yet described in fossil Equidae; the smooth deep median groove (fig. 10 B) represents the opercule vermien of Albrecht (1884, p. 145), "très manifeste chez les Equidés"(Le Double, 1902, p. 77). The mould of this groove—that is, the anterior
facies of the vermis—is the only shaped area in the piece of matrix which forms the
posterior end of the specimen, and is not shown in the figure.

VI. *Mesohippus* sp., PU 12304 (fig. 9; pl. 1, fig. 1) is another skull from the *Oreodon*
beds of South Dakota from which the roof and sidewalls of the neurocranium and
of the posterior part of the nasal chamber have been removed as far as feasible.
The splendid endocast was briefly described by Scott as the brain of a larger animal,

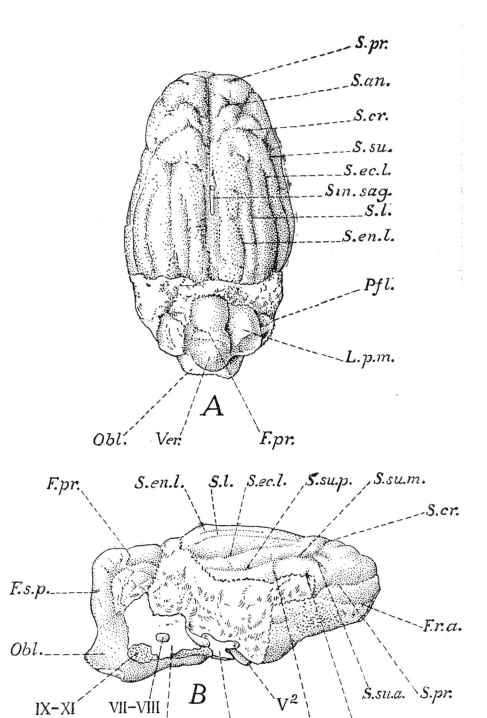

FIGURE 8.—*Mesohippus*

Specimen no. I.   (A) Dorsal, (B) right side view.   × 1

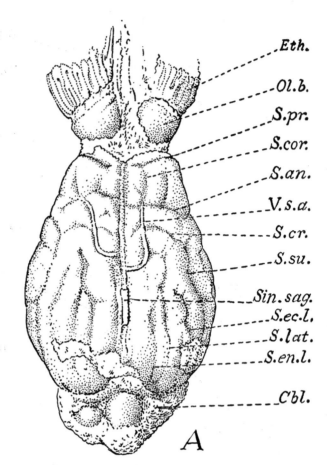

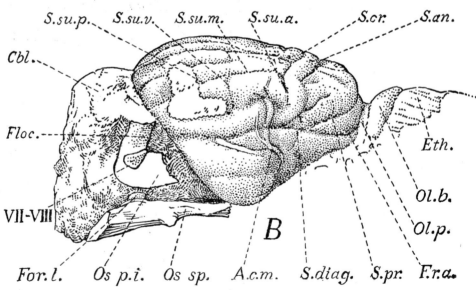

FIGURE 9.—*Mesohippus*

Specimen no. VI. **(A) Dor**sal, (B) right side view. ✕ 1

46

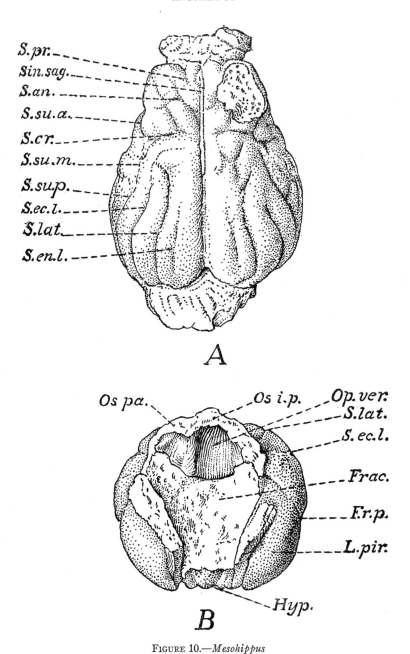

S.pr.
Sin.sag.
S.an.
S.su.a.
S.cr.
S.su.m.
S.sup.
S.ec.l.
S.lat.
S.en.l.

A

Os pa.
Os i.p.
Op.ver.
S.lat.
S.ec.l.
Frac.
Fr.p.
L.pir.
Hyp.

B

FIGURE 10.—*Mesohippus*

Specimen no. V.   (A) Dorsal, (B) postero-ventral view.   × 1

and perhaps larger species than Osborn's (our No. III) specimen.   Both animals were old, the teeth ground down even more in III than in VI.   The distances from the lateral notch of the foramen magnum to the anterior border of the second pre-

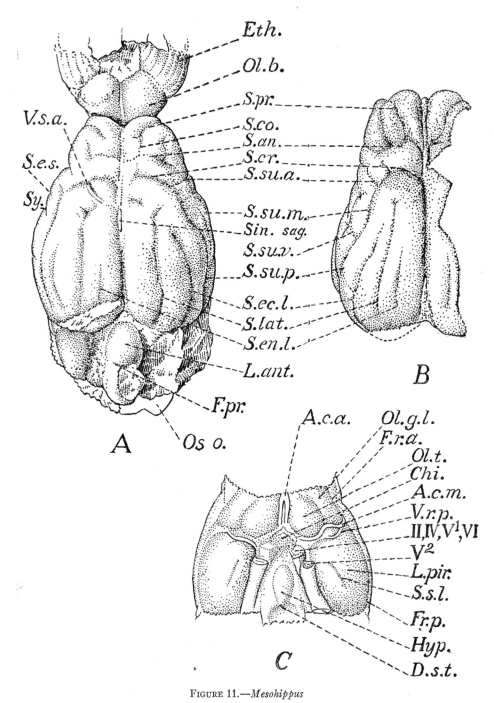

FIGURE 11.—*Mesohippus*

(A) Specimen no. III, (B) specimen no. IV, dorsal views. (C) Specimen no. II, ventral surface. (Specimens II and IV are shown only as far as well preserved.) × 1.

molar are 146 mm. in VI and 134 mm. in III; they differ by 1/11th.   P² to M³ lengths, 68 and 64 mm., respectively, differ by 1/16th.   Cerebral lengths, however, differ only by 1/20th, and in total brain length there is no difference.   The animal VI indeed must have been larger than III, but the brain, as usual, was not correspondingly

TABLE 1.—Mesohippus, Cephalophus *and* Ovis

Measurements of the *Mesohippus* endocasts Nos. I-VII, and of two similar-sized Recent artiodactyls: an endocast of *Cephalophus nataliensis* (Ce), and a brain of *Ovis aries* (Ov).

	I	II	III	IV	V	VI	VII	Ce	Ov
LENGTH									
total			91	97		98		94	92
cer. + cbl.	77		78			81		79	80
cbl.	>20		22			>18		18	28
cer.	57	53	56	63	60	63		65	61
ol. b.			12	11		13		11	3
BREADTH									
obl.	17	15	16	17				16	10
cbl.	(34)		35			(34)		35	36
neopall.	47	48	49	(49)	52	53	55	51	59
pal. pall.	44	44	47	(47)	48	49	51	44	44
front. lo.	23	27	28	28	29	30	30	20	
ol. b.			26	24	(25)	30		21	27
HEIGHT									
obl.	14	15	15	17		(13)		18	7
cer.	36	38	40	41	43	43		37	37

larger.   Bone hides the brain stem and the lower half of the posterior left side of the brain.   The attachment of the olfactory bulbs is obscured by plaster.

VII. *Mesohippus bairdii*, AMNH 11863, from the Lower *Oreodon* beds of the White River group, head of Bad River, Cheyenne River, South Dakota, is a snout with medium-worn teeth and part of the endocast of the forebrain chamber.   The dorsal surface is badly weathered.

A. I further studied both halves of the medio-sagitally sectioned *Mesohippus* skull PU 10503 whose right half is figured by Scott (1891, pl. xxiii, fig. 17).

DESCRIPTION

Cerebellum.—The cross section through the oblongata cast in the foramen magnum is almost circular.   Only for a short distance inward from its posterior end is the steeply rising dorsal side of the oblongata not overlapped by the cerebellum.

Tilney (1931, p. 481), remarked of the cerebellum merely that the vermis is very prominent and sharply demarcated from relatively small lateral lobes, and Scott (1891, p. 312; 1941, p. 918) states that the cerebellum was not overlapped to the same degree as in the Recent horse.   These observations have been verified.   Osborn's figure of "a large central lobe with transverse simple furrows" (1890, p. 88), however, does not represent the cerebellum as preserved in specimen III but reconstructs it; of the two transverse furrows shown on the vermis, the posterior one could not be retraced on the specimen.   There is much damage on the surface of all *Mesohippus* vermes except in specimens I and II, and considerably more on all lateral lobes. Only III shows the outline of the left hemisphere; only I shows some of the dorsal surface of the hemispheres; VI has part of, and I and IV yield some indirect information about the flocculi. However, the variously incomplete specimens taken together suffice for a picture of the *Mesohippus* cerebellum.

The posterior facies of the vermis is vertical. The vermes of I and II rise 20 and 21 mm., respectively, above the oblongata. The summit does not reach quite the same height as the forebrain. Anteriorly it projects for about 3 mm. between the forebrain hemispheres on the surface. The forward and downward extent of the opercule vermien in V (fig. 10 B) shows that the vermis extended at least 10 mm. below the level of the fissura magna cerebri and reached to a transverse plane about 5 mm. anterior to the posterior forebrain poles. It follows that about one fourth of the cerebellum lay in the telencephalic area.

There is no indication of a twist in the vermis; it was straight and symmetrical. The two principal fissures are moulded in I and II, showing the vermis distinctly tripartite. The suprapyramidal fissure delimits the posterior lobe at 10 and 12 mm. height, respectively. Only laterally on the median lobe of endocast I is there an indication of the lobuli into which the vermis cortex was folded. Remnants of a pair of transverse sulci are seen on both sides, and a third sulcus is suggested by an irregularity on the right side of the median lobe surface which otherwise is quite smooth. Between the middle and anterior lobes, the primary fissure is a conspicuous furrow in these specimens. It lies in about the middle of the antero-posterior extent on the dorsal surface of the vermis in III. In I and II the anterior end of the free part of the vermis is not revealed. As in both these brains the fissura prima is only 10 or 11 mm. anterior to the hind end of the vermis, it seems that the lobus anterior was relatively longer in the (probably) primitive I and in the young II than in the old III.

The paramedian lobes were somewhat narrower than the vermis. On the dorsal surface of the right incomplete parafloculus of I some of its sulci are seen, while from the mostly rough left side the breadth of the paraflocculi can be guessed; they were hardly, if at all, broader than the paramedian lobes. The cerebellum expanded to somewhat less than forebrain breadth. The latero-basal, petrosal lobe is seen in VI exactly above the meatus acusticus internus, 6 mm. long. On the internal surface of the detached periotic bone of IV more of its outline is revealed. At 4 to 5 mm. above the internal acoustic meatus this specimen contains the lower part of the floccular fossa. Seen from above, it has the shape of half an egg, with the blunter end anteriorly. Its posterior end is above the posterior rim of the acoustic meatus; medially it is 7 mm. long; it bulges outward about 3 mm. In I, there is on the left side a partial cast of this fossa, 5 mm. high, with two parallel 3 mm.-long sulci curving up from its basal to its posterior side. On the right side of this specimen, the inner plate of the petrosal adheres to the endocast as far as it is perpencidular; as the cast is here broken in a perpendicular plane too, it offers a sagittal section of the flocculus where it entered into the floccular fossa. The flocculus in I, too, lay just above the internal acoustic meatus and anterior to it, being 7 mm. long.

The midbrain has disappeared from the brain surface in *Mesohippus*.

Cerebral hemispheres.—Every former description of a *Mesohippus* brain stresses its "well advanced" or "modernized" appearance. Such statements made about single specimens do not make much sense without comparisons. Now that the full picture gained from many cerebra of *Mesohippus* can be set against the impression obtained from the revealing fragment of the *Orohippus* cerebrum, the advance is found to be great indeed. Comparison with the later stages of brain evolution, however, shows that the brain of *Mesohippus* was far from "modern."

In the endocranial casts of *Mesohippus*, the cerebral hemispheres are high; they are broad, particularly their temporal lobes; and they extend backward over the cerebellum, to above the nervus acusticus entrance.

Convoluted neocortex covered their dorsal halves. The fissura rhinalis had disappeared from dorsal views; the neocortex bulged distally over the less broad palaeopallial formations, especially above the posterior rhinal fissure. This is a deep, horizontal furrow in mid-height of the hemispheres, posteriorly turning up to end on their posterior convexities. The anterior rhinal fissure forms a downward arc except on the right hemisphere of VI where it appears as an almost straight continuation of the posterior rhinal. On the left hemisphere of this brain it forms an arc less curved than in the smaller specimens and VII. To a various extent, therefore, neocortex covers more than half of the brain surface height in the frontal lobe.

On the whole, the "angle" between the posterior and anterior fissurae rhinales is similar in specimens II–V and in Moodie's; but in VI it is more obtuse. No comparison was possible of right and left rhinal fissures of the same brain; in each specimen the fissure is preserved *in toto* only on one side, and on neither side completely in I and in VII.

The site of the apex of this "angle"—*i.e.*, of the Sylvian fossa—seems to vary with the size of the forebrain. Tilney described the Sylvian fossa in I at "about one third the distance from the frontal to the occipital pole" (1931, p. 481); however he mistook for the fossa the anterior end of the unmodelled area in which no Sylvia is recognizable. If measurements on but one hemisphere of five forebrains have any significance, the root point of the Sylvian fossa lay farther anteriorly in the larger *Mesohippus* brains. In our specimens II to VI, the proportion of presylvian to postsylvian lengths changes continuously from 1:1.1 to 1:1.7.

The Sylvian fossa is distinctly modelled only on one side of specimens II–VII, excepting VI in which the lower parts of both fossae are clear. It is almost perpendicular in VII, runs slightly backward in its upward course in II and V, and more so in III, IV, and VI.

The Sylvia is a well-marked groove, surrounded by a prominent ectosylvian convolution, the gyrus arcuatus secundus. The greatest depth of the fossa is dorsally, where it has a forked processus acuminis; basally it appears shallow on the endocasts. The median cerebral artery (preserved on the right hemisphere of VI; fig. 9 B) lies in the fossa, but it is not operculized.

The arcuate constellation (gyrus sylviacus, gyrus arcuatus primus) apparently was not fully developed. However, the following traces of the ectosylvian sulcus were observed on the one side of each specimen with well-moulded surface: the ramus anterior sulci ectosylvii (fissura antica), short in I and III, but 5 mm. long in VI (left side) where it is parallel to the anterior part of the suprasylvian, in the latter's mid-height; a long ramus posterior sulci ectosylvii (fissura postica) in IV; antica and postica in II, as 2-mm. long lines which slightly converge dorsally toward the Sylvian fossa, from which they are both about 4 mm. distant.

Whereas this sulcus, which sets off the "primary" circumsylvian gyrus, thus was incomplete in *Mesohippus*, the suprasylvian sulcus was so far developed as to set off a "secondary" arcuate gyrus.

The literature is almost unanimous in stating that the circumsylvian gyri of ungulates are not really arcuate, in contrast to those of carnivores. Holl (1900, p. 295–296) objected to this view and argued that at least the dorsal portions are as arched in ungulates as in carnivores. Holl admitted, however, that one or both descending legs have a sagittal course in ungulates so that the arch is "more flat and stretched" than the "steep" arch of carnivores. In the "simplified" horse brain, that of *Mesohippus*, where no sulcus branches or other accessories of complication obscure the picture, the impression of a steep circumsylvian arch is quite definite. It is produced not so much by a definite gyrus as by the constellation of three of the four parts of the sulcus suprasylvius. The dorsal pars media is obliquely longitudinal and slightly arched dorsad. It is not continued in an anterior direction as happens in later forms through branching; but from its anterior end there descends, continuing it in ventrad direction, the pars anterior sulci suprasylvii. More or less parallel to this anterior leg of the circumsylvian arch, and at a similar distance from the Sylvian fossa, there descends posteriorly what is called the ramus ventralis of the pars media sulci suprasylvii. This nomenclature implies that the posterior leg of the arch is less fundamental than the anterior leg. However, in *Mesohippus*, this "ramus" would be the only branch of the suprasylvian sulcus. Its development is similar to that of the pars anterior. In I and II, both are almost perpendicular; completely preserved in II, both pars anterior and ramus ventralis are 6 mm. long. In III, the two appear to descend as far as the rhinal fissure on the right, but not on the left side. In IV, the left side (which alone is preserved) shows both legs oblique, directed antero-ventrally. In V, the ramus ventralis is larger than the pars anterior; they converge somewhat ventrally. On the left side of VI, the parallel pars anterior and ramus ventralis are both 8 mm. long; on the right side, both are longer.

The pars posterior of the suprasylvian sulcus continues the arched course of the pars media on the lateral surface of the cerebral hemisphere. The ectolateral sulcus is parallel to it. The lateral and endolateral are almost straight. None of these sulci have branches except in V and VI, where one or two branchlets occur; but there is an occasional bifurcation anteriorly. There is some variation in the course of these long sulci, either between the two hemispheres of each brain or between individuals.

For example, in V, the left ectolateral sulcus has an antero-posterior length of 31 mm., the right one 26 mm. The left lateral is one long slightly sinuous line whose anterior end is split in two short branches, while the right lateral appears much shorter because the branched formation lies medio-anteriorly to and is separate from the main stem. This is similar in III where, however, the medial branch of the left lateral is not straight but sinuous. The endolaterals are alike on the two hemispheres of V, but the left one seems to have a shallow anterior continuation. In VI, both endolaterals are short, and they join the laterals. They are entirely straight, unbranched, and without connections in IV.

Between the posterior suprasylvian and the posterior rhinal, the sulcus posticus (of Krueg; sulcus obliquus of Holl; konstante Nebenfurche of Flatau and Jacobsohn; postsylvian sulcus of other authors) is in an interesting stage of its evolution. It is just starting to change from the one horizontal furrow that it was in *Orohippus* to the multibranched complex of one or two horizontal and many oblique and vertical furrows which it is in *Equus* (hence the designation "System der Fissura postica" in Haller's horsebrain figure, 1934, fig. 200). In this area, II has a short horizontal, and behind and above it a short, slightly oblique, furrow; III has a longer horizontal one, with a short downward branch; IV has only a short one that curves upward posteriorly; V and VI have a long horizontal sulcus posticus with a dorsal perpendicular branch. None of the disconnected curlicues belonging to the posticus complex in the horse and even in the sheep were developed in *Mesohippus*.

The sulcus diagonalis is more appropriately so termed in *Mesohippus* than in *Equus* where it is arched and branched and spreads to the dorsal surface of the hemispheres. In all *Mesohippus* brains it is really a diagonally vertical unbranched sulcus of the anterior lateral surface. It rises from the praesylvian sulcus from which it is usually somewhat removed in the horse.

The praesylvian sulcus is developed as in *Equus* except that it has no branches. It begins in the anterior rhinal fissure very near the Sylvian fossa and from there runs forward, then upward, arching around the frontal pole onto the dorsal side to end, as in the horse, either blindly (I, III, V, VI left side) or in joining the coronate sulcus (IV, VII; right side of III and VI).

Dorsal views of the *Mesohippus* cerebral hemispheres display the original pattern of fissuration which in the modern horse is obscured by the sinuous course of the principal sulci and their many branches and connections. In *Mesohippus* the dorsal convexity of the cerebrum is divided into a posterior two-thirds with four longitudinal sulci—endolateral, lateral, ectolateral, and suprasylvian—and an anterior third with three transverse sulci—the cruciate, the corono-ansate, and the transverse branch of the praesylvian. The last-named crosses the frontal lobe far anteriorly somewhat below the dorsal level. However, as the frontal facies of the hemispheres is low in *Mesohippus*, this third transverse furrow is visible in dorsal views, whereas it may be invisible from above on the high frontal lobe of *Equus*.

As the sulcus cruciatus of artiodactyls is variably developed or absent (*e.g.*, in sheep), and that of the modern horse is occasionally described as only a continuation of a notch in the median wall of each hemisphere, it is significant that the dorsal part of the cruciate of *Mesohippus* is a transverse arc which spans up to four fifths (I, VI) of the breadth of the hemisphere. As in *Equus*, it runs from the median longitudinal fissure to the suprasylvian sulcus. The cruciate of *Equus* is usually said to divide the hemispheres into an anterior third and posterior two thirds. This is only roughly true, as there are variations in both directions. The same is the case in *Mesohippus*. The cruciate lies between the anterior and middle thirds of the hemispheres, with slight variations, in III, IV, V, and VI. It lies farther anteriorly in I than in all the other *Mesohippus* brains.

Considering the general variability of sulci, the question whether this forward position of the cruciate sulcus is a primitive character of I cannot be decided from the material at hand but only by Lower Oligocene *Mesohippus* brains. With only an indication of one branchlet in III and IV, the cruciate has two rostrad rami in V, VI, and VII as has the cruciate of *Equus;* but the rami are straighter and shorter in *Mesohippus*. In I, the cruciate is unbranched on the right hemisphere and has one short anterior branch on the left hemisphere.

We have above introduced the term "corono-ansate" for the sulcus which lies anterior to the cruciate in the *Mesohippus* brain. Descriptions of the brain of *Equus* report the presence only of a coronal sulcus. Surface configuration in this area indeed has undergone, during the evolution from *Mesohippus* to *Equus*, a gradual change due to which *Equus* appears to lack the sulcus ansatus. It is necessary to sketch here conditions in the modern horse brain, in order to show that a sulcus name had to be changed because the term used in descriptions of the horse brain applied to a secondary condition. Although one would expect the term "coronal" to designate a transverse sulcus (actually, Tilney (1931, p. 481) gave this name to the more posterior of the transverse sulci of the *Mesohippus* brain—that is, to the cruciate), the ungulate sulcus coronalis is an anteriorly situated longitudinal sulcus. In *Equus*, it can become connected posteriorly with the sulcus lateralis, so that Flatau and Jacobsohn describe the coronal as forming one arcuate sulcus with the lateral (1899, p. 410). The coronal of the horse has several transverse branches. Of those bifurcating its posterior end, the lateral branch runs toward, and in some cases reaches, the anterior suprasylvian; the medial posterior branch has a relatively short course on the dorsal surface of the hemispheres toward the median longitudinal fissure where it is, however, continued on the median wall of the hemispheres downward almost to the splenial sulcus. On the dorsal surface this medial "branch" (pl. 2, fig. 3, "6") can be so inconspicuous that only Krueg gave it a separate name, "Bügel a" (bridle a; 1878, p. 328).

The sulcus ansatus of ungulates is a transverse sulcus posterior to the coronal. For the frequently occurring connection of the two, Kappers, Huber, and Crosby (1936, p. 1531) suggested the term sulcus corono-ansatus. The ansatus is conspicuous on living artiodactyl brains such as that of the sheep (pl. 2, fig. 2). The only mention made of the ansate in connection with *Equus* is the statement of Ellenberger, after his investigation of 15 horse brains: It is impossible to decide whether an ansate sulcus is present (1892, p. 288). Incidentally, Krueg (1878, p. 320) designates the sheep's sulcus ansatus (described as such by Landacre, 1930, p. 39) also as bridle a.

In the horse the coronal generally has so many branches, none of them being strictly transverse, that no one ramus appeared as a feature sufficiently distinct to be taken for a major sulcus. Conditions were different in the sheep-sized ancestor. They show that the Equidae do possess the sulcus ansatus. What in *Equus* may appear as the two short end branches of the coronalis is in *Mesohippus* one long, deep, slightly arched transverse sulcus—an ansate, from which the coronalis extends forward at right angles. As is the case with the cruciate, this other transverse sulcus too is more markedly dorsal in *Mesohippus* than in *Equus*—so much so that the conspicuousness of ansate and coronal is reversed. Whereas the ansate of the horse appeared to the authors as a branch of the coronal, and indeed is medio-dorsally not more than a "bridle" between the coronal and the fissura magna cerebri, in *Mesohippus* the coronal appears as one of two longitudinal branches extending forward from the sulcus ansatus.

The ansate of the *Mesohippus* endocasts disappears medially where it passes onto the medial side of the hemispheres. It ends laterally in about the same transverse plane as the anterior end of the suprasylvian sulcus, but at various distances from this. There is always a prominent gyrus between the two, in contrast to both horse and sheep in which this gyrus may be buried so that the ansate joins the suprasylvian on the surface. Of the two longitudinal branches, the lateral one is present on all seven *Mesohippus* specimens. The medial one, the homologue of the coronalis of *Equus*, was not found on the left hemispheres of I and III. It is short on the right hemispheres of I and II and on the left hemispheres of V and VI. On the left hemisphere of II, the right one in III and VI, and on both hemispheres of IV and VII, the coronal condition of the horse is attained—that is, the sulcus is confluent with the dorsal presylvian. It may be noted that in the sheep, as in *Mesohippus*, the junction of sulcus coronalis and sulcus praesylvius (*see* our specimen, pl. 1, fig. 2) occurs only "sometimes" (Landacre, 1930, p. 40).

As the anteriormost point of the transverse ansate arc is in most hemispheres on the same transverse level as the widest bulge of a lateral gyrus, this level was chosen for measuring frontal lobe breadth (table 1). At least at this point, frontal lobe breadth varies only according to the general brain size. As Scott has already remarked, the frontal lobes of VI are broader, and its convolutions are richer, more sinuous, and more oblique than in III. That they, consequently, are "more modern in appearance" (Scott, 1891, p. 312; 1941, p. 918) is possibly correlated with the body-size of the respective individuals; VI was the brain of a larger, consequently a "more modern" animal.

Olfactory bulbs.—Although in *Mesohippus* the cerebrum had become high and had developed an anterior facies, the height of the anterior cerebral regions and the height of the olfactory bulbs differ only slightly. The ethmoidal chamber reaches up to the skull roof in such a manner that, in a medio-sagittal skull section (Scott, 1891, pl. XXIII, fig. 17), it was mistaken for a frontal sinus (Scott, 1891, p. 307, 406). The endocasts show that it was the olfactory bulbs which occupied this cavity in front of the hemispheres; they extended into an area which indeed is occupied in *Equus* by the frontal sinus. Anterior and ventral surfaces of the olfactory bulbs are not laid open in any *Mesohippus* specimen; but the dorsal and lateral surfaces displayed in several specimens, together with breaks across their cerebral sides in I and III and a cross section of II (fig. 22, A, B), show that from broad olfactory tracts there rose large bulbs (fig. 9 A, 11 A).

The brain cast broke from the snout portion of specimen III in such a way that there appeared a perpendicular section of the posterior end of the right olfactory bulb. Perpendicular height of the brain in this region, which may well be called a short olfactory peduncle, is 13 mm. laterally. Mediad the break slants baso-posteriorly, in particular on the left side which thus exhibits an oblique cross section of peduncle plus tract. Their combined height is, perpendicularly, 17 mm. From the peduncles forward, the bulbs bulge outward considerably, while their dorsal surface rises (in III, IV, VI, VII) in a 5 to 6 mm.-long slope and becomes almost plane at a level 5 to 6 mm. above the peduncles; this is immediately under the skull roof. The sections through the olfactory bulbs of II, at 3 and 4 mm. anterior to the peduncles (fig. 22) show that the lower surface of the peduncles rises rostrally too. Perpendicular bulb height is 13 to 14 mm. at this level in II and at the lateral side of VI. The position, and in part also the formation of the anterior extremity of the brain, can be deduced from the imprint of the rim of the lamina cribrosa and the ethmoturbinal impressions which radiate from it in III, IV, and VI. The olfactory bulbs had an anterior facies which was almost perpendicular dorsally; the baso-posterior slant was slight.

It follows that the olfactory bulbs of *Mesohippus* were relatively large, subglobular, and placed quite anteriorly to the cerebral hemispheres where they extended upward to the skull roof.

Brain base and cranial nerves.—Most of the lower surface of the brain is laid open in II (fig. 11 C). About the same area is exhibited in V, where it extends somewhat farther forward. In this specimen the medial and lateral olfactory striae (or gyri) can be seen to join, forming the olfactory tract. Lateral parts of the lower brain regions are exhibited in VI (fig. 9) and VII.

Basal views show most graphically how large a portion of the *Mesohippus* brain was the rhinencephalon. The neocortex appears only as a framing line, 1 to 2 mm. broad, 3 mm. anteriorly in V. The picture is dominated by relatively bulky piriform lobes. The sulcus sagittalis lateralis runs along the convexity of each piriform lobe. The olfactory tubercles are prominent. The medial and lateral olfactory gyri are well set off.

The lower side of the pituitary gland is represented by an oval protuberance. This is 10 mm. long in II. Its greatest breadth is 5 mm. in II, and is 6 mm. in V in which the posterior end is apparently not preserved.

The conservative cranial nerves XII to VII and V³ present no features different from either *Eohippus* or *Equus*. However, in *Mesohippus* the exits and entrances into the skull of the anterior nerve groups still were more concentrated than they are in the horse. Inside the horse skull, the maxillary nerve canal branches from the eye muscle nerves canal 23 mm. behind the latter's entrance into the skull wall. In *Mesohippus*, foramen is a more appropriate term than canal, and the foramen rotundum (V²) is only 4 mm. behind the foramen sphenorbitale. In the latter foramen, the abducent (VI), ophthalmic (V¹), trochlear (IV), and oculo-motor (III) nerves left the skull immediately behind the entrance of the optic nerve (II). The sphenorbital foramen adjoins the optic foramen posteriorly; only its lateral half reaches farther laterad, whereas inside the *Equus* skull the two foramina are 11 mm. apart, and the sphenorbital is quite lateral to the optic foramen.

The optic nerves are represented by the endocast of the unpaired optic foramen.

Its dorso-anterior to baso-posterior slant is reproduced in the break both in II and V. This foramen had almost the same height as it has in *Equus*. In *Equus*, however, it is a slit 24 mm. broad, and 21 in the pony; its ratios to forebrain breadth are 1:4.6 and 1:4.5, respectively. Its breadth is 8 mm. in *Mesohippus* II, 7 mm. in V, with 1:6 and 1:7.4 ratios to forebrain breadth. This difference of course does not indicate any difference in the proximal portion of the optic nerves. The distance between the pituitary body and the optic nerve entrance leaves no doubt that in *Mesohippus* too the chiasma lay behind the foramen. But the narrow foramen shows that the peripheral optic nerves did not immediately diverge in *Mesohippus* as they do in *Equus*. Likewise, Scott found the optic foramen on the outside of the *Mesohippus* skull "placed in front of the foramen lacerum anterius" (the sphenorbital), "not above it" (1891, p. 309; 1941, p. 916).

Closely spaced furrows mould the endocranial casts of *Mesohippus* skulls anterior to and below the olfactory bulbs. They correspond to the bases of the ethmoturbinals and show that the fila of the olfactory nerves radiated from the bulbs anteriorly as well as basally.

Bloodvessels.—Besides delicate vessels of the pia mater, the following large vessels left marks on *Mesohippus* endocranial casts.

On the base, the stem of the arteria cerebri media crosses in front of the piriform lobe in II. It passes upward on the lateral surface toward the Sylvian fossa where in this specimen the median branch is obscured while the anterior branch dives into the neopallium 3 mm. anterior to the fossa. In VI the median branch is running upward in the Sylvian fossa where its upper part is overlapped by the ectosylvian gyrus.

The anterior cerebral arteries of the horse unite to form an unpaired vessel already above the optic chiasma (Sisson, 1917, p. 641) or immediately anterior to it (Hofmann, 1900, p. 291, pl. XX, fig. 26), in contrast to the artiodactyls investigated by Hofmann in which the paired course is longer. In *Mesohippus* II, the anterior cerebral arteries run forward from above the chiasma for about 6 mm. before uniting.

The largest basal venous blood collector of the horse brain is the vena rhinalis posterior; it penetrates into the dura mater posteriorly (Hofmann, 1901, p. 277), thus becoming a sinus which can be quite prominent on endocranial casts. In *Mesohippus*, as in the horse, it lies either laterally on the piriform lobe (II, left side) or just below the fissura rhinalis posterior (II, right side). This condition makes the posterior rhinal vein a really basal vessel in *Equus*, but in *Mesohippus* the posterior part is invisible in basal views because the rhinal fissure lies high up on the lateral surface of the forebrain hemisphere. Anteriorly, this vein curves medially and here receives blood from the optic chiasma and olfactory tubercle regions in a transverse branch moulded in II as the only basal vein. This is the strongest ramus of the posterior rhinal vein in *Equus* too.

While only some short parts of the superior sagittal sinus are left on the casts (due to its intimate connection with the falx bone) the largest, most anterior of its dorsal tributaries is distinctly moulded on several hemispheres. Having collected blood from basal, anterior, and medial cerebral regions, the variable course of this vena cerebri superior anterior becomes distinct when, directed caudad and mediad, it approaches the superior sagittal sinus which it enters at approximately right angles somewhat posterior to the cruciate sulcus.   In the horse, the anterior superior cerebral vein has a relatively shorter dorsal course than in *Mesohippus*, and it joins the sinus at an acute angle, while 5–7 pairs of superior cerebral veins behind it join at right angles.   Apparently in the smaller *Mesohippus* brain the anterior cerebral vein could drain a relatively larger brain area.

COMPARISON

Living ungulates.—Various artiodactyls are extant whose sizes correspond to the divers body sizes reached in the *Mesohippus* stage of the horse ancestry.   In contrast to the two earlier stages described above, there is now a general similarity with living brains of similar size.   This is demonstrated by comparison of most of the measurements of two living Bovidae with those of *Mesohippus* (table 1).   One specimen is an MCZ duplicate of the endocranial cast of a duikerbok, *Cephalophus nataliensis*, No. D. 463 of the Royal College of Surgeons' Museum (Elliot Smith, 1902, p. 336; our pl. 1, fig. 4).   The cerebrum, somewhat more slender than in *Mesohippus*, shows a similar degree of fissuration: little branching, no accessory sulci.   The last column of table 1 contains the measurements of the brain of *Ovis aries* shown in figures 2 and 3 on plate 1.   This sheep's forebrain is broader than those of *Mesohippus*. Its sulci are more sinuous and more ramified; but simpler patterns also occur within the species.   The variable configuration of the sheep's circumsylvian area (Landacre, 1930, p. 41–42) definitely recalls the various conditions found in *Mesohippus*.   Naturally, both the bovid brains differ from that of *Mesohippus* by certain artiodactyl characters such as having the splenial sulcus continued laterad on the dorsal forebrain surface (in front of the ansate sulcus; *see* pl. 1, fig. 2).

The more elaborate infolding occurring in sheep is not the only macroscopic manifestation of the fact that the sheep's neocortex is more extensive and consequently more highly developed than was the neocortex of *Mesohippus*.   The situation of the fissura rhinalis in *Mesohippus* on the one hand, and in similarly sized living artiodactyls on the other hand, strikingly shows that *Mesohippus* was far from having achieved complete resemblance to present-day brains.   Important "modern" characters were definitely developed in *Mesohippus*, such as the cerebro-cerebellar contact and the main sulci of the equid brain.   Moodie's (1922, p. 368) summary of the *Mesohippus* brain briefly expresses the generally accepted opinion—"while it is somewhat primitive, it is remarkably modern in its development."   Detailed comparison, however, reveals that the subordinate clause states facts so substantial that the meaning of the principal clause is considerably restricted.

To begin with, the forebrain of *Mesohippus* was more primitive than not only the large forebrain of *Equus*, but also than the similar-sized forebrains of living ungulates of *Mesohippus* size, in that it had a less extensive neocortex.

In the cerebral hemispheres of all living ungulates, neocortex forms by far the greater portion of the surface.   In basal views it is a broad frame surrounding the basal rhinencephalon parts lobus piriformis, tuberculum olfactorium, olfactory gyri, and tract.   In *Mesohippus*, neocortex covers only the dorsal half of the hemispheres; the rhinencephalon is preponderant in the ventral half.   The rhinal fissure lies in mid-height of the hemispheres, curving lower only at the frontal lobe; below it, the rhinal portions are widely exposed on the lateral surface. In *Cephalophus nataliensis*, at the lowest points of the two curves of the rhinal fissure, the heights of suprarhinal and infrarhinal portions are: anteriorly, 14 and 10 mm., posteriorly, 26 and 11 mm. In the sheep, these proportions are 25 and 3, 30 and 5 mm.—the latter a 6:1 ratio whereas the ratio is 1:1 in *Mesohippus*. In consideration of the role of body size in neocortex formation, we note also that in living ungulates much smaller than *Mesohippus* the neocortical area is relatively larger. The 51 mm.-long cerebral hemispheres of the small living Cervidae *Moschus moschiferus* and *Hydropotes inermis* (Elliot Smith, 1902; figs. 187, 192) have a fissure pattern similar to *Mesohippus* except that, as they are small arteriodactyls, they lack endo- and ecto-lateral sulci. However, suprarhinal height is somewhat over twice infrarhinal height in *Moschus*, and posteriorly in *Hydropotes*. In the frontal lobe region of *Hydropotes* neocortex covers up to five sixths of the cerebral height. Conditions in the hyrax are shown in figure 5 B.

The other strikingly primitive feature of the *Mesohippus* brain is another demonstration of rhinencephalon preponderance—viz., the position and height of the olfactory bulbs. Today, high olfactory bulbs situated quite anterior to the hemispheres are characteristic of lowly developed mammals such as the insectivores (e.g., fig. 4 A). In these, however, such voluminous olfactory bulbs belong to forebrains whose surface is about one third neocortex; the "smell-brain"—bulbi and olfactory portions of the cerebrum—has been estimated to constitute three fourths of the forebrain surface in *Erinaceus* (Economo, 1929b, p. 87). *Mesohippus* had these primitive bulbs along with an ungulate neocortex which in many ways was like that of similarly sized living ungulates. They differed not only in position, but they were also larger, as is at once evident when the *Mesohippus* endocasts are compared with that of the duikerbok and the brain of the sheep (pl. 1).

These differences cannot easily be demonstrated in numbers, because the lower side of the bulbs of *Mesohippus* is not entirely revealed in any of our specimens. In a plane corresponding to the section (fig. 22) in which the bulb height was 14 mm. in *Mesohippus*, bulb height is 12 mm. in *Cephalophus*. Thus, the ratio to the maximum forebrain heights—38 and 37 mm., respectively—is hardly different in the fossil and the living brain at about one third the postero-anterior extent of the olfactory bulbs. However, when a line is drawn forward from the base of the piriform lobe horizontally, parallel to the dorsal forebrain surface, one finds that the olfactory bulbs of the *Cephalophus* endocranial cast rise only 18 mm. above the brain base, but from 34 to 39 mm. in the *Mesohippus* endocranial casts. In brains this difference in height between the Oligocene and living ungulates appears even greater. The height of the hemispheres of our sheep brain is 37 mm., bulb height above their base is 12 mm. The ratio is likewise 3:1 in the *Moschus* brain mentioned above, but in *Mesohippus* it was almost 1:1. Correspondingly, in living ungulates the lamina cribrosa is a baso-posteriorly slanting plate in the lower parts of the skull, whereas in *Mesohippus* it descends immediately from the skull roof.

I found only one living ungulate whose olfactory bulbs have almost the same relative height as those of *Mesohippus*. The endocranial cast of an American tapir

(*Tapirus terrestris*) "shows the enormous flattened olfactory bulbs, like those of the elephant" according to Elliot Smith (1902, p. 311). The Museum of Comparative Zoölogy possesses a duplicate of this specimen of the Royal College of Surgeons' No. D. 395. Olfactory bulb height is 50 mm., against 66 mm. maximum forebrain height. Yet while this is certainly one more character noteworthy among the many which make the tapir a "living fossil," the brain of these "belated survivors from a more ancient world" (Scott, 1937, p. 432) does not have the other primitive characters of the Oligocene perissodactyl brain. The ratio of neocortex to paleocortex height of the temporal lobe, 1:1 in *Mesohippus*, is 2.3:1 both in the large tapir endocast and the small brain figured by Elliot Smith (1902, figs. 179, 180). This brain is not much larger than *Mesohippus* VI, but its sulci are sinuous and have many branches.

The cerebellar feature which we found of evolutionary significance—the position of the fissura prima—is not reproduced in the duikerbok endocast, and I was unable to identify it in Elliot Smith's figures of the tapir brain. There is a shallow transverse furrow in the vermis of the tapir endocast which probably corresponds to the primary fissure; the exposed vermis surface is divided by this furrow into anterior 10 mm. and posterior 15 mm. In sheep, the fissura prima is in a still more anterior position. In four sheep cerebella 29–32 mm. long, the fissura prima is 1–5 mm. behind the anterior border of the exposed vermis surface, 5–8 mm. behind the submerged anterior end of the vermis. Variable as it is, the primary fissure of *Ovis* thus is never in a position as far back as in *Mesohippus*.

Contemporary ungulates.—The brain of *Merycoidodon* (*Oreodon*)—a protoselenodont artiodactyl which lived together with *Mesohippus*—is well known, in particular from Black's (1920–1921) detailed description of five natural endocranial casts.

Piglike in appearance, the most common species of this ruminant genus, *M. culbertsonii*, was somewhat smaller than *Mesohippus bairdii;* shoulder height of a mounted skeleton is 420 mm. (Thorpe, 1937, p. 280). The skulls are so differently shaped from *Mesohippus* skulls that it is meaningless to say that they are shorter (from 180 to 220 mm., Thorpe, 1937, p. 47); they are much broader than *Mesohippus* skulls.

The endocranial casts of *Merycoidodon* are only slightly smaller than those of *Mesohippus*, and the brain must have been very similar in the two genera. (The present writer sees no reason for showing the corpora quadrigemina exposed in a *Merycoidodon* brain restoration, as Black did in his figures 23 and 24—"largely matters of surmise," p. 301.) The main difference consists in the shorter, less slender cerebrum of *Merycoidodon*. The cerebral hemispheres of Black's two complete *Merycoidodon* forebrains are 45 and 46 mm. long, and 47 and 46 mm. broad, respectively. The differences in the forebrain fissuration of *Merycoidodon* and *Mesohippus* may well be paralleled to those existing between the brains of pig and horse. *Merycoidodon* has a very short ectolateral sulcus—this sulcus is much shorter in *Sus* than in *Equus;* and *Merycoidodon* lacks the endolateral sulcus which, in contrast to that of *Equus*, is short and shallow, or absent in *Sus*.

The most significant similarity between the two Middle Oligocene brains is their mutual possession of characters which contrast them with living ungulate brains.

Merycoidodon, like *Mesohippus*, has high olfactory bulbs anterior to the cerebral hemispheres. Black's plates V and VI show that their absolute height is half the forebrain height and that their vault rises two thirds of the cerebral height above the brain base. Correspondingly, the course of the rhinal fissure is similar to that in *Mesohippus*, near midheight of the hemispheres. Unfortunately, Black's specimens must have been oriented differently for drawing and photographing, for rhinalis heights appear different in text figures and plate figures of the two lateral views of the same specimens. After measuring all Black's figures and Moodie's (1922, fig. 20) side view of another *Merycoidodon* brain, it was deduced that neocortex covered in the temporal lobe of *Merycoidodon* slightly more than half the hemispheres and in the frontal lobe from two thirds to three fourths of the cerebral height.

Such relatively extensive olfactory surfaces, which distinguished the two American Lower and Middle Oligocene genera from similar-sized living ungulates, also characterized the brains of two similar-sized European Lower Oligocene protoselenodonts, the anoplotheriids *Anoplotherium* and *Diplobune*. Palmer's (1913) *Anoplotherium* was a small representative of that genus; its cerebral length and width were 56 and 45 mm., respectively. Cerebrum lengths of the smaller *Diplobune* were 51 and 53 mm.; the corresponding breadths were 44 and 39 mm. (Edinger, 1928, p. 394). In both, the olfactory bulbs are quite anterior to the forebrain; "the olfactory peduncles are distinct thick stalks" (Palmer, 1913, p. 888). If the oblongata is imagined not horizontal as it is drawn in Palmer's figures, but rising anteriorly as it certainly did, the olfactory bulbs rise to at least two thirds the forebrain height. Both in *Anoplotherium* and in *Diplobune*, "the rhinal fissure divides the hemisphere horizontally into two equal parts" (Palmer, 1913, p. 888; similarly, Edinger, 1928, p. 396); only anteriorly does it curve lower down.

The cerebella too appear similar in the four similar-sized Oligocene ungulates. The fissura prima of *Oreodon* is distinctly moulded only in Black's specimen IV whose photographs (Black's figures 41, 42, and 44) all show it in the middle of the vermis (in contrast to Black's restoration figures). The fissure which in *Anoplotherium* "divided into two almost equal parts . . . the dorsal part of the vermis" (Palmer, 1913, p. 891) was misnamed by Palmer fissura suprapyramis. This misconception of a zoölogist is interesting in connection with our discovery of the "forward move" of the fissura prima in the evolution of the equid brain. Palmer must have had in mind the fissura prima of highly developed living ungulates when he wrote that in *Anoplotherium* he could find only "a suggestion of a groove in the place where it nearly certainly must have lain, on the dorsal part of the anterior face of the vermis" (1913, p. 891). As in *Mesohippus* and *Merycoidodon*, the fissura prima of *Anoplotherium* crossed the middle of the vermis.

The general similarity of these four Lower and Middle Oligocene perissodactyl and artiodactyl brains, and their common possession of primitive characters absent in living Perissodactyla and Artiodactyla, might recall our remarks concerning the Lower Eocene. They might suggest that in the earlier stages of the *Oligocene*, too, certain standard features characterized the ungulate brain. However, this is not the case. We can safely assume that it was not even true within the suborders of which we have discussed only *Mesohippus*-sized genera. Body size had long ago begun to play its role in neocortex formation; besides, the ungulate stock now was greatly diversified. One contemporary of the earliest *Mesohippus* was the giant titanotheriid *Menodus* (*Brontotherium*). The cerebral hemispheres of *Menodus* were subglobular; their well-fissured neocortex extended to the brain base; the olfactory bulbs, though bulky and quite anterior to the forebrain, rose to less than half the forebrain height (Osborn, 1929, fig. 716 D_1 and D_2).

As *Menodus* was the last of a short-lived perissodactyl suborder, and we are comparing its brain with that of *Mesohippus*, one recalls Marsh's hard-dying "law" of Tertiary brains, in particular forebrains—to refute it. "The brain of a mammal of a declining race is smaller than the average brain of its contemporaries of the same group" (Marsh, 1884, p. 59). *Menodus giganteus*, with a large and definitely modern brain, is the embodiment of an evolution drawing to its close. *Mesohippus*, whose slender brain combined modern with primitive characters, represents the beginning of the bloom of a family still flourishing today.

Lacking Upper Eocene material, we do not know when the equid brain turned from its preparatory stage into a brain comparable to living ungulates. In our series, the latter stage is reached in *Mesohippus*. The brain of *Mesohippus* almost conforms to modern standards; its fissuration had developed equid characters, but its rhinencephalon has characters which today occur only in brains of the lower mammalian orders. This stage is well described in Black's summary on the contemporary, similar-sized artiodactyl, *Merycoidodon* (*Oreodon*); "it is evident from a study of its endocranial morphology that *Oreodon* was a primitive, macrosmatic, artiodactyl ungulate . . . and that any edentate (*e.g., Orycteropus*) resemblances are of a superficial nature and wholly confined to the rhinencephalon" (1920–1921, p. 312).

SUMMARY

Seven endocranial casts of *Mesohippus* were studied. They differ from each other in minor details but they do not reflect the diversity of Oligocene equid skeletons and teeth.

In *Mesohippus*, brain evolution had greatly advanced over the *Orohippus* stage. As we have no knowledge of the *Epihippus* brain, we do not know how much of the progress had taken place during the Upper Eocene.

This progress consisted mainly in expansion of the neopallium and the concomitant expansion of the cerebrum as a whole. The cerebral hemispheres had become broader than the cerebellum. They overlapped, posteriorly, a considerable part of the cerebellum; but they did not overlap, anteriorly, the olfactory bulbs. The lower half of the cerebrum was still exclusively rhinencephalon. The upper half of the cerebral convexity was fissured neopallium. All the chief sulci of the horse pallium had appeared. They were straight—longitudinal in the posterior two-thirds, generally transverse in the anterior third. There was little ramification of the sulci, and no accessory sulci were developed.

Although *Mesohippus* had a brain with equid features, the evolutionary level of similar-sized Recent ungulate brains had not been attained in the Middle Oligocene. The neopallium was smaller, and the olfactory bulbs were more prominent. These primitive features were likewise observed in similar-sized artiodactyl contemporaries of *Mesohippus*.

UPPER OLIGOCENE (WHITNEYAN): *MIOHIPPUS*
STAGE IN PHYLOGENY

Miohippus is distinguished from its ancestor *Mesohippus* only by slight changes in structure; size, however, was considerably greater. Skull lengths taken from Robb, Scott, and Osborn's figures are 216, 220, 230, 242, 248, and 256 mm. The AMNH mounted skeleton of *Miohippus intermedius* from the *Protoceras* beds, Cheyenne River, South Dakota, stands 640 mm. at the withers; its skull is 225 mm. long (Colbert, M.S.). Of *M. validus* from the same strata, Osborn records (1918, p. 56) shoulder height 711 mm. and skull length 250 mm. (p. 55). Another adult skull of this species, the predominant form in the *Protoceras* bed channel sandstones, is also 250 mm. long (Scott, 1941, p. 950).

MATERIAL

Miohippus sp., PU 11127 (fig. 12); a neurocranium from the *Protoceras* beds of South Dakota. Upon removal of the bones, the endocast proved satisfactory only where the gray coarse matrix is glazed with a thin smooth post-diagenetic yellowish coat. This is the case on most of the dorsal surface of the cerebral hemispheres, and laterally on most of the left side. Only rough stone fills the anterior part of the cerebellar chamber, and the occiput is not preserved. Nor did the removal of the cancellate osseous tissue, which dorsally extended forward from the anterior end of the cerebrum, reveal any smooth surface in the ethmoidal chamber; only part of the lateral surface of the left olfactory bulb is cast.

The posterior extremity of the maxilla is preserved with the last tooth of the functioning row, an unworn M^1; the M^2 crown was found fully developed within the jaw, with the tips of its cusps descended almost to the level of the alveolar border. The animal thus was as young as an *Equus* somewhat over a year old. At this age the details of the brain surface are fully developed. There are, however, no data on size differences between the brain of a 1-year-old colt and an adult horse. It is from the development of the neurocranium of *Equus* that we can deduce that the length of our young *Miohippus* forebrain was perhaps 6 mm., certainly less than 10 mm., less than adult size; that is, these cerebral hemispheres would have increased in length by somewhat over one tenth had the animal not died in its second year. Robb's list of "cranium lengths" in horse ontogeny does not contain data of exactly corresponding age; besides, his measurement includes the orbit. This length, in an 11-months-old colt, differs from adult horses only by 15–21 mm. (Robb, 1935, p. 48). The difference can be assumed to have been less than half as great in *Miohippus* whose adult neurocranium proper was about half as long as that of *Equus*.

Measurements. Cerebral hemispheres: length 65 mm., height 33 mm. or more; greatest breadth (2 times left hemisphere, at temporal lobe) 64 mm.; frontal lobe breadth at sulcus coronalis 37 mm. Olfactory bulbs: length >8 mm., breadth >26 mm.

DESCRIPTION

The cerebral hemispheres of this young *Miohippus* are only 3 mm. longer than in the largest of our *Mesohippus* brains. Anterior frontal lobe breadth is identical

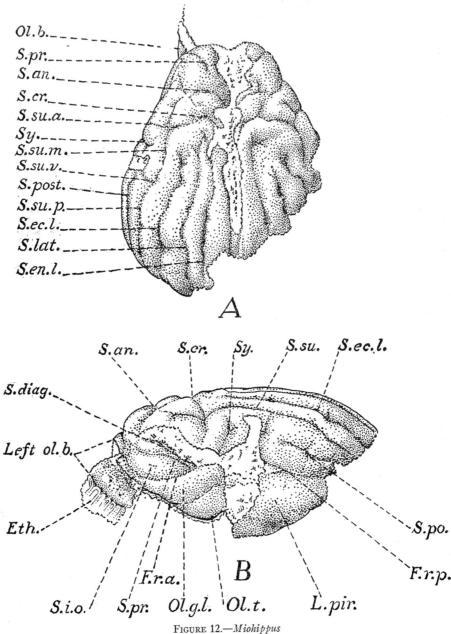

FIGURE 12.—*Miohippus*

Fragmentary natural endocranial cast.   (A) Dorsal, (B) left side view.   × 1.

in the two specimens. Posterior frontal lobe breadth, however, is 7 mm. greater, and temporal lobe breadth about 11 mm. greater in the *Miohippus* brain. It would seem that the young *Miohippus* forebrain was a slightly enlarged and considerably broadened *Mesohippus* forebrain if comparison is made only with the *Mesohippus* specimen nearest to it in size. Possibly the relatively large cerebral breadth of this *Miohippus* was a character of its youth; length of cerebral hemispheres has been observed to increase more than breadth in mammalian ontogenies (Kappers, 1928, p. 74–75).

The neocortex does not protrude laterally over the palaeocortex as it does in all *Mesohippus* specimens. The fissured portion is not broader than the piriform lobe. A small part of the basal side of the piriform lobe is preserved so that probably the entire forebrain height is contained in the specimen. If so, the preserved remnant of the fissura rhinalis posterior is slightly below mid-height. Due to a large unmoulded area between the preserved parts of the posterior and anterior rhinal fissures, the lowest of three more or less horizontal furrows in the anterior lateral region can be mistaken for the fissura rhinalis anterior. However, the most dorsal of the three identifies itself, by curving upward to the dorsal facies, as the presylvian sulcus. The lowest lies within the rhinencephalon; it is the sulcus endorhinalis (s. arcuatus), which medially delimits the gyrus olfactorius lateralis. The anterior rhinal fissure is the middle one of the three furrows; its development has remained similar to that observed in *Mesohippus*.

The extensive unmoulded area which interrupts the rhinal fissure also obscures the Sylvian region. The upper end of the Sylvian fossa emerges from this area as a dorsally bifurcated, nearly vertical sulcus. There was no anterior ectosylvian branch; the region of possible median and posterior ectosylvian branches is within the unmoulded area.

The ventral ramus of the suprasylvian sulcus is basally cut off by the unmoulded area. The pars anterior sulci suprasylvii is preserved somewhat longer. The two converge basally, and with the pars media they form an arch. The pars media continues into a rather straight pars posterior sulci suprasylvii, but the course of the other longitudinal sulci is somewhat more undulating than in *Mesohippus*. The left ectolateral in particular is sinuous; it has two branchlets, but these are very short. The longitudinal sulci are not connected with each other. The sulcus posticus is an almost straight longitudinal furrow which rises dorso-anteriorly; it has two tiny dorsal branches.

The presylvian and diagonal sulci are similar to those of *Mesohippus*. However, a new sulcus has appeared, as a short horizontal furrow, between the presylvian sulcus and the anterior rhinal fissure. This region, the proreal convolution, had been smooth in *Mesohippus*. The sulcus it contains in *Equus* is rarely mentioned in the brain descriptions,—presumably because in the horse it may be continuous with the presylvian sulcus and/or the rhinal fissure, and may extend so far as to join the rostral sulcus of the mesial brain surface. It was described as a separate unit in the horse first by Bradley (1899, p. 220–221) who named it intra-orbital fissure (sulcus supraolfactorius Holl, 1900; sillon orbitaire Anthony and Grzybowski, 1930; intra-proreal Kappers, Huber, and Crosby, 1936). The separateness of this sulcus is definitely established from its first appearance in the evolution of the horse brain; in the Upper Oligocene, the intraorbital sulcus did not have contact with the neighboring sulci.

The sulcus cruciatus is as in *Mesohippus;* the left one has a short, the right one a longer longitudinal branch anteriorly. The right coronal is short, the left seems not to have been developed. The left ansate, however, laterally turns backward and joins the suprasylvian sulcus; a condition is thus established which was not achieved in *Mesohippus* but occurs in all later equid brains.

Although the anterior side of the cast consists mostly of rough surface, the outline of the window into the ethmoidal chamber is satisfactorily represented. A double arc is seen dorsally on the cephalic facies of the hemispheres, at a level about 9 mm. below their summits, separating their smooth surface from the rough stone representing a section through the olfactory tracts. Each of the latter was 13 mm. high, their common breadth 17 mm.

Very little of the olfactory bulbs is directly shown in the specimen. The only part cast is the lateral wall of the left bulb, lacking, however, lower and upper ends. The rest of the matrix anterior to the cast of the cerebral hemispheres was loose and rough. However, its removal revealed on the right side a longitudinal, baso-medially slanting bone fragment *in situ*. The exposed inner surface consists of two areas. A smooth region is a part of the outer wall of the right olfactory bulb chamber; since it has irregular broken rims, it tells nothing about shape or extent of the bulbs. Basally, it abuts upon bone ribbed by the insertion of ethmoturbinals. The border line between these two areas of the bone fragment discloses, in part, the position of the lamina cribrosa. The fila olfactoria entered here through a baso-posteriorly slanting, transverse plate.

The transverse distance of the preserved fragment of the right ethmoidal chamber wall from the cast of the outer side of the left olfactory bulb is 26 mm. This was also the breadth of the medium *Mesohippus* bulbs. As the upper vault of the *Miohippus* bulbs is not preserved, their full breadth was probably slightly larger. The level of the upper surface of the olfactory bulbs remains unknown. In the contemporary but much smaller artiodactyl *Caenotherium*, the olfactory bulbs were, relative to the cerebral hemispheres, more voluminous than they are in living artiodactyls. The bulbi also extended higher up, but not to the skull roof; this is well shown in Hürzeler's (1936) medio-sagittal section (fig. 33) and in his x-ray photo (fig. 19) of *Caenotherium* skulls.

SUMMARY

The data on the brain of *Miohippus* are fragmentary. The only specimen at hand consists of the incompletely preserved cerebral hemispheres of a young individual, with a remnant of one olfactory bulb attached.

This cerebrum was slightly longer and somewhat broader than the largest of the *Mesohippus* cerebra. Its fissuration exhibits but little progress over *Mesohippus*. One sulcus was more undulating. One sulcus connection had been achieved. However, an accessory sulcus had been developed, and it seems possible that the temporal lobe cortex had somewhat enlarged.

MIOCENE I: *PARAHIPPUS*
STAGE IN PHYLOGENY

The *Parahippus* group of species intergrades between *Miohippus* and *Merychippus*. In this stage the Equidae were in transition between the brachyodont, three-toed forest dwellers and the hypsodont, functionally one-toed plains dwellers. Cement appeared on the tooth surfaces. The shortened side toes gradually ceased to be used in running. There is a far wider size variation than in the smaller Oligocene genera; large forms occur already in the Lower Miocene (Arikareean), and a dwarf form existed in the late Miocene (Barstovian). Shoulder height of the only mounted skeleton, the particularly long-limbed Lower Miocene (Upper Harrison) *Parahippus wyomingensis* (MCZ 6390), is 1055 mm.; skull length of this specimen is 312.17 mm. (Schlaikjer, 1937, p. 261). Other recorded complete Upper Harrison skulls are larger—*P. nebrascensis* 370 mm., *P. nebrascensis primus* 390 mm. (Osborn, 1918, p. 79–80).

MATERIAL

I. *Parahippus* sp., MCZ 17878, an incomplete neurocranium. The label reads: Lower *Parahippus* Level, Deer Creek, Torrington, Wyoming. From Deer Creek, Schlaikjer (1935) records *Parahippus* finds only in the lower part of the Upper Harrison (Upper Lower Miocene). The cranium was not fully filled; the brittle sandy matrix inside presents mostly rough surfaces. Only in some of the areas laid open by the removal of bone does the endocast reveal single features of cerebellum, cerebral hemispheres, olfactory bulbs, and the pituitary body. In this fragment, the distance from the anterior rim of the orbit to the supraoccipital crest is 185 mm.; as this distance is 173 mm. in *P. wyomingensis* (Schlaikjer, 1937, p. 261), our fragment suggests a skull about 334 mm. long.

II. *Parahippus cognatus* Leidy, AMNH 14305 (fig. 13); probably Hemingfordian (Middle Miocene), Hemingford group, exact horizon uncertain, 5 miles north of Marsland, Nebraska. Both a rubber and a plaster endocast were taken from the skull figured by Matthew (1924, figs. 44, 45). In this individual the milk teeth are retained, PM^1 and M^1 are ready to erupt—as in a horse about 6 months old. The skull lacks the occiput with the cerebellar chamber. Inside, the ethmoidal chamber is broken, and the right cerebral chamber is distorted; the outline of the left one is preserved, but much of its lateral and lower surfaces is disturbed. The youth of this individual is apparent also in the endocast; the imprint of the fronto-parietal suture (not shown in fig. 13) crosses the cerebral hemispheres, and the gyri are well moulded in the undisturbed regions.

Measurements (mm.).—Length: total, I: 140; cerebellum and cerebral hemispheres, I: 115; cerebral hemispheres, I: 84, II: 79; olfactory bulbs, I: 15.—Breadth: cerebral hemispheres, I: 2 times 32, II: 2 times 30; olfactory bulbs, I: 32.—Height: Medulla oblongata, I: 25; cerebral hemispheres, II: 45 mm.

DESCRIPTION

A medio-sagittal section of the occiput of I shows, through the formation of the inner plate of the occipital bone, the following configuration of the posterior side of the brain. The upper surface of the medulla oblongata rises steeply anterad from the foramen magnum. Its free part is 15 mm. long. Measured horizontally, the medulla extends to 9 mm. in antero-posterior direction from the upper rim of the foramen magnum. In this plane the inner plate of the occipital becomes perpendicular, to form the posterior wall of the cerebellar chamber. The 26 mm. height of this wall is divided into a lower and an upper posterad convexity by (the section of) a low transverse crest which protrudes forward into the chamber. This crest projected into the fissura suprapyramis; it crossed the vermis 17 mm. above the free lower posterior end.

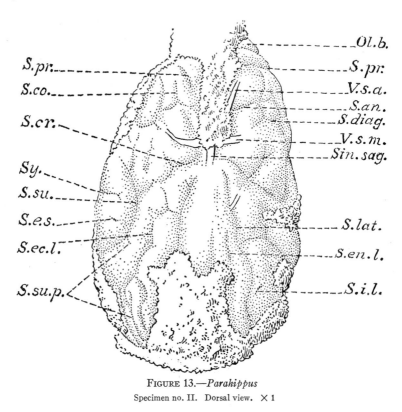

FIGURE 13.—*Parahippus*
Specimen no. II. Dorsal view. × 1

We have no whole cerebral hemisphere of this particularly important stage of equid evolution. From the material at hand, only a general impression is obtained of a cerebrum more slender than that of *Miohippus*. This is in correspondence with the characteristic features of the *Parahippus* skull—viz., elongated and narrow. The cerebral hemispheres of the 6-months-old *Parahippus* were not broader than those of the almost 2-year-old *Miohippus*, but they were longer. The ratios of maximum breadth to maximum length of the hemispheres were the same in the young and the adult *Parahippus*.

Fissuration details could be studied only in the colt. The few sulcus remnants preserved in the adult brain (I) suggest a general similarity with the pattern found in the colt's brain (II). Whereas Anthony and Grzybowski's figures of the brain of a horse fetus (1930, fig. 14) do not quite bear out their contention that with regard to fissuration "ce stade peut être considéré comme semblable à un adulte" (p. 160), this is certainly the case at the age of 6 months.

The regions of both posterior rhinal fissures of I are too disturbed to permit drawing conclusions. Most of the left anterior rhinal is very clearly moulded, and some of the right one. Their position has undergone a striking change since the Oligocene. In the side views, the anterior rhinal is seen to arch down to hardly 3 mm. above the brain base. The basal view in particular shows to what extent the neocortex has expanded to the lower brain surface in *Parahippus*—at least in the frontal lobe which, unfortunately, is all which can be studied in this respect. Fissured cortex is no longer a narrow frame of the brain stem but forms a considerable portion of the lower side of the brain. The progress of evolution, of the neocortex exclusively, which thus manifests itself to the eye, can be illustrated by contrasting measure-ments. The most baso-median points of the right and left anterior rhinal fissure arcs are 23 mm. apart in the young *Parahippus*. This transverse measurement, the width of the rhinencephalon across the medial and lateral olfactory gyri, was about the same in *Mesohippus:* 23 mm. in V, 24 in VI, 25 in VII. Total brain breadth in this plane, however, is 41 mm. in the young *Parahippus*, as against 31 mm. in the three *Mesohippus* specimens.

The lower Sylvian region is not moulded. The upper end of the left fossa Sylvii is bifurcated, and a posterior ectosylvian sulcus (fissura postica) is developed behind it. On the right side the Sylvian region is disturbed to such an extent that the supra-sylvian sulcus is distorted. The left suprasylvian sulcus of *Parahippus* II gives an even stronger impression of an arch than was the case with the preceding stages. This is only partly due to the fact that only a short division of the pars posterior is moulded on the endocasts where it adjoins the pars media—a longer portion is pre-served posteriorly. Pars anterior, pars media, and ramus ventralis together form one arched furrow. The ventral ramus has a short posterior branch. The pars anterior has a long anterior branch. Whereas the region just in front of this branch is somewhat obscured on the left hemisphere, a sulcus coming up from the lateral surface ends here on right hemisphere; this must be the diagonal sulcus whose lower part can be seen ascending obliquely only on the left hemisphere.

The area between the cruciate and ansate sulci is longer than it was in the Oligocene brains. Its length results not· only from the cruciate's lateral backward course (which will remain thus in the later Equidae), but medially, too, the cruciate is farther behind the ansate than it used to be, and than it will be later on. This area seems particularly elongated in *Parahippus*.

The left coronal is a short sulcus. The right one seems to have joined the pre-sylvian, but the furrow which apparently represents it is also (and may be only) the medial side of a vena cerebri superior anterior. The junction of this vessel with the sagittal sinus is not preserved; more posteriorly, a pair of such veins join the sinus at right angles. The intra-orbital sulcus appears as a downward branch of the presylvian. Between the lateral and ectolateral sulci a transverse connection has been achieved in rather different regions on the two hemispheres. Posterior to this transverse branch, a short accessory sulcus, obliquely longitudinal, is developed on the right hemisphere. This is the first appearance of that accessory sulcus which is so irregularly developed in *Equus* (where it may consist of two or three separate parts) that it has been given a name only by Alouf: sulcus interlateralis dorsalis (1929, p. 16).

On the lower surface of II, only the olfactory gyri and the end of the right olfactory tract are well recognizable.   In I, only the central part of the brain base was laid open.   There is a low convexity corresponding to the pituitary body.   A transverse groove along its posterior borders—the imprint of a very low dorsum sellae—and an 8 mm.-long mould of the cavernous blood sinus groove on its right side are the only definite limits; the whole surface is rough sandstone.   However, the sphenoid bone which was removed from this area shows the pituitary groove distinctly. It suggests a roundish pituitary body 13 mm. long and up to 10 mm. broad.

The region anteriorly adjoining the frontal poles of the cerebral hemispheres has considerably changed since *Miolippus*.   The usual epithet of the *Parahippus* skull, elongated, is the best description of what has taken place here.   A mass of cancellate frontal bone, more extensive than the corresponding region of the frontal bone of *Miohippus*, was removed here in I in search of the cast of the olfactory bulbs.   With regard to the brain form, the important feature of this wall between cerebral and ethmoidal chambers is its depth—it extended to 23 mm. below the outside of the skull roof.   From beneath this transverse wall, the olfactory bulbs rise forward. The dorsal surface of the right bulb was revealed complete, and the preserved posterior half of the left bulb supplemented the evidence.   The bulbs of *Parahippus* rose less steeply than those of its Oligocene predecessors.   Nine mm. from the anterior poles of the hemispheres, the highest vault of the bulbs is reached; it is 14 mm. below the skull roof—that is, the upper surface of the olfactory bulbs rises only 9 mm. above that of the olfactory tracts.   The highest vault of the forebrain is at least 20 mm. above the latter.   In contrast to the stout olfactory bulbs of *Mesohippus* those of this *Parahippus* appear to have an elongated egg shape in the dorsal (the only exposed) view.   Furthermore, it seems that the *Parahippus* bulbs were separated by an ethmoidal crest of greater breadth than in *Mesohippus*; this bone, however, could not be further investigated without destroying the preserved parts of the bulbs.

SUMMARY

Fragmentary endocranial casts of one very young and one adult *Parahippus* indicate the following advances since the Oligocene stage of brain evolution:

The cerebrum had become considerably higher than the olfactory bulbs.   The frontal lobe neopallium had spread over the lower cerebral surface.   Sulcus branching had led to some connections.   The sulcus interlateralis dorsalis had appeared.

MIOCENE II: *MERYCHIPPUS*

STAGE IN PHYLOGENY

Thirty-six Middle Miocene to Lower Pliocene species are united in the genus *Merychippus*.   They "intergrade almost imperceptibly with those of *Parahippus* on the one hand and those of *Pliohippus, Calippus, Nannippus, Hipparion,* and *Neohipparion* on the other" (Stirton, 1940, p. 178).   In this stage occurred the definite transition from the use of three toes to one; the lateral metapodials are usually more reduced than in *Parahippus*.   The transition took place from low- to high-crowned teeth, from the short to the long muzzle.   During the long lifetime of the genus, the body size of the smallest living horses was reached. Variation was great. On the whole, the Middle Miocene Sheep Creek species are small and primitive; the Upper Miocene Pawnee Creek species are larger and more progressive (Matthew, 1926, p. 160–161). Of the former group, the skull length of the *Merychippus primus* of Matthew's figure 55 (1924) is 274 mm., and that of Abel's reconstruction (1926, fig. 268) even as little as 225 mm. From Osborn's (1918) and Matthew's (1924) figures I measured the following skull lengths from the early Upper Miocene: *M. paniensis* 334 mm., *M. sphenodus* 304, *M. isonesus* 310, *M. sejunctus* 322; Robb's (1935, p. 48) *M. sejunctus* skull lengths are 321 and 329 mm. Skull length is 330 mm. in a small Shetland pony, 330 and 380 in two newborn horses (Robb, 1935, p. 48). The smallest Shetland pony measured by Brydon (1890, p. 208) was 830 mm. at the withers. The AMNH mounted skeleton of a Sheep Creek *Merychippus isonesus*, with 312 mm. skull length, likewise stands 830 mm. at the withers (Colbert, MS.). The greatest height of the back—at the fifth dorsal vertebra—is 895 mm., and the length of this skeleton, as mounted, is 1615 mm. (Simpson, 1932b, p. 5). The Amherst *Merychippus sejunctus* skeleton is 990 mm. high at the withers (Loomis, 1926, p. 127).

MATERIAL

Middle Miocene (Hemingfordian).—I. *Merychippus* sp., CNHM, P. 26032 (fig. 15 A): an incomplete endocast of a fragmentary skull of a "primitive member of the genus" (Mr. Bryan Patterson, personal communication). It is from the Marsland formation east of Marsland, Nebraska, which is older than the Sheep Creek beds and is characterized by the first appearance of *Merychippus* (Cook and Gregory, 1941, p. 549). This *Merychippus* thus was older than or contemporary with our *Parahippus* II. The left half of the brain cavity is cast, of the frontal poles also its right one, with both ethmoidal chambers. However, the walls of the right ethmoidal chamber are broken, and its cast consequently is irregular, as is also the dorsal side of the left olfactory bulb. The entire cast, made of black rubber, is interspersed with patches of irregular surface; very little of the fissuration is reliably reproduced.

A, B, and II. *Merychippus* sp., AMNH 32671, 32672. These two lots of skull fragments from the Sheep Creek beds of Stonehouse Draw, Nebraska, each contain one fragment of the braincase roof. In 32671 (A) it is the anterior portion, including part of the roof of the ethmoidal chamber. Specimen 32672 (B) contains a posterior portion of which a mould was taken in plasticine (II; fig. 14 A). In both these skull roofs the lamina interna was moulded by brains just the size of specimen I.

Lower Upper Miocene (Lower Barstovian).—C and III. *Merychippus* sp., AMNH 9393: a sectioned neurocranium (pl. 2, fig. 1), complete except anteriorly, and its plaster endocast (fig. 14, B, C); from the Pawnee Creek beds, 4 miles northeast of Pawnee Buttes, Colorado. Only the right side is preserved far enough forward to contain the lateral wall of the ethmoidal chamber. The skull does not appear distorted in spite of many breaks patched up with plaster The flatness of the dorsal side of the endocast, however, appeared strange, and in the compilation of the brain measurements of all Equidae (table 6) those of this specimen are so aberrant that post mortem dorso-ventral compression is strongly suggested.

D. *Merychippus* sp., AMNH 9420: Skull fragments from the Pawnee Creek beds, 5 miles northeast of Pawnee Buttes, Colorado, three of which represent most of the neurocranium of a small individual.

Of the four skull roofs (A–D) studied with the endocranial casts, two possess a conspicuous feature which is mentioned here because no attention has been paid to it before. Besides the group of pits and foramina in and along the posterior part of the parieto-temporal suture which occurs, in increasing number, from *Eohippus* to *Equus*, both B and D possess three paramedian foramina opening from the tabula externa of the parietal bone into the diploë or into the brain cavity.

B has an almost symmetrical pair 32 mm. from the back of the occipital crest. One of them is a pit, the other a complete parietal foramen. They are subcircular on the bone surface with 3 mm. diameter, and they lie at 7 and 8 mm., respectively, from the midline. Besides, there is a smaller and shallower pit at 24 mm. from the occipital crest, extending from 4 to 6 mm. to the right of the midline. A similar group of three lies in the larger D skull, 34 to 42 mm. anterior to the occipital crest. A pair, 4 mm. from the midline, consists of (1) a 2 mm.-wide foramen into whose posterior extremity slopes a groove indicating its former occupation by a venous emissary from the diploë, (2) a small pit. Seven mm. anterior to the latter, there is a deep 1 mm.-wide subcircular pit at 9 mm. from the midline.

Paired parietal foramina were observed only in one of 144 *Equus* skulls investigated (Edinger, 1933, p. 275). Looking over pictures of fossil equid skulls, I found foramina, or pits, nearer the midline than the parieto-temporal group, only in Osborn's side view of *Miohippus meteulophus* (1918, fig. 30; Pl. I, fig. 7: a group of three).

IV. *Merychippus isonesus* (Cope), AMNH 8105 (fig. 15 B). On this natural endocranial cast from the Deep River beds, Deep River (Smith Creek), Montana, are based Cope and Matthew's (1915) figures 8 (left lateral view) and 8a (superior view) of plate 148a. These pictures are all that was heretofore known of the brain of *Merychippus*. They are published without comment and thus are misleading. The specimen is not shown in natural size but in two-thirds natural size. Although not indicated in the figures, only parts of the surface are moulds of the endocranium, and this endocast is strongly distorted by lateral compression. Figure 8a is mostly reconstruction. The olfactory bulbs are not present. The occipital portions of the forebrain are missing. On the lump of rock which is preserved of the endocast of the posterior endocranium, only the base is moulded except for the cast of the foramen magnum region which is preserved almost undistorted. The distortion of this specimen is much to be regretted because of the excellent quality of those moulded areas it possesses. What there is of the left hemisphere shows little sign of distortion. However, most of the right half of the brain is pressed against and under the left half so that in dorsal view the right hemisphere now has less than two-thirds the breadth of the left one. Yet lateral features of the cerebellum and some details of the brain base are well represented on this distorted side. Cope and Matthew's dorsal view of this specimen is probably a good reconstruction of the general brain shape. We have not figured a dorsal view because, except for the anterior two-fifths of the left hemisphere and an 18 mm.-broad strip in the anterior region of the right hemisphere, the cerebral vault of this cast is too disturbed to yield reliable brain data.

DESCRIPTION

Cerebellum.—The casts of the cerebellar chamber of *Merychippus* are more or less disturbed by the dorso-posterior evaginations (fig. 15 A*) which have been described in the chapter on brain-endocranium relations. Not even the vermis can be recognized in specimen I. In III the vermis profile forms a rounded angle of almost 90°; its caudal facies is perpendicular, and its dorsal facies slopes slightly anterad. At the anterior end of the vermis, below the cerebral hemispheres, there is in this speci-

TABLE 2.—Merychippus *and* Tapirus

Measurements of the *Merychippus* endocasts No. I, III, IV, endocranium D, and of an endocast of *Tapirus terrestris* (Ta).

	I	D	III	IV	Ta
LENGTH					
total			(117)		128
cer. + cbl.	88		103	>118	112
cbl.			24		30
cer.	70	73	87	>107	92
ol. b.	7		>10		12
BREADTH					
obl.		22	27	(24)	30
cbl.	(48)		51		50
neopall.	(58)	53	77	2 × 37	80
palaeopall.	(50)		66		73
ol. b.	26		(40)		51
HEIGHT					
obl.		21	26	27	21
cer.	35	43	50	63	64
ol. b.	19		24		50

men a lower, flat, 5 mm.-long portion which can easily be mistaken for a very short anterior lobe. However, checking in the cranium (pl. 2, fig. 1) showed that on the tentorium there is no counterpart to the sudden bend of the vermis profile. Thus it does not correspond to a brain feature but is an irregularity of the cast. The anterior lobe of the vermis is not delimited. Only the suprapyramidal fissure is present; it crosses the vermis 15 mm. above the lower free end.

The vermis was relatively narrow, and in its antero-dorsal part it was straight. Posteriorly, its outlines are asymmetrically dented and arched. Whereas vermis breadth is between 9 and 12 mm. on the anteriorly sloping facies, breadth attains 17 mm. posteriorly. Thus the vermis had, in *Merychippus* (or in *Parahippus*, of whose cerebellum too little is known), begun its irregular coiling.

As the parasagittal fissure is moulded posteriorly in III on the right side, it is seen that the paramedian lobe had remained relatively narrow, while the paraflocculus is a voluminous formation. The flocculus is well seen above, and extending behind, the internal acoustic meatus, while in IV (right side) it is just above the meatus only, perhaps due to the distortion. The length is 6 mm. on both sides (checked in the petrosal fossa of the skull) in III, 7 mm. in IV. Greatest height also is 6 mm. in III, 7 in IV. While neither the measurements taken of the little floccular fossa of three *Mesohippus* nor those of two *Merychippus* can tell the exact size of the whole flocculus, they do indicate that in this cerebellar portion the least (or no) progress in size was made.

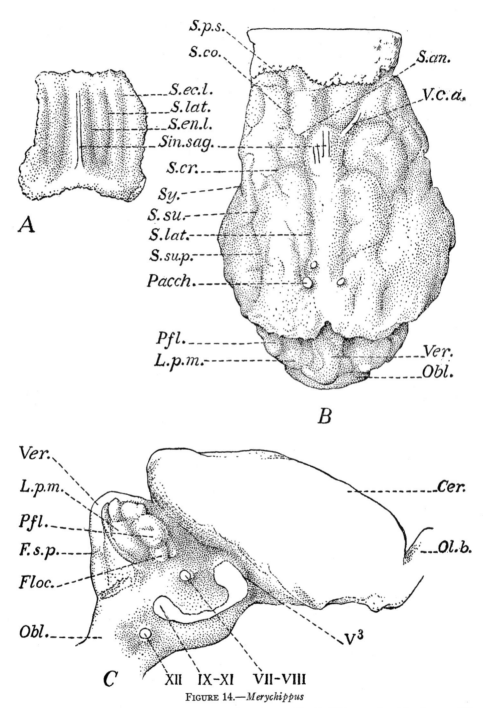

A

B

C

FIGURE 14.—*Merychippus*

(A) Plasticine impression of posterior part of skull roof, specimen no. II.   (B, C) Plaster endocast (specimen no. III)
dorsal and right side views. × ⅜.

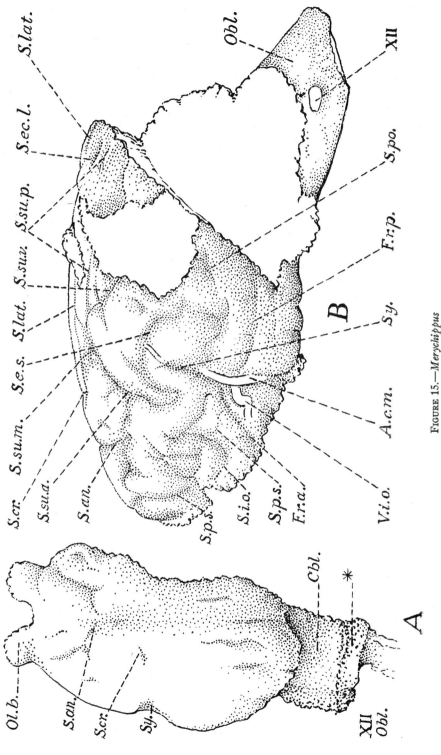

FIGURE 15.—*Merychippus*

(A) Rubber endocast (specimen no. I), dorsal view.   (B) Natural endocast (specimen no. IV), left side view.   ×1.

75

Cerebral hemispheres.—Corresponding with the wide variation otherwise observed within the genus *Merychippus*, in particular with the progress in body size, the cerebral hemispheres of our Middle Miocene specimens are rather different from the Upper Miocene brains. In the following description the contrasts are pointed out. Two specimens from each of the two periods presumably do not characterize the whole brain situation of the respective equid stages; they only show that a great step was taken within the genus *Merychippus*.

The cerebral hemispheres were slender in the Middle Miocene, but not as slender as in *Parahippus*; they were broader and considerably larger in the Upper Miocene. The outline can no more be described as egg-shaped in either stage. Through broadened frontal lobes the subquadrangular shape of the *Equus* hemispheres was approached. The neopallium had equally expanded to the brain base in both stages. It occupies somewhat over three-fourths of the forebrain height at the lowest curve of the posterior rhinal fissure in I and IV. (The anterior rhinal fissure region is not complete in any specimen.) The actual neocortex surface, however, was far larger in the Upper Miocene. The plaster endocast III suggests, and the natural endocast IV shows, that these larger *Merychippus* had complexly convoluted cerebra. Even the anterior and posterior rhinal fissures each had a dorsal branchlet. The few sulci recognizable in the lower Miocene *Merychippus* brains are straight or almost straight and seem to have had hardly any branches.

Below the posterior rhinal of IV a short longitudinal furrow indicates the first appearance of fissuration of the lower lip of the posterior rhinal fissure.

The Sylvian fossa is a deep and wide perpendicular groove in the middle of the lateral side of I. Only a trace of the left Sylvia is preserved in III. Although the hemispheres of IV are not complete, both show that the Sylvia lay somewhat anterior to the middle of the length of the hemisphere. The left Sylvian fossa of IV is a deep perpendicular groove which broadens basally to form a triangular sunken area, the central part of the island of Reil. It is surrounded by a prominent gyrus arcuatus primus (g. sylviacus). The ectosylvian sulcus is a complete arc which anterobasally connects with the pars anterior sulci suprasylvii. Pars anterior, pars media, and ramus ventralis sulci suprasylvii form one highly arched line from which the pars posterior sulcii suprasylvii branches off to run to the posterior end of the hemispheres, ramified and rather high up on the dorsal surface.

There is much connection by branching between the diagonal, presylvian, and intraorbital sulci. The intraorbital also connects with the anterior rhinal fissure.

The longitudinal sulci were of the simplest kind in II and, as far as they are recognizable, also in I. In the Upper Miocene specimens III and IV, however, the ancestral contrast on the dorsal surface between an anterior area with mainly transverse and a posterior area with mainly longitudinal fissuration is somewhat obliterated by branching and connections of the principal sulci, and by the appearance, between them, of little accessory sulci.

The endolateral sulcus is not identifiable in I; in II it is just as it was in *Mesohippus*. It is hidden in the median unmoulded area in IV. The most median longitudinal sulcus in III is in a position which suggests that it is the endolateral, but I rather think it must be the lateral because it extends forward to the cruciate and, through an anterior branch of the cruciate, associates with the coronal. Lateral and ecto-lateral sulci seem to have had sinuous courses in the Upper Miocene specimens. Various sulcus connections existed in this phase. Figures 14 B and 15 B show these as far as they are clearly reproduced on the casts. They seem to have varied as much as they do in *Equus*. The cerebral sulci of the modern horse have more branches, and there are more accessory sulci in horse brains than are shown in our *Merychippus* endocasts III and IV; but the main characters of the fissuration of *Equus* were achieved in the Upper Miocene *Merychippus*.

Olfactory bulbs.—The few data concerning the olfactory bulbs of our specimens are confusing.

The left bulbus of specimen I appears to be completely cast, as its front end is dotted with what I take to be fila olfactoria casts. This anterior surface is mostly perpendicular but curves back basally so that there was also a short horizontal portion of the cribriform facies. The bulbus appears to have been short and in a low position. It did not rise higher than to a level 22 mm. below the summit of the cerebral hemispheres.

In the roof of the ethmoidal chamber of specimen A, likewise Middle Miocene, the imprint of the olfactory bulbs is well seen. These bulbs were broader, dorsally, and must have extended farther dorsad than those of I; the bone above their summit is only 5 mm. thick.

The bulbi of the Upper Miocene specimen III apparently were rather high, too. The partially preserved right bulb reached dorsad only 14 mm. less than the upper vault of the temporal lobes. The fragmentary evidence about the Upper Miocene olfactory bulbs furthermore suggests that they were broad as well as high. Breadth across the two bulbi of III possibly was, as it is in A, two-thirds of the frontal lobe breadth; however, we do not know the breadth of the ethmoidal crest which lay between the bulbi.

At the anterior end of the left hemisphere of IV there is a perpendicular break across the upper part of the cast of the ethmoidal window. This cast is 14 mm. broad.

Blood vessels.—Specimens III and IV show pieces of some of the brain vessels. Differences from the *Mesohippus* stage were observed in the surface course of the vessels which may be connected with the new phase of brain evolution in the Upper Miocene *Merychippus*.

The arteria cerebri media of IV was a large vessel. On both sides of the specimen it can be seen approaching the Sylvian fossa and disappearing into the lower region of the fossa. Thus, while in *Mesohippus* this artery was overlapped by the outer, the ectosylvian convolution, in *Merychippus* it was operculized also by the inner, or sylvian convolution. The branching of this vessel was in the operculized area. On both hemispheres one branch emerges dorsally to cross a part of the dorsal leg of the Sylvian gyrus in dorso-posterior direction. On the left side, the further course was either overlapped by the ectosylvian gyrus, or too thin to be moulded on the surface. On the right side, however, a continuation is present as a small vessel crossing the dorsal leg of the ectosylvian gyrus in dorso-posterior direction, beginning in a transverse plane 12 mm. behind the center of the exposed part of the island of Reil.

Another prominent undulating vessel lies in the subinsular area. This vessel was not found in *Mesohippus* where indeed it cannot have had the caliber found in *Merychippus* which corresponds to that in the horse (Hofmann, 1901, pl. XX, fig. 27, "i.o."). It is the vena insulo-opercularis which in *Equus* collects the blood from a number of strong veins on the island of Reil into which flows the blood both from the insula and the adjoining convolutions.

The anterior superior cerebral veins of III apparently were as in *Mesohippus*. Those of IV, however, drained a relatively shorter area in this higher and more complicated brain, as they joined the sagittal sinus more anteriorly, at the ansate sulcus (as in *Equus*; in *Parahippus* II the junction appears to have been between the cruciate and the ansate sulci). The right anterior superior cerebral vein of *Merychippus* IV had a diagonal course throughout. The left one had a 9 mm.-long transverse course before it joined the sagittal sinus at right angles. According to Hofmann (1901, p. 279) this is the case only with the more posterior cerebral veins in living horses, and this was the condition also in *Parahippus* II (fig. 13).

COMPARISON

In the Upper Miocene *Merychippus*, the Equidae attained skull lengths which equal those of the smallest living perissodactyls—Shetland ponies and tapirs.

The brain of a pony (pl. 4) is on a far higher evolutionary level than that reached in the *Merychippus* stage of its ancestry.

The tapir brain of Elliot Smith's (1902) figures 178–180 has certain general similarities with the Upper Miocene *Merychippus* brains. Its fissuration may appear simpler in these figures than in *Merychippus* IV, but the sulci are described by Elliot Smith (p. 310) as having "numerous offshoots, so that the appearance of the surface is very complicated". Elliot Smith's figure 179 suggests that the neocortex, at least at the temporal lobe, does not extend as far basad in the tapir as did that of *Merychippus*. This impression was verified in an MCZ duplicate of the tapir endocast of the Royal College of Surgeons (no. D. 395; Elliot Smith, 1902, p. 311). Both in the side view of the brain and in this endocranial cast (of another, larger individual), one-third of the cerebral height in the temporal lobe region is piriform lobe. The endocast also shows—obviously better than the brain—"the enormous. . . olfactory bulbs." The bulbi of this tapir were larger and, in particular, higher than those seen in the *Merychippus* specimens. Thus it seems that the tapir level of brain evolution had been surpassed, at least in some respects, by the Equidae in the Upper Miocene.

SUMMARY

Judging from one incomplete endocranial cast and skull roof fragments of two other Middle Miocene *Merychippus* individuals, it appears that little if any advance was made in the brain over the stage exemplified by our *Parahippus* material. Only a relatively greater breadth of the frontal lobes can be regarded as a progressive feature.

The neopallium of the posterior regions (whose limits are not recognizable in the *Parahippus* specimens) had greatly expanded basad since the *Miohippus* stage.

Two Upper Miocene *Merychippus* endocasts, although distorted, reveal remarkable progress in brain evolution within this genus. The vermis cerebelli began to coil. The paraflocculus apparently was another center of particular expansion. Variously undulating, branched, connected, and accessory sulci show that vigorous expansion of the neopallium by infolding had occurred. A modern type of fissuration was accomplished in the Upper Miocene *Merychippus*. In this phase the ancestors of the horse reached the size of the smallest living Equidae—the new-born horse and the pony.

PLIOCENE I (LATE LOWER CLARENDONIAN): *PLIOHIPPUS*

STAGE IN PHYLOGENY

Pliohippus was the first really monodactyl equid. Lateral digits still did occur, but only as slender splints along the robust middle toe, which is like that of *Equus* except in size. There is no sharp division between this Lower to Middle Pliocene genus and its ancestor, the protohippine *Merychippus* group. The teeth became gradually more hypsodont. The body size of an ass was attained already in the early Pliocene (in *P. pernix*; Osborn, 1918, p. 151). The AMNH mount of a skeleton from the Lower Pliocene Upper Snake Creek beds of Nebraska, with 1070 mm. shoulder height and 483 mm. skull length (Colbert, M.S.), suggests a large pony. This skeleton belonged to a young adult *P. leidyanus*; the last molar had not cut the gum (Loomis, 1926, p. 143) so that the age of this individual must have been just over 3 years. Another skull of *P. leidyanus* is 434 mm. long (Robb, 1935, p. 43). Smaller species lived at the same time. Robb's (1935, p. 43) *P. lullianus* skull is 380 mm. long, and the skull of the *P.* sp. whose brain is described below is only 377 mm. long. The size range of adult *Pliohippus* skulls thus corresponds to that of domestic horses between the ages of 1 month (skull length 367 mm.) and almost 2 years (500 mm.) (Robb, 1935, p. 48).

MATERIAL

I. *Pliohippus supremus* (Leidy) AMNH 10844 (figure 16); Little White River formation, Canyon of Little White River, South Dakota. This plaster cast of a forebrain chamber was described by Tilney (1931, p. 481–484). Tilney's figures 27 and 28 are dorsal and right side photographs and key drawings which, as well as the text, show that he did not notice all sulci present on this brain. The complex convolutional pattern appeared to Tilney "perplexing" and "confusing" (p. 482). He tentatively identified five sulci and pointed out what general advances had been made over the far-removed ancestor, *Mesohippus*. Redescription of the specimen was thus called for. Tilney, furthermore, was not aware that the individual was immature. Its fragmentary skull (Matthew and Gidley, 1906, figs. 8, 9) shows that milk premolars were functioning, and M^1 had not pushed out farther than to the alveolar border. This animal was a colt about 9 months old.

II. *Pliohippus* sp., CNHM, P. 15870 (figure 17); Big Spring Canyon, South Dakota: a rubber endocast not so well sculptured as specimen I. The poorer

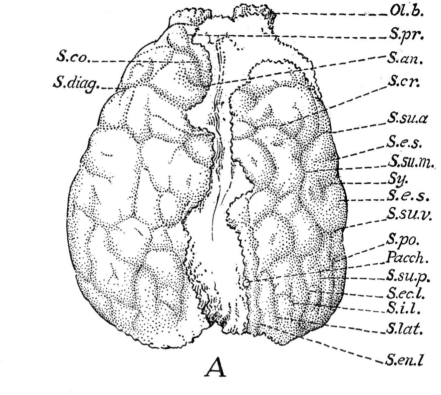

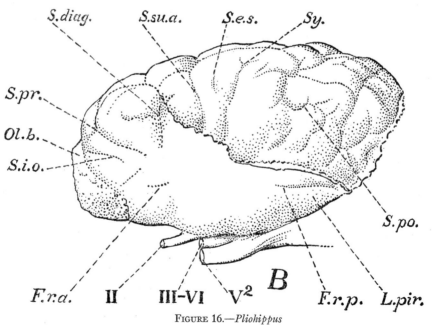

FIGURE 16.—*Pliohippus*

Plaster endocast (specimen no. **I**, colt).   (A) Dorsal, (B) left side views.   × 1.

sculpturing is due partly to the greater age of the animal (an adult, with M³ worn), but there are also disturbed areas as large as the anterior half of the right lateral surface. Sulci appear interrupted which in the real brain must have been contin-

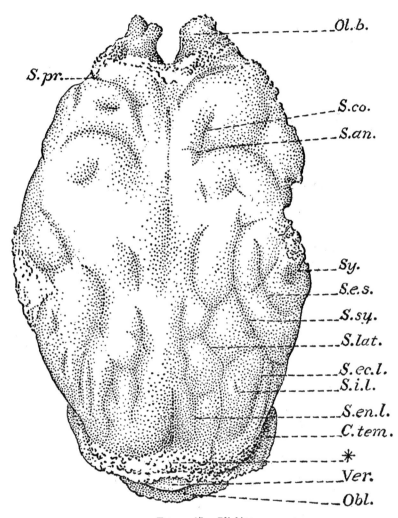

FIGURE 17.—*Pliohippus*
Rubber endocast (specimen no. II). Dorsal view. × 1

uous. The shape of the whole brain is preserved; the specimen lacks only the basal side of the brain stem posterior to the pituitary region.

Measurements (mm.).—Length: total, II: 130; cerebellum, II: 14; cerebral hemispheres, I: 86, II: 103; olfactory bulbs, I: 9, II: 11. Breadth: cerebellum, II: 48; neopallium, I: >78, II: 86; palaeopallium, I: 63, II: 70; olfactory bulbs, I: 29, II: 30. Height: cerebral hemispheres, I: 50, II: 56; palaeopallium (piriform lobe), I: 11, II: 9; olfactory bulbs, I: left 24 (right 30), II: 29.

DESCRIPTION

Cerebellum.—The cast of the cerebellar chamber (in II) shows details of the cerebellum only on the posterior surface. On this facies the right paramedian fissure is
almost straight, while the left one curves laterally; at 18 mm. height, the right side
of the vermis is 5 mm. broad, but the left side extends 12 mm. laterad from the midline. Above this level the twists in the vermis are further expressed in the cast
by the irregular, yet well-moulded surface. The dorsal surface of the cerebellum
is not cast at all; instead, irregular rough masses (fig. 17, *) show that the cranial
tabula interna was incomplete in this area. These masses are continued laterally
into ridges which slope forward and somewhat outward alongside the cerebral hemispheres. These formations correspond only partly to dorsal parts of the cerebellar
hemispheres; antero-laterally, they are casts of the entrance into the temporal canal.

The exposed portion of the cerebellum of this *Pliohippus* is very short. The
conservative position of the internal acoustic meatus also helps to indicate that a
major portion of the cerebellum was overlapped by the forebrain. The cerebral
hemispheres extend to a transverse plane 17 mm. posterior to the entrance of the
acoustic nerves.

Cerebral hemispheres.—Tilney (1931, p. 482) believed that the portion of the brain
containing the rhinal fissure is not included in specimen I. It is true that the per-
fectly moulded surface does not represent the whole neocortex. The neocortex has
an unnatural border which looks like a low crest and has different irregular longitudinal courses on the lateral surfaces of the two hemispheres. This gives the false
impression that the neocortex hung over the hemispheres like a caparison and was
not continued on the lower surfaces. In these almost smooth lower regions, however, the left side contains impressions which seem to me to be parts of the rhinal
fissure (*see* fig. 16 B). The only remnant of the rhinalis in II corresponds to that
part of the posterior rhinal which is preserved in I. The posterior rhinal fissure of
Pliohippus was in a low position. The preserved part is straight. At the greatest
lateral extent of the piriform lobe and of the neopallium, the latter (temporal lobe)
covers about four-fifths of the cerebral height in I and approximately five-sixths in II.
It bulges broadly laterad.

The Sylvian fossa rises dorso-posteriorly in the middle of the lateral surface of all
four hemispheres. Its lower end part is not moulded in any of the hemispheres.
The processus acuminis is bifurcated in each case. The ectosylvian sulcus is satisfactorily shown only on the right hemispheres. It is a complete arc in II, but I do
not see in I the arc shown in Tilney's figure 28a. The horizontal branch was not
found on the left hemisphere of I, and the right horizontal is not connected with the
anterior and posterior portions—a frequent occurrence in *Equus*. The suprasylvian
middle and posterior parts are in a very dorsal position. The high arc formed by the
suprasylvia, its sinuosities, short branches, and many connections with neighboring
sulci are seen in figure 16. Conditions were probably similar in the brain of
Pliohippus II, but they are not well represented in the endocranial cast (fig. 17).

The lateralis group of sulci is so sinuous, branched, and interconnected that a
dense network of fissuration, different on the right and left hemispheres, has replaced
the ancestral group of longitudinal furrows. Tilney did not register the presence

of the ectolateral. It is indeed only at their posterior ends in I that one finds the original state of separateness of ectolateral, lateral, and endolateral sulci. The ectolateral of II runs toward the suprasylvian; in I the ectolateral turns mediad anteriorly and joins the lateral sulcus which here has turned laterad and continues its sinuous course forward. It reaches the cruciate sulcus on the right hemisphere of I. Between the ectolateral sulci, the sulcus interlateralis dorsalis seems to have been only an oblique cross-bar on the left hemisphere of I, but it is more elaborately developed on the right hemisphere. Conditions are obscure in this region of II. The sulcus posticus, while chiefly a longitudinal sulcus, has a tortuous course. On both sides of I, it has five transverse branches. Short accessory sulci were scattered particularly over the posterior areas of the *Pliohippus* cerebrum.

The cruciate sulcus is not moulded in II but is deep and branched in I. The diagonal is continued over the dorsal vault of the hemispheres as a branched transverse sulcus between cruciate and corono-ansate. The ansate is now in that stage which explains why it was not recognized as a definite sulcus in *Equus*. Medial from its junction with the coronal sulcus, the ansate has only a short dorsal course which in I is no longer transverse, but oblique. The presylvian sulcus forms one anterad arc on the left hemisphere of I; it is not preserved on the right hemisphere, and only pieces of it could be traced in II. Here it seems that there was a transverse part of considerable extent on the right hemisphere, crossing an anterior frontal lobe facies which was steeper than in I.

Olfactory bulbs.—The olfactory bulbs appear (in the casts) planted upon the lower half of the anterior facies of the cerebral hemispheres. The two bulbi of specimen II are so differently shaped that they cannot be reliably cast; the chief dimensions, however, are the same on both sides. In I, the anterior facies of the bulbs is dotted with the fila olfactoria entrances; however, these imprints of the two laminae cribrosae are at different levels. The 21 mm.-high and 11 mm.-broad, oval anterior facies of the right bulb has suffered an upward shift. The 20 by 11 mm. imprint of the left cribriform plate is the anterior end of the cast of the only undisturbed ethmoidal chamber in the present material. In I, the right lamina cribrosa appears to have been perpendicular; the undisturbed left one was almost perpendicular, sloping but very slightly baso-posteriorly. The anterior facies of the olfactory bulbs of II suggests a somewhat more pronounced inclination of the cribriform plate in this adult *Pliohippus*.

As far as the unsatisfactory *Merychippus* material allows comparison, there appears to have been no increase in the length of the olfactory bulbs. In comparison with *Parahippus*, the bulbs have become shorter. This was not a reduction in size; the space occupied by the bulbs was closer to the hemispheres in *Pliohippus*. The bulbs are no longer brain portions anterior to the cerebral hemispheres; the peduncular area has disappeared. Perpendicular height of the olfactory bulbs has increased, and their largest oblique diameter is in I 1 to 2 mm., in II 3 mm. more than the perpendicular height given above. The bulbs were separated by the ethmoidal crest to the extent of 3 mm. in I, 5 mm. in II.

A significant difference from the early ancestral condition is the position of the olfactory bulb chamber within the skull. As observed in *Parahippus*, but as seems to have been the case in only one of the *Merychippus* brains, the olfactory bulbs of *Pliohippus* are confined to a lower area in the head than they had occupied in the Eocene and Oligocene; that is, the cerebral hemispheres have come to be much higher than the bulbi. The topographical relation between bulbi and hemispheres is furthermore changed in that anterad expansion of the cerebrum overlapped the proximal parts of the bulbi. The highest point of the bulbi is in our *Pliohippus* specimens not at some distance from the cerebral hemispheres, but immediately adjoining them. As the bulbi lie along the lower side of the frontal lobe, they are tilted into a more oblique position. Their dorsal surface is 25 mm. below that of the cerebral hemispheres in I, 31 mm. in II; they were only half, or somewhat over half, as high as the cerebrum.

Brain base.—The olfactory gyri and tubercles are not reproduced. In specimen I, "no structural features are recognizable on the basal surface, except the roots of the second and fifth pairs of cranial nerves" (Tilney, 1931, p. 484). In addition to these, there are the bundles of the eye-muscle nerves. The region between these nerves is quite smooth; the *Pliohippus* sphenoid had no pituitary groove. The sulcus sagittalis lateralis on the piriform lobe, however, is well seen in I and partly moulded in II. In II several sulci are developed laterally on the piriform lobe. The fissuration of the lower lip of the fissura rhinalis posterior in *Pliohippus* II appears to have been similar to this constant and conspicuous feature of the rhinencephalon of *Equus*, whereas in *Merychippus* it had only been indicated by one sulcus.

Only insignificant short portions of blood vessels are reproduced on the two *Pliohippus* endocranial casts.

SUMMARY

The brain picture gained from the endocranial cast of an adult and a cerebral chamber cast of a young *Pliohippus* illustrates continued evolution in the following features. There was an increase of the vermis twist, of cerebrum expansion over adjoining brain parts, of complication and concomitant variability in cortex fissuration. A high frontal lobe partly overlapped the olfactory bulbs which had become established in a relatively low position.

PLIOCENE II (PONTIAN, CLARENDONIAN): *HIPPARION* AND *NEOHIPPARION*
STAGE IN PHYLOGENY

The hipparions were three-toed, European and North American descendants of *Merychippus*, varying from ass size to over zebra size. They are generally considered a side branch of the *Equus* lineage. Only Abel, Antonius, and Schlosser (Abel, 1926, p. 432) contend that the small *H. matthewi* from Samos is the ancestor of the Old World *Equus*. The North American *Neohipparion* was distinguished from *Hipparion* Christol 1832 only in 1903 by Gidley, and the validity of separating these forms with elongated protocone from those with oval protocone is not generally acknowledged. It is "practically impossible to separate lower teeth of *Hipparion* and *Neohipparion*" in Lower Pliocene American faunas (Stirton, 1940, p. 182). The upper teeth are in some respects less, in others more progressive in *Hipparion*; the limbs and feet are more slender, the lateral digits more reduced—*i.e.*, more modern—in *Neohipparion*. According to Abel certain American Pleistocene horses are descended from *Neohipparion*.

MATERIAL

Hipparion.—Two brains of *Hipparion* have been made known previously; a third one is described below. All three are natural endocranial casts from Balkan Peninsula localities.

I. Lartet mentioned a specimen from Pikermi in one sentence; "le cerveau de l'*Hipparion* se montre encore un peu moins riche en circonvolutions que celui de nos chevaux actuels" (1868, p. 1121). This specimen consists mainly of the cerebral hemispheres. I saw it in 1926 and found it as richly convoluted as endocasts of living horses (Edinger, 1929, p. 176).

II. Simionescu (1934) described a dorsally and laterally exposed endocast in an otherwise complete adult skull of *H. gracile* from Cimişla in Romania (our fig. 18 B). The anterior end of the brain is not disclosed, but cerebrum and cerebellum are so "parfaitement conservés" that Simionescu speaks of "l'encéphale pétrifié" (p. 163) as opposed to a "moulage intérieur du crâne" (p. 166).

The cerebral length of the Pikermi specimen (I) and the cerebral length as measured by Simionescu in the Cimişla specimen (II) happen to compare as the skull lengths of *H. matthewi* (about 360 mm., according to Abel's figure 372, 1926) and of the Cimişla *H. gracile* (467 mm.); namely, as 1:1.3. The Pikermi brain, therefore, may have belonged to an individual of that small size, which (together with cheek teeth and skeletal characters) made possible the insertion of *H. matthewi* into the horse ancestry. This small *Hipparion* brain is in the Musée national d'histoire naturelle in Paris, France. No figure of it has been published.

III. *Hipparion gracile* Kaup AMNH 10732a from Samos (fig. 18 A) is prepared much as is the Cimişla brain. The basal parts of the occipital and sphenoid bones and the anterior wall of the forebrain chamber remained attached to the endocast. Under the removed tabula externa of the frontal bone cancellate structure is revealed due to which this skull region is completely infiltrated with matrix. Whereas 100 mm. of the length of the cerebral hemispheres is exposed dorsally, the position of the transverse constriction of the neurocranium in the lateral sides of the specimen shows that the anterior poles of the hemispheres are hidden to the extent of 12 mm. or more. Comparison of this specimen with Simionescu's figures shows that the Cimişla brain, too, is not completely revealed anteriorly. The Samos and Cimişla specimens are similar in size but apparently not in quality of preservation. In the one specimen at hand, the Samos endocast, only the lateral areas of the dorsal surfaces of the cerebral hemispheres, and very little of the basal surface of the right hemisphere, are smooth enough to reproduce brain details. The endocast of the cerebellar chamber is a rough block of coarse stone, with much of the petrosal bones left *in situ*.

Neohipparion.—CNHM 15871 (fig. 19) is a black rubber endocranial cast of the 387 mm.-long skull of an adult *Neohipparion occidentale* (Leidy) from the Big Spring Canyon local fauna, Bennet County, South Dakota. It represents the whole brain, excepting two regions. At the dorsal surface of the oblongate and the posterior

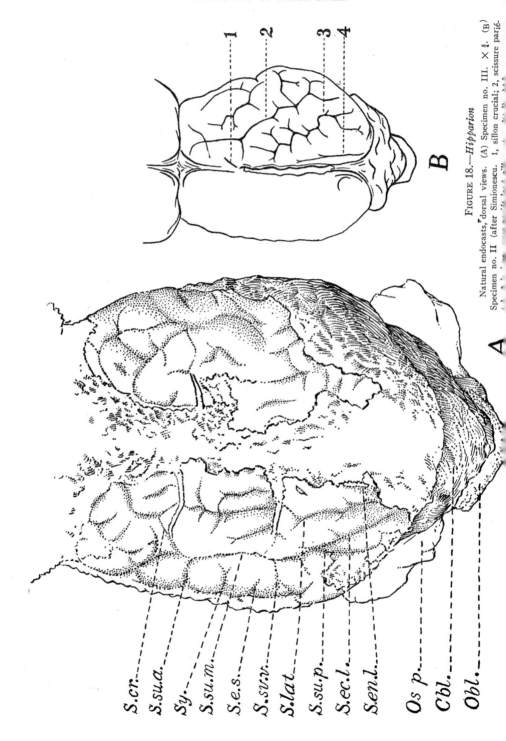

FIGURE 18.—*Hipparion*

Natural endocasts, dorsal views. (A) Specimen no. III. × ¾. (B) Specimen no. II (after Simionescu. 1, sillon crucial; 2, scissure parié-

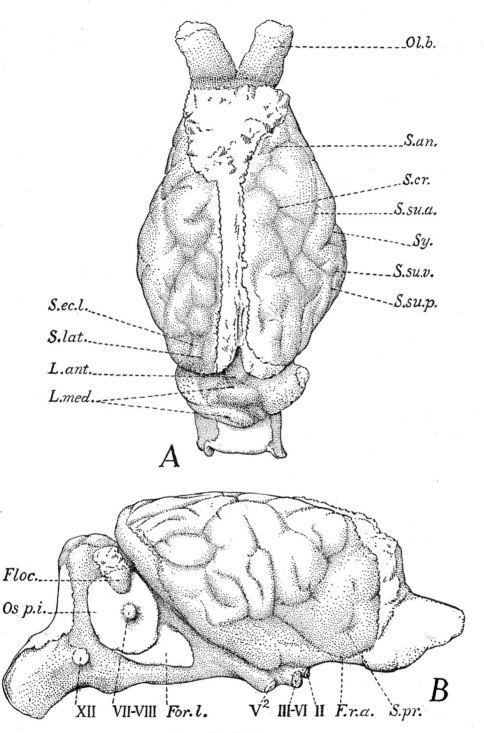

Ol.b.

S.an.

S.cr.

S.su.a.

Sy.

S.su.v.

S.su.p.

S.ec.l.

S.lat.

L.ant.

L.med.

A

Floc.

Os p.i.

XII   VII-VIII *For.l.*   V^2 III-VI II *F.r.a.* *S.pr.*

B

FIGURE 19.—*Neohipparion*
Rubber endocast. (A) Dorsal, (B) right lateral view. × ⅔.

facies of the cerebellum a gap in the endocranium has been patched up in the cast by plaster (posterior unshaded area in fig. 19 B). A dorso-median strip of the cerebral surface, and much of the frontal lobe region do not represent brain surface but are rough rubber. The quality of those cerebral surfaces which are moulded is good only in some parts; in particular, the left lateral surface is unsatisfactory.

TABLE 3.—*Hipparions and pony*

	Hipparion			Neohipparion	Pony
	I	II	III		
LENGTH					
total				140	146
cbl. & cer.			122	l. 115, r. 111	140
cbl.			15	26	30
cer.	l. 85, r. 88	>110	(112)	l. 98, r. 97	122
olf. b.				25	6
BREADTH					
obl.			33	27	38
cbl.				44	65
neocortex	67	90	92	69	97
palaeocortex			73	(57)	72
olf. b.				38	50
HEIGHT					
obl.			27	25	33
cer.		60	65	l. 56, r. 60	76
olf. b.				l. 25, r. 23	24

DESCRIPTION

Cerebellum.—A cross section of the medulla oblongata is disclosed posteriorly in *Hipparion* III; its form is a transverse oval. The oblongata of *Neohipparion* is also broader than high. If the *Hipparion* II and III specimens include the cast of the foramen magnum—that is, are posteriorly complete brains—the medulla oblongata was much more overlapped by the cerebellum than in the *Neohipparion* specimen.

In *Hipparion* III, nothing is moulded of the cerebellar surface except patches of the perpendicular posterior facies, including the junction with the dorsal facies of the oblongata. The cerebellum of *Hipparion* II has been described as follows: "Le Cervelet est situé en partie au dessous du bord du lobe occipital, en partie à l'extérieur de celui-ci. On distingue des lobes latéraux, plissés, mais aussi une partie du lobe médian" (Simionescu, 1934, p. 166). Simionescu's figure 2 (our fig. 18 B) shows that the "exterior" part is present only on the right side; it is actually an endocast of the temporal canal. Without it, cerebellar breadth was 56 mm. in *Hipparion* II. The ratio of this breadth to greatest forebrain breadth is the same as in *Neohipparion*, viz., 1:1.6. The exposed cerebellar surface is 15 mm. long medially in *Hipparion* II and III.

The cerebellum of our *Neohipparion* is less overlapped by the cerebral hemispheres than must have been the case in *Hipparion* II and III.

In the cleft between the occipital poles of the *Neohipparion* forebrain a part of the vermis is visible as a symmetrical tongue whose smooth surface slopes anteriorly to about 17 mm. below the cerebral vault. It is set off from the vermis portion posterior to the cerebrum by a furrow which is transverse in the middle and turns anterad at the sides to join the paramedian fissures. The contrast between the smooth and narrow surface of the vermis portion anterior to the furrow on the one hand, and the high, fissured bulge behind it on the other hand, shows that the furrow corresponds to the fissura prima cerebelli. The exposed length of the anterior lobe is 10 mm. It lies almost entirely in the forebrain region; therefore it is probable that this endocast exhibits the whole antero-posterior extent of the anterior lobe. The length of the anterior lobe was about two-fifths of the entire vermis length.

The lobus medius of the vermis continues laterally into the cerebellar hemispheres. The major markings on its high vault consist of a transverse ridge anteriorly and a crooked ridge posteriorly. The latter is asymmetrical, and it is continued down the right side of the posterior facies in a hemicircular protuberance which curves around a large, lower protuberance on the left side of the dorsal facies of the vermis. Such complicated sculpture is the expression, on the endocranium and its cast, of a median vermis lobe which consisted of irregularly coiled groups of lamellae.

Irregular markings on the cerebellar hemispheres indicate their lamellation. The flocculus is represented on each side by a protuberance above, and slightly behind, the internal acoustic meatus. These two protuberances are somewhat differently shaped. Both have their greatest antero-posterior extent (8 mm.) near their dorsal end; both are about 9 mm. high.

Cerebral hemispheres.—The cerebrum of *Hipparion* has been described by Simionescu (1934, p. 164–169, figs. 1–4). It is very true that "La forme du cerveau ressemble beaucoup à celle du cheval" (p. 164). Even though the anterior facies is not exposed either in Simionescu's or the AMNH specimen, and Simionescu was not aware of this circumstance, his statement that "la bordure frontale est rectiligne" (p. 164) is presumably true—because this was the case in *Pliohippus* and in *Neohipparion*. *Equus* endocranial casts show that undistorted frontal lobes of some horses (*see* pl. 3, fig. 1) might be called quadrangular.

The shape of the cerebral hemispheres of our *Neohipparion*, however, differs from that of the *Hipparion* and *Equus* cerebra. In length, the cerebrum of *Neohipparion* was intermediate between the small and the large *Hipparion* brains. The cerebrum to skull length ratio was similar—about 1:4.2 in *Hipparion* II, 1:3.9 in *Neohipparion*. But the cerebral hemispheres were more slender in *Neohipparion* than in *Hipparion*. This fact is expressed in the ratios of greatest (temporal lobe) breadth to greatest length of the cerebral hemispheres—1:1.29 in the small *Hipparion* I, about 1:1.22 and 1:1.23 in the large *Hipparion* II and III, but 1:4.2 in *Neohipparion*. The slenderness of the *Neohipparion* brain is even more apparent when the frontal lobes are compared. Frontal lobe breadth in the plane of the transverse part of the presylvian sulcus is 63 mm. in *Hipparion* III and compares to temporal lobe breadth as 1:1.45; in the *Neohipparion*, this anterior frontal lobe breadth is only 33 mm., and its ratio to temporal lobe breadth is 1:2.09.

Our *Neohipparion* endocast represents the brain of a fully adult animal. Its M^3

were well worn, and its skull was not smaller (387 mm. long) than that of the type of the genus (377 mm.—*N. whitneyi*, Gidley, 1903, p. 469). Thus we can reasonably assume that we are dealing with a normal *Neohipparion* brain. It was a brain more slender not only than the brain of the three *Hipparion* specimens, but also than our two *Pliohippus* brains.

. The neocortex had reached a definitely modern extent in the hipparions. The fissura rhinalis is a basal feature in all these brains. Simionescu failed to identify the fissura rhinalis in *Hipparion* II; parts of it, however, are shown in his figure 4. Only parts of the posterior rhinal fissures can be traced in III. In the *Neohipparion* specimen almost the whole right rhinal fissure is moulded. The neocortex overhangs the piriform lobe more broadly in *Hipparion*, particularly in II, than in the slender *Neohipparion* brain.

In *Hipparion* the general pattern of neocortex fissuration, like the brain shape, agrees with that of *Equus*. It is a network of branched sulci. The gyral meshes, wholly circumscribed or confluent, are less numerous than in the horse. This is in correspondence with the smaller size of *Hipparion* and the *Hipparion* brain. The diameters of individual meshes are similar to those of *Equus* endocranial casts. Even in the small *Hipparion* I, fissuration was found to be relatively as rich as in an *Equus* endocast (Edinger, 1929, p. 176). Although Simionescu's figures of *Hipparion* II do not give this impression, I believe that fissuration was as similar in II and III as it is in two horse brains. It is expressly stated that in II "La surface supérieure des hémisphères est tout aussi fortement plissée que celle d'un cerveau de cheval" (Simionescu, 1934, p. 165). The pictures of II show that there was as much branching in II as in III. That the branches are shown shorter in II (fig. 18 B) than in III (fig. 18 A) may be due either to poorer preservation of intersulcal areas in the former specimen or to the fact that the investigator of II was more interested in gyri than in sulci. He traced only six of the latter, and, incidentally, his nomenclature differs from the international one. On the lateral surface of the cerebrum, Simionescu (1934, fig. 3) identified the presylvian sulcus and labels as "Sillon ectosylvien" what seems to me an anterad branch of the suprasylvian sulcus. On the dorsal surface (our fig. 18 B), Simionescu identified the cruciate and endolateral ("ectosagittal") sulci. The line labelled "scissure pariétale", however, contains most elements of the suprasylvian sulcus; but, if one of the shorter anterior sulci of Simionescu's figures represents the pars anterior sulci suprasylvii, its connection with the pars media was overlooked. Simionescu's "incisure suprapariétale" combines elements of the lateral and ectolateral sulci. The fact that through this interpretation there seem to be three instead of four posterior longitudinal sulci makes it obvious that not all connections which had existed in the brain of *Hipparion* II were represented on the endocranial cast.

Figure 18 A shows how much detail of the dorsal cerebral surface is represented in the only *Hipparion* specimen at hand. Between the borders of the extensive median rough area and the lateral sulcus a few pieces of otherwise destroyed sulci are preserved. At least those two which, posteriorly on the left and more anteriorly on the right hemisphere, run sagittally close to the border of the rough region are, I suppose, remnants of the endolateral sulcus. The *Hipparion* specimen is the largest of our series of endocranial casts on which this sulcus appears on the dorsal surface; geologically speaking, this is its last appearance on endocasts. In *Equus*, this cerebral region is no more in contact with the endocranium. The lateral sulcus, best preserved on the left hemisphere of *Hipparion* III, is continued forward across cruciate and ansate sulci so that there existed that long, undulating, multibranched line from the posterior to the anterior end of the hemisphere which is regarded as a characteristic of *Equus* brains. A similar, but shorter, longitudinal line consisted of the pars posterior sulci suprasylvii, the pars media, and an anterad continuation of the pars media (above and beyond the pars anterior) which joins the diagonal sulcus. On the left lateral surface, the suprasylvian partes anterior, media, and the ramus ventralis enclose a quadrangular area, in which a posterior ectosylvian sulcus is developed behind the Sylvian fossa. On the right side, the suprasylvian arch is inclined antero-basally. Both types of configuration occur both in earlier equid and in modern horse brains. Further differences in the fissuration of right and left hemispheres are readily seen in figure 18 A. Such variation, too, recalls conditions in modern horse brains. We can indeed terminate the study of single sulci in this phase in which the variability of sulcus details makes their description meaningless, and their identification on endocranial casts uncertain.

It remains, however, to compare briefly the fissuration of the two hipparionid brains at hand, those or *Hipparion* III and *Neohipparion*.

The only definite difference in fissuration is that the suprasylvian arcs of our *Neohipparion* form angles so acute that there is practically no longitudinal section in the pars media sulci suprasylvii. The anterior portion of the pars media runs upward to a point about 4 mm. above and 4 mm. medial to the processus acuminis fossae Sylvii, and the posterior one runs from this point steeply downward over the lateral surface. The pars posterior (preserved on the right side) thus branches off at a much lower level than in *Hipparion*. Correspondingly, the ectolateral sulcus, which longitudinally divides the area between pars posterior sulci suprasylvii and sulcus lateralis, is also in a position somewhat different from that which it occupies in our *Hipparion* specimen.

Although fissuration is generally similar in *Hipparion* and *Neohipparion*, the two cerebra are rather different in appearance. In a study like this, the question arises whether the differences signify different stages in brain evolution—that is, whether the brain of our *Neohipparion* was more primitive, or only smaller than the *Hipparion* II and III brains. I find myself unable to answer this question, as the data are conflicting.

Hipparion III, and probably also II, have a few more accessory and branch sulci than the *Neohipparion* endocast. This, however, does not necessarily mean that the same difference existed in the brains; the Balkan specimens are natural endocasts, whereas the South Dakota specimen is an artificial endocast. Yet, although typical gyrus breadth (*see* table 8) is somewhat narrower in *Hipparion* III than in *Neohipparion*, the diameters of measurable gyri are on the whole similar in the two specimens. Likewise, the rhinal fissures are in about the same position. However, in *Neohipparion* in contrast to *Hipparion* II and III, the occipital lobes leave most of the cerebellum uncovered, and the temporal lobe is but little broader than the piriform lobe. These two features are possibly primitive; but the former can still occur in *Equus*. The frontal lobe is much narrower than the temporal lobe in *Neohipparion;* on the other hand, its anterior facies rises steeply above the olfactory bulbs, and it is a high lobe as is the frontal lobe of *Hipparion*.

Olfactory bulbs.—There are no data on the olfactory bulbs of *Hipparion*. In our *Neohipparion* the ethmoidal chambers are well cast. The bulbi of this endocast end anteriorly in the impressions of the cribriform plates. These were up to 13 mm. broad near their upper rim, and they tapered, slanting baso-posteriorly, to a breadth of 9 mm. in the region where they face downward. As in *Pliohippus*, shape and position of the *Neohipparion* olfactory bulbs differ strikingly from the conditions observed in earlier Equidae. A voluminous ethmoidal crest separated the ethmoidal chambers so that the bulbi diverge anterad. While the bulbi are large and high, the cerebrum rises high above them. The bulbi lie along the lower regions of the frontal lobe. They strongly protrude anteriorly, by about 25 mm. in their mid-height. Their longest diameter is an oblique one; measured along this axis of the bulbi, bulbus length is 32 mm. on the left side, and the right bulbus was 35 mm. long.

SUMMARY

Two formerly described *Hipparion* endocasts and a third one examined in this study indicate that at least the larger hipparions had brains resembling those of living Equidae.

A *Neohipparion* endocast is remarkably different. The brain of this individual was more slender than the *Hipparion* brains; the cerebrum overlapped the cerebellum to a lesser degree; and its fissuration was possibly less complicated.

QUATERNARY: *EQUUS*
GENERAL REMARKS

Size range.—In the Upper Pliocene of North America *Pliohippus* was superseded by generally larger Equidae, with larger, higher, and more complicated teeth. Formerly considered a separate genus, *Plesippus*, this form is now regarded as "representing a slightly more primitive condition in the Upper Pliocene of the genus *Equus*" (Stirton, 1940, p. 194).

The size range of this youngest genus far surpasses the variations of the ancestral genera. Forms much smaller than the equid typical for the period existed both in the Miocene and in the Pliocene, but these were side branches of the horse ancestry— separate forms of generic rank. *Equus*, generally the tallest of the Equidae, contains forms less than half as high as its tallest representatives. *Equus* is the only one of the larger genera of which adults of *Merychippus* size are known. Flower (1891, p. 76) found cart horses between 17 and 18 hands (18 hands = 1828 mm. at the withers) "not uncommon." The hundreds of purebred adult Shetland ponies measured by Brydon (1890) varied in shoulder height from 1118 mm. to 835 mm.—*i.e.*, back to *Merychippus* shoulder height. Cornevin (1889, p. 24, 28) records body weights from 94 kg. (Corsican pony) to 1040 kg. (heavy Belgian horse). The weights in life of the small pony and giant draft horse in the AMNH exhibit were 76.5 kg. and 1066.5 kg., respectively (170 lbs. and 2370 lbs.; Chubb, p. 43). The extremes of endocranial capacity in Cornevin's horse material were 443 cubic cm. (Annam pony) and 852 cubic cm. (Boulonnais breed; Cornevin, 1889, p. 12)—that is, within the living species *Equus caballus* brains occur whose volumes compare as 1:1.92. A striking example of the variations in brain size are the three 9 year-old domestic horses among Mobilio's material (1915, table II). Their endocranial capacities were 650, 670, and 750 cubic cm., respectively. (To each kilogram body weight, these three similar individuals had 2.321, 1.914, and 1.666 cubic cm. endocranial capacity!)

The size range of *Equus* is not a product of breeding. Dwarf horses have developed both from oriental and occidental horse stock before the Neolithic period (Hilzheimer, 1926, p. 104, 126). The Celtic ponies of the British Isles, of which the Shetland pony is the smallest, have branched off the main stem at a more remote period and developed independently from the light Asiatic and heavy European horses (Ewart, 1904, p. 259; Megaw, 1943, p. 100). The Pleistocene *Equus tau* probably was the size of Shetland ponies. On the other hand, the Pleistocene species *Equus giganteus* and *E. occidentalis* contained individuals which were larger than any living horses.

In consideration of the great size range of *Equus*, the question arises in the context of our study: how are the formative influences of body size and of evolutionary standard balanced in the brain? In other words, is regression in body size accompanied by a turn-about in brain evolution; does a Shetland pony brain in any way recall a *Merychippus* brain, or is it in every way a small *Equus* brain?

Unfortunately, we have few data answering these questions directly. Not only is a *Nanippus* brain a desideratum, but it seems that brains of Recent dwarf horses have not been studied either. I found no description of a pony brain in the literature, and I was unable to procure either brain or endocast of a small pony. Our material includes, however, the endocast of a large pony.

The brain of this pony (pl. 4) is a highly developed brain of *Equus* type. Furthermore, the series of equid brains at hand, and the brains of small living members of other mammalian families, indirectly answer the questions concerning the smallest *Equus* brains. Even the smallest pony should have a brain of *Equus* type. Pliocene Equidae had modern, if small, horse brains. Cat brains are in no way more primitive than lion brains; the lesser branching of the cats' neopallial sulci is a function only of their smaller body size. The tiny living artiodactyls have modern brains; the cerebrum of the pigmy antelope *Cephalophus monticola* even "exhibits a wealth of sulci as rich as that of the much larger *Odocoileus*" (Elliot Smith, 1902, p. 335).

If the cerebral hemispheres of the smallest extant dwarf horses should be found to have a fissuration more like that of the larger *Merychippus* species (as exhibited in our specimen *Merychippus* IV) than like the *Equus* type of fissuration, this could be correlated with their smallness. But it seems certain that these cerebral hemispheres have the rhinal fissure in the *Equus* position, largely overlap the cerebellum, are high, and have high frontal lobes partly or completely overlapping the olfactory bulbs which are in a basal position—just as these dwarf horses have feet and teeth which, however small, represent the highest stage of equid evolution.

The endocranial cast of a large pony described below shows that the outstanding achievement of equid brain evolution—the large and high cerebrum—is not as much smaller in small horses as the differences in skull size might suggest (see tables 4, 6). The larger size of large horse skulls is chiefly due to larger muzzles. The size of the neurocranium varies less, and this seems to be true in a greater degree of the cerebrum. Living dwarf horses presumably have not only relatively large brains but, in particular, relatively large cerebral hemispheres.

Anatomy.—The characters which distinguish the endocranial casts of *Equus* (and the brain of the horse) from those of its ancestors have been frequently referred to in the preceding chapters, and they are discussed in Part II. Brains of horses are described in the handbooks of the anatomy of domestic animals (*e.g.*, Sisson, 1917, p. 768–793, fig. 629–644), and they were the object of special studies by Anthony and Grzybowski (1930; also zebra brain), Bradley (1899), Ellenberger (1892), Flatau and Jacobsohn (1899, p. 405–421, fig. 81–83), Holl (1900, p. 324–328, pl. XX, fig. 21–23), Krueg (1878, p. 328–329, pl. XXIII), and Legge (1884).

For completeness, I have included in our bibliography Mobilio's 1914 paper whose existence I discovered when my studies were completed. Mobilio describes 17 convolutions, 27 subgyri and gyral loops, and 37 fissures and sulci (with a nomenclature of his own) in the right and left cerebral hemispheres of 37 ♂ and 14 ♀ horses, 17 ♂ and 11 ♀ mules, and 16 ♂ and 17 ♀ asses. The main results of this investigation (Mobilio, 1914, p. 260) are that (1) in the horse the sulci are more ramified and the gyral loops more curved than in the ass, the mule is intermediate; (2) male and female brains, and the right and left hemispheres of every individual differ by "inconstant and infrequent . . . variations."

The complication and variability of the cerebral sulci in *Equus* is stressed by practically every author. Holl (1900, p. 324), too, found that no one horse brain is completely like any other, and he found identification even of the principal sulci possible only by comparative study of a series of specimens. According to Anthony and Grzybowski (1930, p. 147), the only way to recognize the major sulci and gyri is to trace them through ontogeny. It is indeed a striking difference between the earlier equid endocasts on the one hand, and our Quaternary specimens on the other hand, that in the latter only sulci with particularly characteristic courses can be readily identified with sulci of ancestral brains. For example, the pars media sulci suprasylvii is obviously the same in the Oligocene to Recent specimens and the homologue of an Eocene sulcus. We shall not try to describe the sulci of our Quaternary endocasts. The course of single sulci in the maze of the neopallial surface of *Equus* is irrelevant for our study.

In form, too, the *Equus* brain is extremely variable. The cerebral hemispheres of *Equus caballus* I can be described as very broadly egg-shaped, those of the pony as cubic, and those of *Equus caballus* II are intermediate. Cerebellum and olfactory bulbs are overlapped in various degrees, but always more than in at least the pre-Pliocene ancestors of the horse.

All this is true also of the Pleistocene *Equus* brains briefly described on the following pages (we have no Upper Pliocene brain material). Based on minute differences in tooth structure, more or less slender limbs, or differences in skull length and body size, a large number of Pleistocene species of *Equus* have been distinguished. In view of the variability of the brain of *Equus caballus* I doubt that any of the differences between the Pleistocene *Equus* brains can be regarded as specific; nor do I expect that differences distinguishing all Pleistocene from all Recent *Equus* brains, in particular a difference of evolutionary significance, can ever be found. This is certainly not possible with only single endocranial casts of only four Pleistocene *Equus* species at hand.

MATERIAL AND DESCRIPTION

I. Equus *sp.*—The only Pleistocene *Equus* brain whose description has been published is an incomplete natural endocranial cast, specifically unidentified, from Hungary. It has been described and figured in ventral and right side views by Kubacska (1932, p. 57–65, pl. VIII) who found it "von vorwiegend rezentem Charakter" (p. 65). Apparently no feature exists in this specimen to justify the restricting word "predominantly"—no feature which might not be found in the endocranial cast of a Recent horse. The skull length of this individual was estimated at "560–570 (?)" mm. The brain cast extends from the foramen magnum to the lamina cribrosa; but the dorsal vault, including the suprasylvian region, is weathered away. Measurements were taken only of the cerebral hemispheres (table 4). The olfactory bulbs are described as flat, elongated, and closely appressed to the cerebrum.

II. Equus scotti *Gidley.*—The plaster endocast AMNH 10608 (fig. 20) was taken from one of the individuals found with the type specimen at the head of Rock Creek, Briscoe County, Texas. This whole group consists of young adults of the same age, with the last milk molar and the milk incisors still functioning (Gidley, 1900, p. 113).

Mrs. Rachel H. Nichols informed me that this is the Pleistocene brain seen in the "Evolution of the Horse" photograph of Matthew's AMNH Guide Leaflet (p. 36). Naturally that picture is very indistinct. It looks as if the specimen had reconstructed olfactory bulbs when it was on exhibition. The specimen now consists of the oblongata, the cerebellum, and most of the cerebral hemispheres. Several prominent Pacchionian bodies indicate that a relatively spacious subdural space existed medially over the cerebrum where no brain details are reproduced on the cast. The ventral and lateral surfaces of the cerebrum are likewise without identifiable sculpture, and dorsally only very few of the gyri are represented. The indistinctness of the sulci makes it difficult to decide exactly how much of the cerebrum is missing anteriorly, where the cast ends in an approximately transverse perpendicular plane which cuts across the anterior slope of the frontal lobe. Near the anterior end of the left hemisphere an oblique sulcus is so much like the dorsal part of the presylvian sulcus of the pony endocast that it probably represents a part of the presylvian of *Equus scotti*. The left hemisphere of this brain would then have been only 2–5 mm. longer than it is in this endocast so that the right hemisphere, which is preserved somewhat further anterad, probably represents approximately the complete cerebral length of this individual.

The brain most similar to that of this *Equus scotti* must have been, among our material, that of the pony (pl. 4). Greatest cerebral breadth and height are practically the same in the *Equus scotti* and pony endocasts. The cerebral hemispheres of *Equus scotti* were somewhat longer than in the pony, but still of a similar sub-

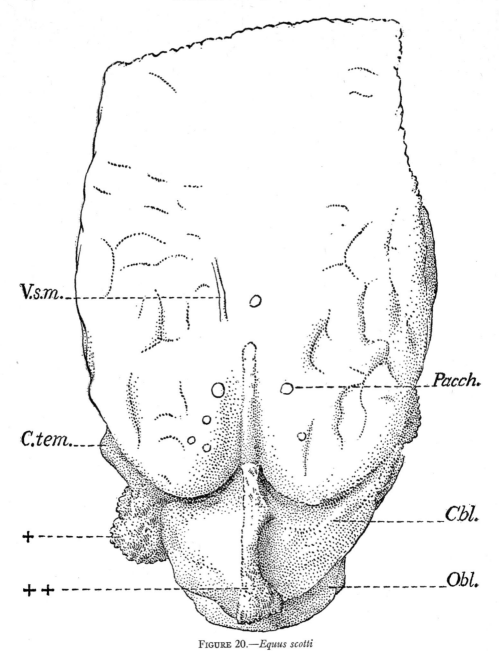

FIGURE 20.—*Equus scotti*

Plaster endocast of a brain chamber which is incomplete anteriorly, and is broken in the left occipito-temporal (+) and posterior median regions (++). × 1.

cubic shape. Gidley characterized *Equus scotti* as a long-faced type of horse, about the size of the largest western pony, but with a much larger head (1901, p. 139–140). He described the posterior skull region as narrower than in the common horse (Gid-

ley, 1900, p. 116).   The type skull is 577 mm. long (Robb, 1935, p. 43; Colbert MS.,
570 mm., shoulder height 1340 mm.); another *Equus scotti* skull is 610 mm. long
(Robb, 1935, p. 43).   However, in full accord with the outer appearance of the
Equus scotti skull, the cerebrum of our *Equus scotti* was hardly, if any, larger than

TABLE 4.—Equus

Measurements of *Equus* endocranial casts (in mm.).   The bracketed skull lengths are taken from other individuals than the endocasts.

	sp.	scotti	niob.	occ.	pony	cab. I	cab. II
Skull length	565?	(577–610)	(530–556)	(535–589)	424	580	600
LENGTH							
total				193	146	179	183
cer. + cbl.				160	140	163	158
cbl.		40		30	30	49	
cer.	126	>126	126	136	122	128	129
ol. b.				17	6	20	15
BREADTH							
obl.		44		45	38	44	41
cbl.				72	65	76	73
neopall.	117	97	105	128	97	105	112
palaeopall.				89	72	85	90
ol. b. each				23	22	26, 30	25
ol. b. both				59	50	57	55
HEIGHT							
obl.		35		34	33	42	39
cer.		78		84	76	87	89
ol. b. perp.				30	28	38	31
ol. b. obl.				50	35	45	40
						(skull 30?)	

that of a pony whose short-faced skull is more than 150 mm. shorter than an *Equus
scotti* skull.

III. Equus niobrarensis *Hay.*—The Museum of Vertebrate Paleontology at the
University of Kansas possesses two natural endocast fragments taken from two
Equus niobrarensis, from the interglacial fauna of the upper part of the Meade forma-
tion of Locality 8 ("*Equus niobrarensis* beds," Frye and Hibbard, 1941, fig. 3c) in
Meade County, Kansas.

The smaller fragment represents the central and anterior parts of the lateral and
basal surfaces of the left cerebral hemisphere.   Dorsally, the preserved area ends
below the pars media sulci suprasylvii; the pars media is not contained in the fragment, only the pars anterior.   The anterior extremity of this specimen is the stump
of the lateral wall of the left olfactory bulb.   It is 20 mm. high, but only 3 mm. of
the length are preserved.   This stump protrudes from the lower half of the preserved
portion of the anterior cerebral facies, which is perpendicular.   On the ventral side
of the fragment, most of the left piriform lobe and gyrus olfactorius lateralis can be
distinguished.   The area posterior to the Sylvian region is much obscured by bone

particles adhering to the cast.   This is also the case with the frontal lobe region in
which, however, the many prominent convolutions are well seen.   There is a conspicuous contrast between the gyri anterior and dorsal to, and those of the Sylvian
region.   The former are undulating and prominent.   In the Sylvian area, four low
gyri radiate upward from the "angle" of the rhinal fissure.   These gyri are for the
most part narrower than those framing this region.   The most anterior sulcus dorsally turns backward into a longitudinal furrow which is first horizontal, then runs
slightly downward, and is confluent with the two posterior ones.   The middle one
of the five furrows is perpendicular and represents the fossa Sylvii.   The most
posterior of the four gyri is partly subdivided by a short sulcus whose course is
parallel to the hindmost sulcus.   These conditions differ from those in our other
Equus endocasts and from those shown by Holl (1900, pl. XX, fig. 21) in a horse
brain said to exhibit relatively uncomplicated conditions of the insula (p. 324).
Holl's remarks concerning the difficulty of identifying gyri in horse brains, in particular those of the insular region without removal of the opercula, definitely prohibit interpretation of these differences.   In a purely descriptive way we can say
that where in the *Merychippus* endocast IV we saw one arcuate gyrus, the gyrus
arcuatus I, there is in this *Equus niobrarensis* an arched sulcus framing four, more or
less straight, gyri.   This framing sulcus probably corresponds to the major part of
the ectosylvian sulcus of *Merychippus*.   It is more a backward leaning arc in the
larger of the two *Equus niobrarensis* fragments.   The region enclosed by the arc is
not well preserved in the larger specimen but what can be seen is different from the
conditions in the smaller fragment described above.

The larger *Equus niobrarensis* fragment is shown in an unretouched photo in
figure 2 of plate 2.   This specimen represents the entire dorsal surface of the cerebral
hemispheres.   The lateral, posterior, and anterior slopes are preserved to an extent
which shows that the whole outline of the cerebrum is present.   The lateral aspects
include most of the Sylvian region.   Between the posterior poles of the hemispheres
there is a mass of cancellate bone, triangular in superior and posterior views.   This
is a remnant of the internal occipital protuberance; it frames the occipital pole of the
right hemisphere from behind and also that of the left hemisphere, though less completely.   Similarly, the presence of crista galli matter at the anterior end of the
midline helps to show that the cerebral chamber is completely cast.   Convolutions,
with deep, winding, branched sulci between them form the surface of the whole
endocast, except for a 13 to 23 mm.-broad medial area in which the original endocast
surface is missing all along the cerebrum except posteriorly.   Posteriorly, the dorso-
median regions are cast, less conspicuously fissured than the other regions, and somewhat obscured by adhering bone particles.   Among these is a remnant of the falx
cerebri which is continuous with the internal occipital protuberance.

The greatest diameters of this *Equus niobrarensis* cerebrum are almost exactly
like those of the *Equus caballus* I endocast.   The frontal lobe of the *Equus niobrarensis* specimen is broader; besides it seems that the frontal lobe was not so highly
vaulted as the frontal lobe of *Equus caballus* I.   If the entire species *Equus niobrarensis* really is, as the type skull suggested, a smaller form than the large domestic breeds,
the equality of the forebrain diameters in those two specimens bears out Hay's state-

ment that in *Equus niobrarensis* "the size of the brain case is remarkably large" (1913, p. 578).

Hay's (1913, p. 578) observation that "The skull is wider in the present species than in the domestic horse" suggests that *Equus niobrarensis* had a particularly broad brain—or, at least, that this was the case in the individual studied by Hay. However, Hay's remark is quoted to point out that there is no exact relation between greatest cranium breadth and greatest brain breadth in *Equus*. Skull width was measured by Hay "above the hinder end of the zygomatic arch" (p. 578). In this region the cranium is not only brain capsule. The temporal bone is thickened, and it contains a considerable layer of spongiosa between tabula externa and tabula interna. Cranium breadth thus includes the root of the zygomatic arch. Hay's statement was based on the fact that this breadth is 122 mm. in the 530 mm.-long *Equus niobrarensis* type skull, whereas in the 550 mm.-long *Equus caballus* skull which Hay used for comparison (p. 577) this breadth is only 115 mm. Unfortunately no skull width is recorded of the brain region of the 556 mm.-long *Equus niobrarensis* skull measured by Merriam (1913, p. 402). Hay's statement is supported by the fact that in our *Equus caballus* I skull, which is 50 mm. longer than the *Equus niobrarensis* type, cranium breadth above the hinder end of the roots of the zygomatic arches is only 5 mm. more (120 mm.) than in the *Equus niobrarensis*. Relatively, the *Equus niobrarensis* type cranium is definitely broader than *Equus caballus* skulls.

Greatest endocranium breadth is somewhat posterior to the zygomatic arches. Here the temporal bone has a compact structure and is not thickened; it forms only the brain capsule. In our *Equus caballus* II this squama region of the temporal bone is horizontally sectioned and was found to be up 6 mm. thick at the juga cerebralia, but down to 2 mm. thin at the impressiones digitatae of the temporal lobe gyri. Consequently, cranium breadth in the region of maximum cerebrum breadth of our *Equus niobrarensis* individual must have been about 110 mm.

To the right and left of the crista galli remnant there are high, perpendicular ovals of rough stone surface. These ovals are the endocasts of the windows between the cerebral and ethmoidal chambers. They represent the area in which the olfactory bulbs were in contact with the anterior poles of the cerebrum. The left one of these cross sections is undistorted, 16 mm. broad for most of its height, 28 mm. high, and apparently incomplete ventrally. The right side section is complete; there is bone matter on its ventral surface. Its shape has suffered from the pressure which also pressed inward and flattened the lateral facies of the right frontal lobe (*see* pl. 2, fig. 2). Whereas the longest diameter of the left oval is perpendicular, that of the right is oblique, from latero-dorsal to medio-basal, and 35 mm. long. Perpendicular height is 30 mm. on this distorted side, but greatest breadth is the same as on the other side, viz., 16 mm. As our *Equus caballus* II endocast likewise does not include the olfactory bulbs, it is in the same condition anteriorly as the *Equus niobrarensis* fragment. The oval endocasts of the cerebro-ethmoidal windows are 32 mm. high and 18 mm. broad in that Recent horse. Thus there was practically no difference between the *Equus niobrarensis* and the *Equus caballus* specimens in the shape and size of the ethmoidal windows. These connections between the cerebral and olfactory chambers are no clues to the shape and size of the olfactory bulbs, but their dimensions show that the bulbi of *Equus niobrarensis* cannot have been small.

IV. Equus occidentalis *Leidy.*—The excellent plaster endocranial cast LACM 3500-17 C-3 (pl. 3, and fig. 24) represents the largest brain in our series. This cast was taken from an incompletely preserved skull from the Rancho La Brea Pleistocene. The *Equus occidentalis* skulls collected up to 1913 equalled or exceeded those of Recent *Equus caballus* in size (Merriam, 1913, p. 400); large size now appears to be characteristic of the species (Schultz, 1938). The brain represented by the endocast surely must have belonged to an individual which, to say the least, had a larger cranium than our *Equus caballus* I and II. It is the largest horse brain ever reported.

It is a modern horse brain. Undulating, ramified sulci are densely spread over the extensive neopallium, running in all directions. Figures 1 and 2 of Plate 3 show this condition. The dorsal view (fig. 1) also shows the voluminous and smaller blood vessels which in some regions obscure the sulci on the cast. There is, for example, a thick, oblique vena cerebri superior anterior. The drawing of this specimen in figure 24 shows only those sulci which are well seen in the cast.

The brain represented by this endocast of *Equus occidentalis* was larger than, but so similar to, the brains of living horses that description is superfluous.

V. Equus caballus *Linné.*—The endocranial casts *Equus caballus* I and II were taken from domestic horses. Specimen I belongs to the skull no. 1713 of the MCZ Department of Mammals. The origin and preparation of no. II are described in the first chapter. These two casts were used only for comparison with the brain of the horse and with the endocasts of fossil Equidae; they are, therefore, discussed in the first chapter of part I of this paper and in several chapters of part II. Their measurements are given in table 4. Only one remark must be made here, a technical one concerning the olfactory bulbs of *Equus caballus* I. This specimen is shown in figure 24 with the bulbi strongly protruding in front of the cerebrum. That is their condition not only in this endocranial cast, but also in those figured by Marsh (1886, fig. 65) and by Matthew (Evolution of the horse in nature, p. 36). The three specimens seem to be as alike as duplicates. Inspection of the *Equus caballus* I skull, however, revealed that the ethmoidal chambers are not so long as our endocast suggests. The casts of ethmoidal and cerebral chambers must have been taken separately and patched together; in casting the no. II specimen it was found impossible to include the two chambers in one cast. The measurements of the no. I cast in table 4 are the diameters of the cast verified, or revised, or supplemented by checking up in the endocranium. Only in length the cast exaggerates the size of the olfactory bulbs of this individual. They were very large, as is shown, for example, by the extent of the cribriform plate.

The pony specimen is the endocast of skull no. 44, AMNH Chubb Study Collection. The individual was a ♀ 18-year-old Shetland pony. From the data given below for comparison, it will be seen that, with 424 mm. skull length, the animal must have been a medium-sized or large pony. Dubois (1923, p. 326) mentions two Shetland pony skulls with lengths of 405 mm. and 410 mm., respectively (shoulder height of the latter individual was 925 mm.). Schotterer (1931, p. 102) records a 4-year-old and an 8-year old Shetland pony with basilar skull lengths (not including the occipital condyles) of 348 and 348.5 mm., respectively, and oblique skull lengths (from superior nuchal line to alveolar border of incisivi) of 380 and 381 mm. Robb's Shetland pony skull length is only 330 mm. (1935, p. 48). Thus our endocast is not representative of the smallest extant horse brains, but it does represent the brain of a dwarf horse.

As is the case in all dwarf forms, the brain of the Shetland pony is relatively larger than the brain of domestic horses. The neocortex is densely fissured. The whole form gives the impression of a large brain being compressed into the shortest possible space. Perhaps it is due to osteological rather than neurological conditions that the frontal lobe is highly vaulted and square, and that the olfactory bulbs are confined to a very low level of the brain chamber. These olfactory bulbs are not small (pl. 4, fig. 2), but they are so closely appressed to the lower anterior facies of the high frontal lobes as to be invisible in the dorsal view of the brain (pl. 4, fig. 1). Although this may be related to the shortness of the pony skull, it nevertheless represents a condition in which neurological tendencies observed in the brain evolution of the Equidae have proceeded farther than in our other *Equus* specimens. The pony endocast represents the most highly developed brain form in our material.

SUMMARY

The modern horse brain existed already in the Pleistocene *Equus*. Endocast material is now known of four Pleistocene species. These brains were rather different from each other, but variability is characteristic also of *Equus caballus* brains.

The endocranial cast of a Shetland pony, with highly vaulted frontal lobes completely overlapping the olfactory bulbs, suggests a continuation rather than a reversal in modern dwarf horses of the trends of equid brain evolution.

PART II: BRAIN EVOLUTION IN THE EQUIDAE

MEDULLA OBLONGATA

Summarizing the contents of the preceding chapters, we shall now discuss the changes undergone by each brain region in the evolution from *Eohippus* to *Equus*.

The fact that height and breadth of the foramen magnum are 10 and 10 mm. in *Eohippus* I and 40 and 50 mm. in *Equus* II might suggest an expansion of the medulla oblongata corresponding to the four- to five-fold increase in shoulder height from *Eohippus* to the living domestic horses. Indeed we have in this paper incidentally discussed material which strikingly illustrates the general relation of oblongata volumen to body size; the brains of three different Lower Eocene ungulates are very similar, but the medulla oblongata is a larger portion in the larger *Phenacodus*, and a far larger portion in the giant *Coryphodon*, than in *Eohippus*. However, for an exact statement about oblongatal size increase in the Equidae the endocast data are not sufficiently reliable.

The relations between the posterior end of the oblongata and the foramen magnum are not at all intimate in *Equus*, and hence no conclusions can be drawn from the diameters of the foramen relative to those of the brain part it surrounds. In breadth oblongata and foramen magnum are not very dissimilar (38 mm. and 41 mm. in *Equus caballus* II); but the mammalian oblongata, usually a transverse oval in section, is not nearly so high, medially, as the foramen magnum. Nor can the considerable increase in the length of the medulla oblongata be traced in the fossil brains. The cerebellum conceals most of the dorsal surface, and either adhering bones or unsatisfactory moulding in most of the endocasts prohibit measuring the expansion of the medulla oblongata on the basal surface. Besides, much of the oblongata area of the brain is not taken up by nerve matter but is ventricle and choroid plexus.

The form of the foramen magnum changed so conspicuously that it is noted here although we cannot know whether a similar change occurred in the oblongata, nor could we explain such a change on either osteological or neurological grounds.

The upper rim or the foramen magnum determines in endocasts the beginning of the medulla oblongata (the condyles are beyond the brain chamber). In this transverse plane the foramen magnum of *Equus* is a transverse oval; its breadth is $1\frac{1}{4}$ of its height. Conditions were similar in *Merychippus*, with breadth $1\frac{1}{5}$ the height.

The foramen magnum of *Mesohippus*, however, was circular. In the two specimens (II and IV) in which the region of the foramen is shown in the cast of the oblongata, its breadth and height are the same (table 1). In III the matrix is excavated to 4 mm. anterior to the (broken) foramen; here, oblongata breadth exceeds height by one fifteenth. I is an endocast freed of bone; the end of the oblongata is broken in this cast, so that we do not know at what distance from the foramen the transversally oval shape (height 14, breadth 17 mm.) was achieved.

The shape of the foramen magnum of *Eohippus* differs still more from that of the horse. It has not been previously described. In our *Eohippus* I, breadth and height are equal. The outline of the foramen is not circular but rhomboidal. In this case it is obvious that the medulla oblongata, round or oval in transverse section, did not entirely occupy the rhomboidal foramen.

CEREBELLUM

SIZE RELATIONS

The cerebellum lay entirely behind the mesencephalon in *Eohippus*. It was as broad as the cerebral hemispheres, and its vermis rose to forebrain height. The cerebellum had bulged upward, and also forward over the midbrain, in *Orohippus* (whose forebrain diameters are not known). In *Mesohippus*, cerebellar height had increased none or very little over that of *Orohippus*. In our material *Mesohippus* represents the first stage in which the vault of the cerebral hemispheres surpasses in height that of the vermis cerebelli. There seems to have been little change in this height relation later on, but there was, and is in *Equus*, much variation. Cerebellar breadth was only about five-sevenths of the breadth of the cerebral hemispheres in *Mesohippus*. With slight variations, this 1:1.4 proportion remained unchanged in the further evolution of the equid brain.

In this steady increase of the cerebellar width, the various portions of the cerebellum have participated in different degrees.

Cerebella in which the lateral portions are set off from each other are few among our endocast materials; in particular, paramedian lobes and paraflocculus can rarely be distinguished. This material does show, however, that the rates of evolutionary enlargement were dissimilar, on the one hand, in the palaeocerebellum of L. Edinger (1910) (vermis and flocculi) and, on the other hand, in the neocerebellum (paramedian lobes and paraflocculi): those lateral portions which are new in mammals. The progressive evolution of the neocerebellum involves the median lobe of the palaeocerebellar vermis which, anatomically, forms a unit with the paramedian lobes.

FLOCCULUS

In the evolution of the Equidae there occurred no size increase of the flocculus comparable to that undergone by all the other measurable parts of the brain. Length and height of the fossa subarcuata were 8 mm. and 6 mm. in *Eohippus*, 8 and 8 in *Orohippus*. Lengths of 6 and 7 mm., one height of 5 mm. were observed in *Mesohippus*. Lengths and heights were 6 and 6, 7 and 7 in two *Merychippus* specimens, 8 and 9 mm. in *Neohipparion*. They are 9 and 9 mm. in the pony. The fossa subarcuata of *Equus* is too poorly developed to be accurately measurable. The flocculus appears to be variably shaped in the horse brain, to judge from the figures in the literature. It seems to be partly overlapped from above by the paraflocculus in Bolk's specimen (our fig. 6 C) in which the length is 9 mm.; length and height are 10 and 8 mm. in the horse brain of Flatau and Jacobsohn (1899, fig. 82), 8 and 11 mm. in Sisson's fig. 632 (1917). In the *Equus* II brain, the flocculus is 9 mm. long and 9 mm. high, and it is thin; it does not protrude as far laterad as the paraflocculus.

In *Eohippus* and *Orohippus* the flocculus bulged laterad 1 mm., and 2 or 3 mm. in *Mesohippus*. Thereafter, its thickness seems to have not increased at all. It is a tiny portion of the brain of *Equus*, never visible in dorsal views of the cerebellum.

The flocculus was never large in the Equidae. It did not keep step in evolution with the other parts of the brain and thus in the living horse certainly is—as Kappers, Huber, and Crosby (1936, p. 817) say of the flocculus of living mammals in general—"one of the most primitive portions of the cerebellum." It may be recalled here that the flocculus was, relatively, very large in the Upper Jurassic mammal *Tricono-don* (Simpson, 1927, p. 262, 265).

The mammalian flocculus is known to have but two functions, functions which surely were of equal quality in the tiny *Eohippus* and the tall *Equus*; the flocculus is concerned with the musculature of the tail and, through its connection with the vestibular region, with eye muscle coördination.

VERMIS

Lobus anterior.—There are further centers for tail muscles in the median palaeo-cerebellar part to which the flocculi are joined, viz., the lobus posterior of the vermis. Authors are not agreed in all details about functional localization in the cerebellar cortex. It seems that the areas which co-ordinate the posture and movements of the different parts of the body overlap. It is established, however, that the basal and posterior vermis parts are concerned with trunk and tail, the major part of the median vermis lobe co-ordinates bilateral movements of the extremities, the lobulus simplex of the median lobe controls the neck muscles, and the anterior lobe is the center which regulates the muscles of the head.

The lobus anterior of the mammalian vermis extends from the margo mesen-cephalicus to the fissura prima. In medio-sagittal sections this deepest fissure of the vermis may seem to separate the arbor vitae into two halves. Study of the outer surface only—which is shown in fossil material—disclosed to Bolk (1906) that in living mammals, without exception (p. 80), the anterior lobe is much less developed than what Bolk called the lobus posterior (the median and posterior lobes of Ingvar).

The opposite was the case in *Eohippus*. The surface of the *Eohippus* vermis was divided by the fissura prima into a posterior third and anterior two-thirds. It may be mentioned here that also in the contemporary *Phenacodus* the fissura prima was in a more posterior position than in living ungulates; three fifths of the vermis length was anterior lobe.

The greater development of the median than of the anterior lobe, so characteristic of modern mammals, was started, in the Equidae, in the Middle Eocene. From *Eohippus* to *Orohippus*, there occurred a considerable forward shift of the fissura prima; the fissure moved to almost the middle of the antero-posterior length of the vermis. This was due to expansion behind the primary fissure. The surface length of the anterior lobe had remained the same, in *Orohippus*, as it was in *Eohippus*, viz., 10 mm. Vermis length posterior to the primary fissure, however, increased from 5 mm. in *Eohippus* to 9 mm. in *Orohippus*. In *Mesohippus* I, 10 mm. of the anterior lobe length is seen, but at least 2 mm. is hidden under bone remnants which cover the cerebro-cerebellar border. Median and posterior lobe length is 10 mm. The anterior lobe thus was the somewhat longer portion in this small and probably primitive representative of the genus. In *Mesohippus* III, which shows the entire free surface of the vermis, lengths anterior and posterior to the primary fissure both are 12 mm.; half of the dorsal side of the vermis was anterior lobe.

In our post-Oligocene material, the fissura prima is not marked except in the *Neohipparion* specimen in which the cerebral hemispheres recede laterally, laying open between them apparently the whole dorso-anterior vermis surface. The anterior lobe occupies 10 mm. of the 26 mm. vermis length—that is, two fifths.

I round no reference in the literature to the fissura prima or the size of the anterior lobe in *Equus* except Bradley's remark that "fissure I is almost as deep as Fissure II" (1904, p. 233). In most published figures of unsectioned horse cerebella the primary fissure cannot be identified in the maze of surface furrows. It is readily seen, however, in Bolk's figure of a somewhat flattened specimen (1906, fig. 178; our fig. 6 C), setting off less than the anterior third of the vermis, and it is found in a similar position in Sisson's medio-sagittal section (1917, fig. 639; our fig. 21 B). In the specimen shown in Bradley's medio-sagittal section (1903, pl. XXIII, fig. 109) and in my *Equus caballus* brain, the forward shift of the primary fissure has gone beyond this condition; the fissure is close to the anterior end of the dorsal facies, setting off anteriorly one fourth of the vermis length in the former specimen and less than that in the latter. (I have observed similar variation of the position of the primary fissure in sheep brains.) Thus in the living horse there occurs a condition in which the Lower Eocene length proportion of anterior lobe to middle and posterior lobes is reversed, and one also finds a condition in which the anterior lobe cortex, which had been largely a dorsal portion in *Eohippus*, has become the anterior facies of the vermis.

The problem arises whether a posterior position of the fissura prima within the vermis surface, the primitive condition in the evolution of the Equidae, might be generally regarded as a primitive feature in mammalian brains.

This question has not been definitely asked before, and indeed appears futile, and is ostensibly answered in the negative when only the living mammals are surveyed—those living representatives of the "lower" and "higher" mammalian orders whose brain evolution we do not know. The share of the anterior lobe in the vermis cortex is extremely different in the Recent genera of an order. Bolk states that in rodents—lower mammals, certainly, from the standpoint of forebrain anatomy—anterior lobe cortex constitutes the larger part of the vermis surface (1906, p. 90). Kuithan (1895, p. 32) observed that the anterior lobe is larger in the cavy than in the sheep. This is well seen in Kuithan's figures of the two brains, in which the length ratio of the anterior lobe to the posterior portion is 1:2.2 in *Cavia* and 1:3.5 in *Ovis;* even shorter anterior lobes occur in sheep. However, the primary fissure is in the anterior facies of the vermis of a bat (*Vesperugo*, Ärnbäck, 1900, fig. 1) and of most insectivores (Ärnbäck, 1900, fig. 5; Le Gros Clark, 1932). Among the insectivore cerebella figured by Le Gros Clark, those of *Erinaceus* (1932, fig. 5c) and of the primitive *Centetes* (our fig. 4 A) appear to have the longest anterior lobes. The anterior lobe of the opossum (fig. 5, fig. 21 A) is far shorter not only than that of *Eohippus*, but also than that of some *Equus* brains. The anterior lobe of man is (within the human vermis) relatively much larger than that of the horse.

Obviously, the stages of anterior lobe changes observed in the evolution of the Equidae do not represent a standard to which present-day higher and lower brains conform. It is all the more interesting that Bolk (1906, p. 42), from his comparisons of the cerebella of living mammals only, concluded that the dissimilarities in shape are due exclusively to the differently complicated development of the parts posterior to the fissura prima. Bolk (p. 87) sensed the evolutionary significance of his observation, but his test cases, naturally, were no proof; he found that in contrast to carnivores the anterior lobe appears "nicht mehr" in the middle part of the dorsal surface of the cerebellum, but "has become" an anterior part in *Bos taurus, Cervus elaphus, Sus scrofa,* and—*Halmaturus rufus!*

While the anterior lobe was shifted forward, and increasingly more of it disappeared from the outside aspect of the brain, its cortical surface expanded. Its four

TABLE 5.– *Cerebellar diameters*

The "height" and breadth of the cerebellum and the breadth of the vermis lobes with their ratios to total cerebellar breadth. (The *Merychippus* specimen seems compressed dorso-ventrally.)

	Eoh. I	Oro. I	Mes. I	Mes. III	Mes. IV	Mer. III	Neohip.	Pony	Eq. cab. I	Equus II brain	Equus brain (Sisson's figs.)
cbl. height	20	24	24	24	26	34	33	45	57	49	49
cbl. breadth	22	24	—	35	34	53	44	61	76	67	61
lob. ant.	9; 1:2.3	10; 1:2.4	9	—	10; 1:3.4	11; 1:4.8	10; 1:4.4	20; 1:3.0	22; 1:3.5	21; 1:2.9	18: 1:3.7
lob. med.	11; 1:2	11; 1:2.2	12	14; 1:2.5	—	17; 1:3.1	18; 1:2.4	26; 1:2.3	35; 1:2.2	23; 1:2.7	21; 1:3.2
lob. post.	(8; 1:2.8)	10; 1:2.4	12	—	13; 1:2.6	14; 1:3.6	—	24; 1:2.5	27; 1:2.8	16; 1:3.8	—

lobules seem to have been present at least from *Orohippus* onward. The endocranial casts do not reveal the evolutionary development of their few folia, but they show that anterior lobe maximum breadth increased: slowly in the early forms, from 9 mm. in *Eohippus* to 11 mm. in *Merychippus*, but then up to 22 mm. in *Equus.* However, in the Miocene the cerebellum had become so broad that the anterior vermis lobe, in breadth too, became a relatively smaller portion than it originally was (table 5).

The distance between the fissura prima and the antero-basal end of the vermis in the medio-sagittal plane—*i.e.*, the axis of the anterior lobe—is somewhat over 9 mm. in the *Eohippus* endocast, and 22 mm. in the *Equus* II brain. In both, it equals the greatest transverse diameter of the anterior lobe. This axis is almost horizontal in *Eohippus*, slightly sloping anteriorly; the surface curve bulges less than 2 mm. beyond the axis. In the horse brain, the axis is almost perpendicular, and the surface arc extends about 6 mm. anterad.

Whereas the endocranial casts cannot completely show this forward and downward rolling and height increase of the anterior lobe, the evidence of the trend is supplemented by the evolution of the tentorium osseum. The increasing enlargement of this osseous septum between cerebellum and cerebrum is correlated with two factors in the evolution of the brain. On the one hand, the cerebellum became more and more submerged beneath the expanding cerebral hemispheres. On the other hand, the cerebellum itself gradually protruded into the space (*sit venia verbo:*) evacuated by the midbrain, which gradually became a lower portion within the brain.

Eohippus had no tentorium *sensu stricto*; the midbrain intervened between cerebellum and forebrain. The first tentorium of the Equidae, that of *Orohippus*, projects well downward and forward into the brain cavity between cerebellum and cerebrum. It does not extend beyond the posterior poles of the cerebral hemispheres and it reaches medially less than 2 mm. into the cerebral area. The dorsal surface of the *Orohippus* vermis was completely exposed.

The tentorium osseum of *Mesohippus* V (fig. 10 B) extends baso-medially to a point 10 mm. below the level at which cerebrum and cerebellum meet laterally on the dorsal brain surface, and 5 mm. anterior to the posterior cerebral poles. In this specimen, the dorso-median gap between the hemispheres, in which the cerebellar lip thrusts forward on the dorsal brain surface, has about 3 mm. antero-posterior length. Thus at least 2 more mm. of the anterior vermis were overlapped below the surface.

The tentorium of the *Merychippus* skull C (pl. 2, fig. 1) projects into the skull forward and downward to 12 mm. in front of the posterior forebrain poles. A high portion of the cerebellum, about one third of its antero-posterior extent, had come to lie in the forebrain area.

In *Equus* the protuberantia occipitalis interna and tentorium have become a voluminous structure whose forward-downward extent is variable. The published figures of horse brains suggest an equal variability of the corresponding brain feature, the cerebral facies of the cerebellum. Conditions similar to those in *Merychippus*, medial overlapping of one-third, may still occur, but up to half of the vermis may lie in the forebrain area in the horse.

The forward shift of the anterior lobe within the vermis is a phylogenetic phenomenon known at present only in the evolution of the Equidae. No generalized statement can be made on this point, because no attention has been paid heretofore to vermis details in fossil mammals, and because no comparable study of phyletic stages has been made of any other mammalian group.

We have seen that the anterior lobe rolled from a dorsal into an anterior position because of its relatively limited development; the vermis portions posterior to the fissura prima expanded much more in the phylogeny of the horse. Such discriminatory evolution within the vermis was postulated by L. Edinger when he introduced the phylogenetic terms palaeocerebellum and neocerebellum. In contrast to the median vermis lobe, which was known to be very differently developed in the living mammals, the anterior and posterior lobes were seen as one "konstant bleibender Teil" (L. Edinger, 1910, p. 323).

Lobus posterior.—The assumption that anterior and posterior lobes "remained constantly the same" of course did not refer to absolute size, but resulted from comparisons with median lobes. The posterior lobe extends from the margo myelencephalicus of the vermis to the fissura suprapyramis. The junction with the oblongata is invisible in endocranial casts. The suprapyramidal fissure, junction with the median lobe, is represented on several specimens.

The fissura suprapyramis was not found in the *Eohippus* endocranial cast, and the boundary of the posterior lobe may not have been folded into a fissure in the brain of *Eohippus*. This can be assumed for two reasons: (1) The fissura prima is very distinct on this specimen, while the rest of the vermis (of which only a small postero-basal part is hidden under bone) is quite smooth; (2) the fissura suprapyramis is not developed in all living mammals, and its absence is most frequent in small forms (Bolk, 1906, p. 7). *Orohippus* surely had this fissure in its well-lobulated vermis, but it could not be identified because the specimen is incomplete postero-basally. In *Mesohippus*, the suprapyramidal fissure crosses the posterior facies of the vermis at a height of 10 mm. above the medulla oblongata of one specimen, at 12 mm. in another. In the large *Parahippus* II it is found at a height of 17 mm., at 15 mm. in *Merychippus* III, at 17 mm. height in the pony endocast. It is not reproduced in our horse endocasts, not even in the endodural cast. In my horse brain (*Equus caballus* II) and in that of Sisson's figure 639 (1917; our fig. 21 B), this fissure delimits the posterior lobe at 21 mm. above the medulla oblongata.

The height of the posterior lobe is a sounder measurement of its size than we have for the other portions of the cerebellum. True, a length increase of the myelencephalic facies cannot be examined in the endocasts. However, the increase in height expresses posterior lobe expansion clearly, because the posterior facies is by far the largest surface of the lobe, and because it was perpendicular all through the evolution of the Equidae. Even when, in *Equus*, expansion of the median lobe had pressed the distal vaults of the posterior lobe folia from the median plane, they remained exactly above each other and retained the perpendicular profile.

The upward shift of the fissura suprapyramis is, of course, primarily an expression of the general increase in height of the vermis. Considering the forward shift of the fissura prima described above, one can perhaps regard it as another sign of the development rolling forward the surface features of the vermis during evolution.

Posterior lobe cortex must have enlarged, not only by the increase in height traceable in endocasts, but also by increased lamellation. However, the division into three lobules was attained in the *Orohippus* stage; the posterior cerebellar facies is not entirely revealed in our specimen of that genus, but it has at least two transverse sulci. There are altogether six transverse sulci on the posterior facies of the posterior lobe in the *Equus caballus* II brain.

While the posterior lobe thus remained relatively simple structurally, its maximum breadth increased at the same rate as cerebellar breadth. The ratio between the two appears to have remained about the same from the endocast of *Eohippus* to the endocasts of *Equus*. Two specimens in our series suggest that, among the variations occurring in the modern type equid brains, there are cases in which the cerebellar hemispheres had gained more in breadth than the posterior lobe; the posterior lobe is a narrower portion of the cerebellum than in the other specimens in the *Merychippus* III endocast and in the *Equus caballus* II brain (table 5).

Lobus medius.—The fissurae suprapyramis and prima limit posteriorly and anteriorly the lobus medius—the vermis region which is linked to the cerebellar hemispheres.

The median lobe of the mammalian vermis consists of two morphologically rather different parts. The lobulus medianus anterior has only two major sublobules; it is the lobulus medianus posterior which is variably developed. Whereas the whole median lobe appears quite smooth in *Eohippus*, Bolk's terms lobulus simplex and lobulus complicatus are appropriate from *Orohippus* onward. On the 10 mm.-long anterior lobe of *Orohippus* there are two shallow furrows and an indication of a third sulcus, and also on the posterior vermis facies there are only two widely spaced transverse furrows. In contrast to these regions, the 9 mm.-long median lobe cortex of *Orohippus* was folded into at least six lamellae. The two anterior ones differ from the posterior cluster in the same fashion as do the lobulus simplex sublobules in the cerebellum of the horse; they continue smoothly into the paramedian lobes. The lobulus complicatus lamellae are narrower antero-posteriorly, but they are not really "complicated," for the lobus medius of *Orohippus* was a straight, symmetrical formation.

Mesohippus I displays the whole median lobe, and in specimens II and III major parts of it are preserved. Except that in I the lateral sides are marked by parts of two or three transverse sulci, these median lobes have a smooth surface. The lobulation so well shown in the *Orohippus* endocranial cast has disappeared in all three vermis lobes of *Mesohippus* endocasts. Evidently, in this stage infolding of the vermis cortex first crowded the surface with many narrow lamellae; there had come into existence that pattern of minute furrows which the endocranium cannot reproduce. The progress of lobulation to the extreme existing in the median lobe of *Equus* cannot be followed directly in endocranial casts.

This progress is indirectly shown, in the series of fossil brains, in changes of the median lobe outline and profile. The outlines of the anterior and posterior lobes did not change, and the profile changed very little in the anterior lobe from *Orohippus* to *Equus* and not at all in the posterior lobe from *Eohippus* to *Equus*.

The median lobe was still a symmetrical formation in *Mesohippus*. There is no material exhibiting the shape of this region in *Miohippus* and *Parahippus*. In the one *Merychippus* with a complete cerebellum, specimen III, the paramedian sulci have assumed an irregular course; this is the expression, in the endocranial cast, of an asymmetrical lobulus complicatus of the brain. The left paramedian sulcus has a mediad dent just above the fissura suprapyramis; upward from the level of this indentation of the left sulcus, the right paramedian sulcus forms a wide laterad arc. The vermis of *Pliohippus* is not satisfactorily preserved in our material. On the surface of the vermis of the *Neohipparion* endocast there are, between the little-curved profiles of the anterior and posterior lobes, two prominent convexities. The anterior region of the median lobe forms a transverse, broad dorsad bulge; posterior to this, a Ɔ-shaped ridge rises dorsad—and, posteriorly, posterad—from the rest of the median lobe surface. Thus in the Miocene and Lower Pliocene the middle region of the vermis had effected bulges and curvatures of its surface which enlarged the median lobe cortex well beyond the gain in diameters of the median lobe area. Far more lamellae must have built up those arcs than existed in the straight ridge of the ancestral forms; but there cannot yet have taken place that multiplication of lamellae which gives the cerebellum the aspect of a cauliflower in *Equus*. Instead of the strictly transverse sulci so distinctly modelled in the *Orohippus* endocast, and partly reproduced in one *Mesohippus* endocast, the median vermis lobe of the horse brain has innumerable sulci, short or long, which run in practically all directions. As a result of this proliferation, in particular of the lobulus complicatus, a distinct osseous counterpart of the paramedian fissure has been obliterated. *Equus* endocasts have, rather than paramedian fissures, wide paramedian depressions, and these do not follow the up-and-down course of the crooked paramedian fissures of the brain. The endocranial cast of the horse does not suggest that the median lobe of the vermis of the horse brain has developed into a crooked S-shaped mass of clusters of lamellae. The endocranial casts of the fossil Equidae, however, reveal the steps preceding this formation: the symmetry up to the Oligocene, and the simple arc in the Miocene and Lower Pliocene.

Changes in the vermis profile supplement the evidence of greater phylogenetic development of the median lobe than in the anterior and posterior lobes.

The median lobe forms the highest portion of the cerebellar vault in all Equidae. Corresponding to the forward rolling of the vermis surface described above, the top of the median lobe vault is farther posterior in the Eocene and Oligocene than later when it lies at about the middle of the subcircular profile. The median lobe of *Eohippus* is negligibly higher than the anterior lobe. A conspicuous difference between the Lower Eocene and Middle Eocene cerebella, in addition to those noted, is the fact that in *Orohippus* the dorsal profile rises abruptly behind the fissura prima. The median lobe had developed into a hump, extending fully 2 mm. nearer to the horizontal external surface of the skull roof than does the anterior lobe. Thus median lobe evolution in this phase advanced over anterior and posterior lobe evolution not only by cortex foliation but also by an expansion of the surface area in conspicuous contrast to the relative stability of the rest of the vermis. There is no further step so conspicuous in the vermis profile during the later evolution, when increasing lamellation within the slowly expanding median lobe area provided for the cortex increase. The "sudden" height development of the median lobe region in the Eocene, the separate hump it still forms in *Mesohippus*, and its later merging into one roundish vermis profile of which it forms the summit, are best seen in the specimens or our illustrations. To a certain degree the facts are expressed in the figures of cerebellar height. The measurements given in the "height" column of table 5 are not perpendicular heights. Such heights were not taken because the lowest point of the posterior cerebellar facies is difficult to determine in most of the endocasts, and because something like a cerebellar axis was believed to give a better idea of the actual dorsad expansion. "Height" was measured from the baso-anterior end of the flocculus to the dorso-posterior median lobe curve of the vermis profile— this distance being the same, in those later forms with a more anterior summit, as the flocculus-summit distance. It will be seen from table 5 that after the *Orohippus* stage cerebellar height did not increase at the same rate as breadth. In a comparison of *Eohippus* with the *Equus caballus* II brain, the ratio of cerebellar heights is 1:2.5, but the ratio of breadths is 1:3.0. Comparing *Eohippus* with the *Equus caballus* I endocast, the height ratio is 1:2.9, but the breadth ratio is 1:3.5.

It may be mentioned here that length is not included in the comparative list of cerebellar measurements because with progressing evolution an increasingly greater anterior part, increasingly variable within each genus, came to lie below the measurable surface. In the endocasts, median cerebellar length seems to increase far less than height; actually, it about trebled from *Eohippus* to *Equus*.

It follows that no more data than those described above are available concerning the difference between anterior and posterior lobe expansion on the one hand and median lobe proliferation on the other hand. Between the stage of *Eohippus*, with a symmetrical, short, low, and probably smooth median lobe, and the long, wound-up coil of lamellae clusters of the *Equus* median lobe, the following steps were observed in the fossil brains: (1) continuous forward expansion; (2) upward expansion in *Orohippus*, and dense, but straightly transverse fissuration in the same stage; (3) bending of the longitudinal axis in *Merychippus*, more bending in *Neohipparion*. The evolution of the median lobe cannot be expressed in figures. The median was always the broadest lobe, but its breadth increase (table 5) does not disclose that within the slowly expanding area the cortex so expanded by lamellation that the vermis curled up in the median lobe region. A comparison of relative median lobe breadth of *Eohippus* with that of our horse brains (table 5) shows that the median lobe has even become relatively narrower. This is due to the greater breadth expansion of the cerebellar hemispheres.

NEOCEREBELLUM

The greatest expansion of the cerebellum was in breadth. As has been shown above, the flocculus was not involved in this process, and the vermis only to a certain degree. It follows that this expansion consisted chiefly in the evolutionary development of the neocerebellar lateral divisions: the paraflocculi and paramedian lobes.

The functions of the neocerebellum are of a higher order than those of the palaeocerebellum. It regulates unilateral muscle action. In contrast to the vermis, the cerebellar hemispheres apparently do not receive spino-cerebellar tracts; but by way of ponto-cerebellar fibers they are connected with the cerebral cortex.

Traces of the lamellation of the neocerebellar cortex are rarely seen on endocranial casts; nor does our material allow us to follow separately the two parts of the cerebellar hemispheres throughout the evolution of the Equidae. Only three specimens show a distinct parasagittal fissure: *Orohippus* I, *Mesohippus* I—in which the paraflocculus is not completely preserved—, and, on its posterior facies, *Merychippus* III. In posterior views, the paraflocculus is about 2 mm. broad in *Orohippus*, and 7 mm. in *Merychippus*. Paramedian lobe breadth is not correspondingly different but is about 7 and 15 mm., respectively. These figures cannot be regarded as evidence of a relatively lesser expansion of the paramedian lobe than of the paraflocculus; they are figures of only one diameter of formations which in *Merychippus* surely were highly lamellated; and they are diameters only of one Middle Eocene and one Upper Miocene specimen. Because of the lack of more details in our material, we must consider the great increase in size as evolutionary progress of the neocerebellum as a whole.

With the great expansion of the neocerebellum is related that of the median vermis lobe, with which it is intimately connected. Yet, if our very limited material may be regarded as conclusive, there was a difference of tempo in the evolution of the two.

The mammalian type of cerebellum, characterized by breadth, was present, in its simplest form, in *Eohippus*; but in the Lower Eocene the cerebellum was but little broader than the midbrain. The palaeocerebellar section connected with the neocerebellum was the first to show outstanding progress; this consisted in dorsad expansion and cortex infolding in *Orohippus*. Cerebellar breadth, however, increased negligibly from *Eohippus* to *Orohippus*: by one eleventh. The relatively greatest step in the evolution of the cerebellar hemispheres occurred between *Orohippus* and *Mesohippus*, when the median vermis lobe remained practically unchanged (gaining in breadth up to 3 mm.) but the breadth of median vermis lobe plus cerebellar hemispheres enlarged by almost half (by 11 mm.). The three- to three-and-a-half-fold increase of cerebellar breadth from *Eohippus* to *Equus*, and the keeping in step with cerebral breadth expansion of the cerebellum from *Mesohippus* to *Equus*, were mainly achieved by the evolution of the cerebellar hemispheres.

MESENCEPHALON

In the Lower Eocene, the midbrain was quite anterior to the cerebellum, and mostly posterior to the cerebrum; the posterior corpora quadrigemina and a part of the anterior pair were in contact with the endocranium (fig. 2 A). In the Middle Eocene, the midbrain roof had disappeared from the brain surface. With increasing expansion of the forebrain, the midbrain has come to lie deep within the brain, under the cerebral hemispheres. In the living horse, portions of the cerebral hemispheres twice as high as the whole midbrain tower above the tectum mesencephali (fig. 21 B).

The length of the tectum of *Eohippus* is not known beyond the 8 mm. exposed in the endocranial cast; it is 18 mm. in the brain *Equus caballus* II and in the horse brains shown in Sisson's (1917) figures 635 and 639. The greatest tectum breadth, that of the posterior quadrigeminal lobes, was 18 mm. in *Eohippus* and is 31 mm. in the *Equus* II brain. (The tectum of a sheep brain of the size of *Mesohippus* endocasts may be reasonably considered to represent a stage intermediate between *Eohippus* and *Equus*, viz., to show conditions similar to those which existed in *Mesohippus*; it suggests a midbrain roof 16 mm. long and 20 mm. broad for the Middle Oligocene Equidae.) The *Eohippus* endocast discloses no difference in the height of posterior and anterior quadrigeminal bodies. The basal surface of the midbrain is not exposed medially. Midbrain height was 17–19 mm. in the major portion not overlapped by the forebrain. In the *Equus* II brain, height is 21 mm. at the anterior and 27 mm. at the posterior quadrigeminal bodies.

Midbrain breadths of *Eohippus* and *Equus* compare as 1:1.7, posterior midbrain heights as 1:1.5; the length expansion remains unknown.

PITUITARY BODY
SIZE AND SHAPE

The only part of the 'tweenbrain region which can, to some extent, be studied in mammalian endocranial casts is the pituitary body. The lack of a sella turcica in the horse skull, and the consequent lack of representation of the pituitary on endocasts, is a character which became manifest only in the Middle Miocene.

No brain base is known of pre-Oligocene Equidae. The cast of the pituitary groove in the sphenoid bone of *Mesohippus* is a longitudinal oval on two endocasts. It is 10 mm. long and 5 mm. broad in specimen II, 6 mm. broad in specimen V. The pituitary cast of the Lower Miocene *Parahippus* is more rounded—13 mm. long and 10 mm. broad; thus, length had increased by about one third, while breadth had about doubled.

The pituitary body of the living horse shows that breadth continued to gain more than length. Among the 15 horses investigated by Trautmann (1909, p. 618), the average length was 17 mm. in the older individuals, whereas pituitary length in younger horses varied between 21 and 24 mm.; breadth seems to have been 20 mm. in all cases. Lothringer (1886, p. 271) states that he studied only old horses and that length was 21 mm., breadth 25 mm. As these authors fail to mention the number of individuals in which the different diameters were found, we must use for comparison the arithmetical mean of the diameters given by Trautmann and Lothringer. Comparing this average length (20.5) and breadth (22.5) with those of the one *Parahippus* pituitary we know, we find that pituitary length has increased by half, but breadth by five-fourths. From *Mesohippus* to *Equus*, pituitary length has doubled; breadth, however, has become fourfold, and up to fivefold.

The greater increase in breadth than in length in the phylogeny of the Equidae is a surprising parallel to the conditions in pathological and physiological (pregnancy) enlargement of the human pituitary body. In such cases, swelling of the anterior lobe increases the height and breadth of the pituitary body, while length remains unchanged. This is, of course, because the human pituitary is rigidly confined, anteriorly and posteriorly, within the sella turcica, which bony "saddle" is open laterally and dorsally. In the phylogeny of the Equidae pituitary length was dependent upon—or, rather, correlated with—length of this portion of the neurocranium only up to *Parahippus*. One can well imagine that, with the greatly increased size of the body from *Mesohippus* to *Parahippus*, the gland which produced the growth hormone had to occupy more space than was provided by the little increase in length of the sphenoid area assigned to it; this accounts for the change of pituitary form from egg shape in the Middle Oligocene to a more globular shape in the Lower Miocene. The pituitary of the later Equidae, however, was not hemmed in by a sella turcica.

The height of the pituitary body is necessarily unknown in the fossils. The pituitary body of the horse is flat ("discoid," Sisson, 1917, p. 769) and tapers toward the edges ("scharfkantig," Trautmann, 1906, p. 618); greatest height varies from 6.5 to 8.0 mm.

The pituitaries of *Mesohippus* and of *Parahippus* were of simple shape. Oval in the former, round in the latter, they had their greatest transverse diameter in the middle of the antero-posterior length, and their surface does not indicate the shares of anterior and posterior lobes, respectively. When the stage of the living horse is reached, a more distinctive form has developed. The pituitary of *Equus caballus* is described as heart- or chestnut-shaped. It is usually broadest in the middle region of its anterior half (Lothringer, 1886, p. 271; Koller, 1922, p. 190; Sisson, 1917, fig. 629). The gain in breadth, over the fossil forms, thus is located in the anterior lobe. It is no doubt a gain in glandular lobe matter also in the cases reported by Trautmann (1906, p. 618) with the greatest diameter in the posterior half of the pituitary body, and a slight tapering anterad, because the glandular lobe of the horse pituitary is not, topographically, an "anterior lobe" only, but also envelopes the small neural posterior lobe dorsally, basally (fig. 1, fig. 21 B), and laterally. The glandular lobe is normally two thirds of pituitary body weight in horses (and weighs three fourths of the total pituitary in pregnancy; Saito, 1923, p. 309).

RELATIVE SIZE

A general survey of fossil and living Amniota (Edinger, 1942) has shown that, whereas the neural contents of the brain case are not correspondingly larger in large forms than in smaller related forms, there is a closer correlation between body size and the volume of the pituitary body, particularly of the anterior lobe which produces, among its various secretions, the growth hormone. Some of the comparisons between related mammals of different sizes now living seemed to disprove the rule. Their (relatively) similar-sized pituitaries showed that a perceptible difference in relative pituitary size is not necessarily correlated with any and every difference in body size. As a whole, the material investigated suggested that enlargement of the pituitary accompanies the development of very large forms in natural evolution.

Data pertinent to this subject were all the less expected in the present investigation as the quantity easiest to measure for comparison with the pituitary is not the whole brain but the cerebral hemispheres. These are essentially stable units within the groups which furnished the 1942 data: Jurassic dinosaurs, subfossil ratites, and mammals likewise more or less contemporary. In the series compared in the present paper, however, the cerebral hemispheres are that brain portion whose diameters have enormously increased from Eocene to Recent times; hence the method of comparing the pituitary with the cerebrum seemed ill-suited for finding relative pituitary enlargement. Despite this handicap to the disadvantage of the pituitary body, pituitary-cerebrum comparisons do reveal the role played by the pituitary gland in the evolution of the large body of horses.

The ratio of pituitary length to the length of the cerebral hemispheres seems to have remained generally the same since the oldest equid whose pituitary we know. It is 1:5.3 in the one *Mesohippus* whose pituitary length is preserved; it is 1:6.4 in our one *Parahippus*, 1:5.5 and 1:5.1 in Sisson's figures of *Equus* brains (1917, figs. 629, 632). The pituitary is not represented in our *Equus* endocasts. The average of horse pituitary lengths compares with the lengths of the cerebral hemispheres of *Equus caballus* I and II as 1:5.7.

On the other hand, the ratio of maximum pituitary breadth to maximum forebrain breadth has changed considerably since the Oligocene. It is 1:9.3 and 1:8.7 in the two *Mesohippus*, 1:6.4 in the *Parahippus*, 1:4.9 in a horse brain (Sisson, 1917, fig. 629). Average horse pituitary breadth compares to the breadth of the cerebral hemispheres of the two horse endocranial casts as 1:4.7 and 1:5.0, respectively.

Length, breadth, and height of the cerebral hemispheres of *Equus* II are just twice those of *Mesohippus* V. Likewise, pituitary length has doubled. Breadth of the anterior pituitary lobe, however, has increased four- to five-fold from *Mesohippus* to *Equus*. Thus, although changes of pituitary height remain unknown, it appears that the gland which produces the hormone regulating body growth increased its volume, in the evolution from sheep-sized Equidae to *Equus caballus*, more than did the cerebral hemispheres; that is, more than any portion of the brain proper (except the neocortex).

HORMONE EFFECTS?

The modern horse indeed could not have evolved from *Mesohippus* without considerable increase of the activity—that is, considerably increased mass—of the pituitary gland. It is not only body growth in general that is promoted by pituitary hormone. We know from animal experiments that the size development of certain body parts is particularly dependent upon the activity of the pituitary gland. In the skull of hypophysectomized rats and dogs, the cranium does not develop to fully normal size, but the snout is disproportionately short even against this small cranium; the teeth are markedly retarded in growth. (*See*, for example, Mortimer, 1938, p. 225.) It thus appears that two salient features in the post-Oligocene evolution of the Equidae—viz., the elongation of the facial skull and the enlargement of the teeth—are associated with the spectacular increase in volume, during this period, of the anterior pituitary lobe.

Two types of Equidae which were larger than their contemporaries differ from these in features which are among the most prominent results, in the head, of one kind of human hyperpituitarism: enlargement of acral parts.

In acromegaly, the mandible enlarges and becomes thick and heavy, the chin deep and protruding; the frontal bone expands through (?) enlargement of the frontal sinuses, and the thickness of the flat bones is "usually most marked in the calvarium" (Putnam and Davidoff, 1938, p. 716).

Megahippus matthewi was by far the largest equid in the Lower Pliocene. It was known only from teeth and a palate when it was made a separate genus upon the discovery of a lower jaw which is one-fourth larger than a large *Hypohippus* mandible from the same quarry and "displays characters heretofore unknown in the Equidae" (McGrew, 1938, p. 315). These characters are, as concerns the mandibular bone, depth and heaviness; they are very striking in comparison of McGrew's figure 1, *Hypohippus*, and figure 5, *Megahippus*. There is in particular "a deep, short symphysial region in contrast with the flat, long region in all other horses." "The angle of the jaw is large and deep, extending below the basal line of the ramus. The condyle is heavy" (p. 316).

Excepting *Equus giganteus* of which only the giant teeth are published, the Pleistocene species *Equus occidentalis* contained (in its Large Variant, including "*Equus pacificus*"—Schultz, 1938, p. 199–202) the largest horses of all times. *Equus occidentalis* had a mandible which was deeper, broader, and heavier than that of *Equus caballus*, and its frontal bone was more vaulted, both longitudinally and transversely ("the arching of the frontal region which is so characteristic of the species," Schultz, 1938, p. 195).

CEREBRAL SIZE RELATIONS
BRAIN AND SKULL

The axiom that that brain is the highest developed in which the cerebral hemispheres constitute the largest portion, and have the most extensive neocortex, was probably originally an anthropocentric conception. It has been substantiated by the comparative anatomy of living vertebrates. The cerebral hemispheres become increasingly dominant "from fish to man," and today the cerebrum is generally a larger portion, and has a more extensive and more convoluted neocortex, in the higher than in the lower orders of placental mammals.

Only in material such as that presented in this paper can it be actually seen that brain evolution in the Mammalia consists almost entirely of evolution of the cerebral hemispheres.

With very few exceptions, the extensive literature which compares relative brain sizes of living animals bases its calculations on the volume or the length of the brain as a whole. The results, through being regarded as indicating evolutionary stages,

TABLE 6.—*Skull, brain and cerebrum diameters and ratios*

The *Eohippus* skull length is that of the only known complete skull (*E. venticolus*); the brain diameters are those of *E. validus*. The *Mesohippus* measurements are averages of five to seven specimens.

	Eoh.	Mes.	Par. I	Mer. I	Plio. II	Neoh.	Pony	Eq. I	Eq. II	E. occ.
I Skull length	(135)	181	(334)		370	387	424	580	600	
II Total brain length	(64)	95	115	110	130	140	146	179	188	192
II: I	1:2.1	1:1.9	1:2.9		1:2.8	1:2.4	1:3.6	1:3.2	1:3.3	
III Cerebrum length	27	59	84	70	103	98	122	128	129	136
III: I	1:5.0	1:3.1	1:4.0		1:3.6	1:3.9	1:3.5	1:4.5	1:4.7	
III: II	1:2.4	1:1.6	1:1.4	1:1.6	1:1.3	1:1.4	1:1.2	1:1.4	1:1.4	1:1.4
IV Cerebrum breadth	23	50	64	(58)	86	69	97	105	112	128
V Cerebrum height	24	39		(35)	56	(58)	76	87	86	89

by their very absurdity show that brain evolution is not a matter of the brain as a whole. There is, to name one example, Flatau and Jacobsohn's compilation of the approximate proportions of total brain volume to total skull volume in living species of the different orders of mammals (1899, p. 524–527; the ungulates are represented by pig, horse and elephant), according to which "am niedrigsten stehen die Ungulata" (p. 527). Inclusion of horned forms would have assigned the ungulates to an even lower grade in this comparison. Paleoneurology, too, is not innocent of such studies. Marsh, in many publications, attempted to demonstrate the lower or higher evolutionary level of the brains of various fossil mammals through pictures showing the endocranial cast within the skull. The endocast occupies a small area in the forms chosen to represent the early Tertiary, a larger area in the representatives of later periods. The similar compilation, of an ancestral series however, in the three upper columns of table 6, would suggest that among all Eocene to Recent Equidae the modern horses are the lowest developed.

Actually, those columns mainly show the evolution of an entirely non-neurological feature—viz., that the modern horses are the Equidae with the most powerful muzzles. Details evident from the length ratios of brain:skull are that (1) brain expansion was as great as, and possibly greater than, face expansion from the Lower Eocene to the Middle Oligocene;[3] (2) with the elongation of the facial skull in full

[3] The brain expansion during this period is even reflected in brain:body ratios. The proportion of brain volume to body volume of course decreased, in the evolution of the Equidae, with every step toward larger body size. However, the decrease must have been less in this early phase than it was later on. Some ratios of brain diameters to body diameters are surprisingly similar in *Eohippus* and *Mesohippus*. Our calculations are based on brain measurements of *Eohippus validus* and body measurements of *Eohippus venticolus*, average diameters of our *Mesohippus* brains and body diameters of other *Mesohippus* individuals (height: mean of two *M. bairdii*). The ratios thus do not compare the conditions which existed in any actually known individual. However, they show that such ratios—much higher in the later genera—could occur in the Lower Eocene and Middle Oligocene forms:

Brain length (= 1) to body length—*E.* 10.6   *M.* 9.7
Brain height (= 1) to body height—*E.* 13.5   *M.* 12.4
Brain length (= 1) to body height—*E.* 5.2   *M.* 5.2

swing in the Lower Miocene, the brain capsule has become a much smaller part of the head; (3) since the Lower Miocene there has been little variation in the proportion of the whole brain to the skull. Whereas in the Eocene and Oligocene times of short-snouted, low-toothed Equidae the length of the brain capsule was just below or just above half that of the skull, it is more or less over one third in our Miocene and Plio-cene material, and in the Recent material the brain is more or less under one third of the skull in length.

These conditions in our material ostensibly contrast with the constant relative decrease of cranium length against total skull length in the evolution of the Equidae, as shown by Robb (1935, I) and checked and modified by Reeve and Murray (1942).

To prevent misunderstanding, the opportunity is taken here to say that the discrepancy between their results (obtained from 19 fossil equid skulls and, of living forms, 2 *Equus caballus*) and the outcome of our study (of 13 specimens) is not necessarily, and presumably is not a matter of in-sufficient material. The fact is that the "cranium" length measurement used by Robb, and by Reeve and Murray, is the so-called postorbital length and has nothing to do with the brain capsule.

The independence of the evolutionary shift of the orbit from endocranium evolution is illustrated, for example, by the following fact. The orbits are placed farther forward in the skull of *Mesohippus* than in the *Equus* skull where they have come to lie behind the tooth battery. At the same time the cribriform plate—that is, the anterior end of the brain capsule—has "retreated" from a position corresponding to the center of the orbits in *Mesohippus* to the transverse plane of the posterior orbital rims, or behind this plane, in *Equus*.

Robb's cranium length is the distance from the caudal limit of the occipital condyles to the an-terior wall of the orbit—the orbital margin of the lacrymal bone, a bone which does not belong to the neurocranium. The former point is posterior to the brain capsule, and the latter is anterior to it in variable degrees. Thus Robb's "cranium length" of the *Eohippus venticolus* type skull is 74 mm. Our knowledge of the skull and brain at the anterior end of the brain capsule in one *Eohippus venti-colus* and in one *Eohippus validus* suggests a brain length of about 65 mm. in the *Eohippus venticolus* type individual. Robb's five *Mesohippus* crania are 87 to 96 mm. long; our *Mesohippus* III (occi-pital condyle to P^1 length: 134 mm.), IV (140 mm.), and VI (146 mm.) increase the variation shown in Robb's figures by having 106, 110, 110 mm. "cranium length." The length of the brain capsule (upper margin of foramen magnum to lamina cribriformis), however, is 91, 97, 98 mm. in these speci-mens. Thus there is a difference of 15, 13, and 12 mm., respectively between "cranium" and brain capsule length in the three *Mesohippus*. In the *Equus caballus* I skull, the difference is 70 mm. Flatau and Jacobsohn's figure 81 (1899) shows the brain *in situ* in a horse skull; I presume that the reduction of this picture (not stated by the authors) is to one third natural size; the figured skull would then have been 534 mm. long. In this individual the brain was 75 mm. shorter than the "cranium." It is, of course, not so much the endocranium as the structures jutting outward from the lateral side of the cranium which are free to vary within each genus.

It may be pointed out here that no outside measurement can deputize for the inside brain case length. The skull constriction under the postorbital processes corresponds approximately to the anterior end of the chamber housing the cerebral hemispheres, but its relation to the olfactory bulbs is different in each equid genus. A line connecting the points at which the anterior temporal ridges (frontal crests) turn back into the postorbital processes crosses above the olfactory bulb chambers at their posterior extremity in *Eohippus* II and *Mesohippus* A, but crosses the midpoints of these chambers in *Eohippus* III and in *Equus* I.

From these considerations and from the third column of table 6 it follows that relative brain length was more stable in the evolution in the Equidae than changes in certain external features of the skull might suggest. Reeve and Murray were quite right in suspecting that measurements different from Robb's, "such as prosthion . . . to cribriform plate, might bring out a different aspect of facial evolution" (1942, p. 403). As far as the material at hand permits conclusions, the evolu-tionary change of proportion of brain length to skull length did not proceed like that of the "face length to cranium length."

Obviously, the evolutionary expansion of the brain is not correlated with the gradual changes observed in skull evolution and related to the increase in body mass. The length of the whole brain is less than one-third of the skull length in modern horses. It has been almost one-third since the Miocene reconstruction of the skull to carry high-crowned teeth. Before this time, brain length was about half the skull length. If there was any change in the brain:skull length ratio from the Eocene to the Oligocene, the scanty material now known suggests increase rather than decrease (table 6). This would be due to the fact that in this phase the cerebral hemispheres made their greatest evolutionary advance.

CEREBRUM LENGTH

Each portion of the brain has become absolutely larger from *Eohippus* to *Equus*. However (with the possible exception of the median and lateral lobes of the cerebellum), no brain part has achieved such relative increase in size and undergone such structural elaboration as the cerebral hemispheres. From a small portion between midbrain and olfactory bulbs, capped by an almost smooth neocortex, the cerebral hemispheres became the dominant part and were covered by a well-convoluted neocortex.

The lissencephalic hemispheres of *Eohippus* were low and slender; they constituted only two-fifths of the total brain length (*see* table 6) and were neither broader nor higher than the cerebellum. The Lower Eocene equid brain had not reached the evolutionary level of the brain of the lowest living placental mammals.

It has been said of the equid skull that "had there been no evolution of size, there would have been little if any 'orthogenetic' evolution of form" (Robb, 1935, p. 45). However, *Orohippus* was not taller than *Eohippus*, and there was very little progress in skeletal specialization from the Lower to the Middle Eocene; yet in this phase the brain underwent the change from subplacental to placental form, and probably to ungulate specialization. The cerebrum of *Orohippus* was gyrencephalic, and it had expanded backwards, overlapping the midbrain (its diameters are not known).

There exists no brain material of *Epihippus*. We thus do not know how much of the progress exhibited by the Oligocene brains was accomplished in the Upper Eocene.

In *Mesohippus*, we find the cerebral hemispheres established as the dominant portion of the brain. High and broad, they begin to approach the subcubic form of the modern horse brain. They did not overlap the olfactory bulbs, but their backward expansion had extended into the cerebellar area. From *Eohippus venticolus* to *Mesohippus bairdii*, skull length had increased by about half, but the cerebral hemispheres had become twice as long. The cerebrum constitutes almost two-thirds of the total length of the brain. Up to this stage, the expansion of the cerebral hemispheres was so much greater than the other evolutionary changes in the head that the cerebrum, once about one fifth of the skull in length, now occupied about one third of the skull. As long as we have no knowledge of conditions in the Upper Eocene, it seems that this high proportion existed only in the Lower (?) and Middle Oligocene.

Skeleton evolution from *Mesohippus* to *Miohippus* was mainly a size increase. As our *Miohippus* brain material consists only of the isolated forebrain of a colt somewhat over one year in age, the proportions of the hemispheres to the whole brain and to the skull are not known at present. The one young forebrain at hand, however, does disclose that the cerebrum also of an adult *Miohippus* was not considerably different from *Mesohippus* cerebra. In particular, the cerebral hemispheres of *Miohippus* were not so much larger than in *Mesohippus* brains as the gain in body and skull size would imply. In the *Eohippus-Orohippus* phase cerebral evolution had advanced without corresponding progress in body evolution; in the *Mesohippus-Miohippus* stage cerebral evolution was not linked up with body evolution in respect to size. The expansion of the cerebral hemispheres was not like muzzle elongation "algebraically linear and predictable" (Robb, 1935, p. 45). The phase of vigorous evolution was passed; the cerebral hemispheres had assumed their dominant role before *Miohippus* evolved from *Mesohippus*.

With the increasing preponderance, in the skull, of the facial portion, the share of the forebrain chamber in the total length of the skull had already become considerably reduced by the early Miocene. In the later stages of horse evolution there appears to have been great size variation within each genus, and only a small number of specimens are available for measurement. In consequence, there is no clear indication (table 6) of a change in the cerebrum/skull length ratio. It would seem, however, that the relative length of the cerebrum had gradually decreased, for in the larger living horses the proportions have reverted to figures similar to those in *Eohippus*.

On the other hand, there was little change in the length ratio of the cerebrum to the whole brain once cerebral preponderance had been achieved. These ratios (table 6), however, do not signify that the trend toward increasing cerebral preponderance in volume had ended when, in the Miocene, neocortex specialization leading to the modern brain type had begun. Cerebral expansion in the later stages no longer is expressed by the relative length alone.

Expansion in breadth and height will be discussed below. Certain topographical relations shall be mentioned here which illustrate that the cerebral hemispheres gained more in length than the rest of the brain. The forward expansion of the cerebral chamber shifts the ethmoidal chambers downward from their original neighborhood of the skull roof. The main trend of the backward expansion of the cerebrum is illustrated in some of our specimens by the relation of the posterior forebrain poles to a transverse line connecting the centers of the acoustic foramina. The forebrain ends 9 mm. anterior to this line in *Eohippus*, 7 mm. in *Orohippus*, and just above the foramina in *Mesohippus*. The posterior forebrain poles are 10 mm. posterior to the acoustic foramina in *Merychippus* III, and 12 mm. in *Pliohippus* II. In the more numerous material of *Equus* it was found that this condition varies. A relation as in *Merychippus* can occur, and the greatest backward extent of the forebrain is to a line 15 mm. posterior to the centers of the acoustic foramina (*e.g.*, in *E. occidentalis*, pl. 3, fig. 2).

CEREBRUM BREADTH

Maximum breadth of the cerebral hemispheres increased, on the whole, proportionately to cerebral length.

This is shown in the table of inter-generic cerebral ratios (table 7). We cannot profess to have used, in the calculation of these ratios, diameters typical for each genus. This is the case only of *Mesohippus* (the numbers used were the averages of five to seven endocranial casts), of *Equus caballus* (averages of two similar endocasts of large individuals), and probably of *Eohippus* (as there is reason to assume that there was little variation of brain form in the Lower Eocene). We have only one adult brain of *Parahippus* and only one adult brain of *Pliohippus*. The list is,

TABLE 7.—*Inter-generic cerebral ratios*

	Length	Breadth	Height
Eo.: Mes.	1:2.18	1:2.17	1:1.62
Mes.: Par.	1:1.42	1:1.33	
Mes.: Plio.	1:1.74	1:1.72	1:1.43
Par.: Plio.	1:1.26	1:1.33	
Plio.: Eq.	1:1.25	1:1.25	1:1.55
Mes.: Eq.	1:2.17	1:2.17	1:2.21
Eo.: Eq.	1:4.76	1:4.71	1:3.60

furthermore, incomplete; we have no adult *Miohippus* brain, and the only complete *Merychippus* brain is distorted.

However, the similarity of the intergeneric length ratios and the breadth ratios is so striking as to be, in my opinion, convincing proof of the parallelism in length and breadth expansion of the cerebral hemispheres from *Eohippus* to *Equus*. Only between *Mesohippus* and *Parahippus* there occurred, with the elongation of the skull, a greater gain in length than in breadth.

As cerebral length and breadth increased proportionately in the Equidae, forebrain evolution in this phyletic series apparently does not agree with the evolutionary principles deduced by Kappers (1928) from his study of the influence of cephalization and of body size upon the form of the forebrain in living mammals. Kappers investigated the differences of the cerebral breadth index $\dfrac{\text{breadth} \times 100}{\text{length}}$ in two sets of comparisons. (1) Within the mammalian orders the breadth indices of less cephalized members were compared with the indices of more cephalized forms—*i.e.*, whose higher brain centers are more dominant, anatomically in the brain, and physiologically in the functions of the body. Kappers found that within an order the larger species, which are generally the more highly cephalized (as is the case in our material, the Equidae), are more brachencephalic—that is, have the higher breadth index; "their forebrain has a rounder instead of a longer form" (p. 72). (2) Kappers compared the breadth indices of equally cephalized, differently sized representatives of smaller groups. He found that within species, genera, and families the larger forms are less brachencephalic than the smaller forms—that is, have a lower index. As, therefore, within a family, "an increase in body size is accompanied with a decrease of brachencephaly," the greater brachencephaly of the larger members of mammalian orders "is the result of their greater cephalization only" (p. 72–74). As a possible reason for "the elongation of the brain in larger animals" (p. 74), "the fact that the length of the [fore-] brain generally increases more than the width"

(p. 75), Kappers recalls "that the skull itself in the larger animals of the same family is relatively more lengthened" (p. 77).

From our paleontological standpoint, we naturally object to this way of connecting the living members of a family (including the Equidae, horse, and ass, p. 72, p. 75) as if the smaller were ancestral to the larger forms. However, both the last-quoted statements are true of the ancestral series of the horse. The skull becomes more elongated, and cerebral length increases absolutely more than breadth. The Equidae, furthermore, are a group of forms with very different body sizes, and a group with progressive cephalization. Our series of equid brains thus puts to the test the evolutionary implications of Kappers' findings in living mammals.

The cerebral breadth indices of our endocast material are: *Eohippus* I: 85.2; *Mesohippus* I–VI: 84.2, 90.6 (young), 87.5, 77.8, 86.7, 84.1; *Miohippus* (young) 98.4; *Parahippus* I: 77.8, II: 75.9; *Pliohippus* II: 83.5; (sideline: *Neohipparion*: 70.4; *Hipparion* I: 77.5, III: 82.1); pony: 79.5; *Equus caballus* I: 82.0, II: 86.8; *Equus occidentalis*: 94.1.

Kappers' brain indices of a small and a large living representative of the Equidae (p. 75) are: *Equus asinus*: 95.0, *Equus caballus*: 94.2.[4]

These indices reveal, incidentally, that variation of greatest cerebral length and breadth is so great within one genus (*Mesohippus*) or even species (*Equus caballus*) that one or two brains of one form (Kappers' material) do not furnish sufficient data for general conclusions. In Kappers' material, the larger members of a genus or a family have the lower indices; in our material, the indices of the two domestic horses are higher than the pony index, and the index of the giant Pleistocene horse is the highest of the series.

A survey of the cerebral breadth indices from *Eohippus* to *Equus* shows that (as table 7 suggested) no definite change in the proportion of cerebral length and breadth accompanied increasing body size and increasing forebrain preponderance in the evolution of one form. Is it possible that the influences of increasing cephalization (causing brachencephaly, Kappers' first rule) and increasing body size (causing dolichencephaly, Kappers' second rule) have balanced each other in the evolution of the horse brain?

CEREBRUM HEIGHT

Maximum height.—Whereas the gains in cerebral length and breadth of the cerebral hemispheres were steady and directly proportionate, the smallest diameter, height, did not increase proportionately to the other two diameters. Our figures furthermore suggest a rate of increase in the early stages different from that in the latest stages.

Intergeneric height ratios (table 7) show that height was slower to gain than length and breadth from the *Eohippus* to the *Pliohippus* stage; height increased at a greater rate than length and breadth between *Pliohippus* and *Equus*.

---

[4] Kappers measured length not horizontally but along the inclining line of greatest distance between front- and hind-pole of the cerebral hemispheres. In effect there is no difference between the two methods, particularly because of the great variations in brain shape. Actually, the greatest, oblique length of Kappers' horse brain is only 6.2 mm. more than its breadth, whereas the horizontal length is 17 mm. and 23 mm., respectively, more than breadth in the cerebra of our two *Equus caballus* endocasts.

The number of specimens at hand is, of course, too small to afford positive proof of these statements. However, different height increases—different from length increase, and different in different periods—are also suggested by the fact that Eocene, Oligocene, Mio-Pliocene, and Pleisto-Holocene cerebral height indices arrange themselves in four separate groups. The $\dfrac{\text{height} \times 100}{\text{length}}$ indices of our specimens are:

Eohippus I: 88.9

Mesohippus I–VI: 63.2, 71.7, 71.4, 65.1, 71.7, 68.3; (Miohippus: >57.7).
Parahippus II: 56.9; (Neohipparion: 59.2; Hipparion III: 58.0) Pliohippus I: 58.1, II: 54.4.
Equus occidentalis: 65.4; Equus caballus I: 67.9, II: 66.7, pony: 62.3.

Frontal lobe height.—Due to the variability of the outline of the cerebral hemispheres, it is not possible to ascertain precisely differences in the breadth increase of different regions. On the other hand, such a difference is definitely shown in our series of endocasts with respect to height.

The development of frontal lobe height differs from the height increase in the posterior cerebral areas; gains were greater. The profile of the *Eohippus* cerebrum (fig. 2 C) is an unbroken curve; the anterior region was considerably lower than the posterior region. An approximately horizontal dorsal facies had been developed by Oligocene times in the posterior two thirds of the hemispheres; but up to the Middle Miocene the profile of the frontal lobe was a gentle slope anteriorly, ending in a low vertical part above the olfactory tracts. A somewhat higher vertical anterior facies is suggested by the two distorted Upper Miocene *Merychippus* endocasts. In the *Pliohippus, Hipparion*, and *Neohipparion* specimens, the anterior frontal lobe regions are disturbed in different ways; but they all indicate more anterad bulging of the upper frontal region than had been the case in the earlier forms. It seems, for example, that the anterior side of the *Pliohippus* II brain was perpendicular for 15 mm. of its height. In continuation of this tendency, there has developed, in *Equus*, the high, subperpendicular anterior facies of the frontal lobe seen in the endocast profiles (pl. 3, fig. 2; pl. 4, fig. 3).

The frontal lobe type of neocortex ends posteriorly at the sulcus ansatus. In the region of this sulcus, as well as in the frontal lobe itself, our endocast series shows a greater gain in height than in the posterior region of greatest height; but this difference is very small. Height at the juncture of the ansate with the fissura magna cerebri compares to greatest temporal lobe height as 1:1.7 in *Mesohippus* I and V, 1:1.4 in *Mesohippus* III, IV, and VI, 1:1.2 in *Equus occidentalis*, 1:1.3 in *Equus caballus* I and II, 1:1.1 in the pony. In a comparison of the averages of *Mesohippus* and *Equus caballus*, temporal lobe heights compare as 1:2.2, and the height at the posterior end of the frontal lobe in *Equus* is 2.4 times that of *Mesohippus*.

Thus it is only in the region anterior to the sulcus ansatus that there was a gain in height considerably greater than the increase of maximum brain height, in particular in the latest phases of the evolution of the horse brain. It cannot be well demonstrated in figures, but it is unmistakably expressed in the change of the profile of the frontal lobe. This forward-upward vaulting is accompanied by a gain in the breadth of the frontal lobe.   Regarding the special breadth increase of the frontal lobe, our material does not show such a steady trend as was observed in the evolution of frontal lobe height.   From the anteriorly tapering *Eohippus* brain, a subquadrangular form had developed in *Mesohippus,* and existed in our *Merychippus* I and III (and in *Hipparion*), but not in our *Parahippus* (and *Neohipparion*).   All we can say is that at the end of the ancestral line the frontal lobe was relatively much broader than it had been in the early Equidae.   Whereas maximum cerebral breadth has somewhat more than doubled from *Mesohippus* to *Equus,* average frontal lobe breadth became almost threefold.

Thus the frontal lobe expanded considerably more than the other regions of the cerebrum.

Frontal lobe cortex is of the highest developed type, with seven layers of different cells.   Its two sections greatly differ in extent in the hierarchy of living mammals, but both are largest in man.   The regio praecentralis agranularis is concerned with association and complicated motor activities such as isolated movements of single body parts.   It covers in the investigated ungulates (Rose, 1942) the frontal convexity up to the ansate sulcus.   In the area frontalis granularis are located the highest associational activities and, apparently, emotions.   This cell area has not been found in marsupials, insectivores, Chiroptera, and rodents.   The human brain represents its highest development.   In the sheep it is so small that it covers only the walls of the sulcus praesylvius and does not extend to the free surface of the brain (Rose, 1942, p. 30).

The cytoarchitectonic structure of the frontal lobe of *Equus* has not been investigated.   What can it signify that in the evolution of the Equidae the frontal region of the cerebrum expanded more vigorously than other cortex areas, that this was particularly manifest in the latest phase of equid evolution, and that the Equidae developed a frontal lobe more vaulted than that of the sheep?   The question cannot, of course, be answered definitely; but the facts of comparative neurology taken together with the data of our series of endocasts recall the process to which Economo has given the name cerebration:

"Wenn wir . . . die phylogenetische Reihe der Lebewesen bis zum Menschen heraufsteigen, bemerken wir . . . nicht nur die bekannte Zunahme des Gehirns an Masse, welche der zunehmenden Bedeutung des Grosshirnes im nervösen Geschehen und seiner zunehmenden Wichtigkeit für die Motilität und Sensibilität . . . entspricht" [cephalisation], "sondern auch eine zunehmende feinere spezifische Differenzierung der einzelnen Hirngebiete durch Vermehrung der architektonischen Felder und schliesslich eine Neuerwerbung solcher Felder, welche einer Neuerwerbung von Hirnorganen gleichkommt, die notwendigerweise das Auftreten neuer psychischer und geistiger Fähigkeiten beinhalten" (cerebration; Economo, 1929b, p. 119).

Economo himself quotes the Equidae as a case of progressive cerebration; his data, however, are not valid:

"So ist z.B. für die ganze Ahnenreihe des Pferdes vom vierzehigen Palaeotherium zum dreizehigen Architherium, zum Hipparion bis zum heutigen einzehigen Pferde neben der stetigen Entwicklung des Fusses zur Einzehigkeit auch eine stetige, die gleichzeitige Zunahme an Körpergrösse übertreffende Entwicklung des Gehirnes, das heisst der Schädelhöhle charakteristisch" (p. 124).

Perhaps the changes in shape and size of the frontal lobe in the phyletic series of the Equidae signify the acquisition, at some stage of the evolution of the horse brain, of a histologically different cortex area. Probably no cortex of the regio frontalis granularis type existed in the smooth cerebrum of *Eohippus*. The low and narrow anterior region of the early Eocene equid neocortex would then have been the motor association area. A regio granularis was presumably present, but small, in the Oligocene Equidae. In the endocranial casts of the later Equidae the pronounced enlargement of the anterior cerebral regions suggests progressive expansion of both the agranular and the granular, general association area.

NEËNCEPHALON
EXTENT

Morphology.—While the cerebral hemispheres increased in absolute size, and gradually increased their dominance over the other brain portions in volume, their surface (and consequently their structure) underwent striking changes. "Man spricht mit Recht von einer dramatischen Entwicklung des Neocortex in der aufsteigenden Säugerreihe" reports Scharrer (1936, p. 22), contrasting opossum and baboon. "From lower to higher mammals the increased development of the telencephalon is characterized chiefly by the progressive development of the neocortex and its associated fiber bundles" (Kappers, Huber, and Crosby, 1936, p. 1401). But we need not compare opossum and baboon, or lower and higher mammals, to view this dramatic story of progressive development of the neocortex. A wide range of mammalian necortical evolution can be observed within the confines of a single family of higher mammals—the Equidae.

The expansion of the neocortex is exhibited, in our series of fossil brains, in two ways: (1) the shift of the fissura rhinalis downward over the sides to the base of the brain, (2) the increasing fissuration of the neocortex.

The fissura rhinalis of *Eohippus* delimited the neocortex as a straight, generally horizontal border line just above the midheight of the cerebral hemispheres. In *Mesohippus* and in *Miohippus*, the posterior rhinal fissure lay at the middle of cerebral height; the anterior rhinal fissure curved farther ventrally so that in a part of the frontal lobe the neocortex extended to the lower half of the forebrain. Only the anterior rhinal fissure is traceable in our *Parahippus* material; its arc reaches farther down than it did in the Oligocene, to the base of the brain. The transverse distance between the lowest points of the anterior rhinals—that is, the breadth of the prepiriform basal region—was not greater in our young *Parahippus* than it had been in *Mesohippus*, whereas the breadth of the hemispheres in this plane is 10 mm. greater; the gain is purely neocortical. The fissura rhinalis posterior had become a feature of the basal portion of the cerebrum in *Merychippus*, and conditions similar to those existing in modern horse brains were reached in *Pliohippus*.

Thus in the account of the evolutionary changes in greatest breadth and greatest height of the cerebral hemispheres we have discussed a matter different in nature from the changes in cerebral length. Length increase, from *Eohippus* to *Equus*, involved proportional increases in both the paleëncephalic parts of the cerebrum and the neëncephalon, the neocortex. This was not the case with breadth and height. The increase of greatest cerebral breadth signifies mainly increasing width of the neocortex; the share of the piriform lobe and the pre-piriform areas in cerebral breadth decreased. Cerebral height at the temporal lobe comprises piriform lobe and neocortex in proportions different in each stage; the share of the former decreased considerably, from more than half to about one seventh. The "acceleration" of height increase in the late Miocene or after the Miocene was pre-eminently a matter of neocortex expansion.

In the *Eohippus* cerebrum, the gyrus olfactorius protrudes laterally below the frontal neocortex, but posteriorly paleopallial and neopallial breadths are the same. In *Mesohippus* I–VI, breadth of paleopallium to neopallium, at the latter's greatest lateral bulge (temporal lobe), compare as 1:1.07, 1.09, 1.04, 1.04, 1.08, 1.08. In the young *Miohippus* the ratio is 1:1. The gain in breadth of the neocortex over the piriform lobe is shown by the following ratios of piriform breadth (= 1) to neocortex breadth: *Merychippus* I and III: 1.16 and 1.17; *Pliohippus* II: 1.23 (*Neohipparion:* 1.2; *Hipparion* III: 1.25); pony: 1.34; *Equus caballus* I and II: 1.23 and 1.24; *Equus occidentalis:* 1.44.

It has been noted that the fissura rhinalis of *Mesohippus*, in mid-height of the cerebral hemispheres, was at a higher level than in any living ungulate; the neocortical area was in *Mesohippus* a far smaller portion of the brain surface than it is in living ungulates, whether they are smaller or taller than *Mesohippus*. That the period in evolutionary history is a factor more important than size is emphasized if we compare the living sheep with the sheep-sized Oligocene *Mesohippus* with regard to the proportion of greatest piriform lobe breadth to greatest temporal lobe breadth; this figure in the sheep is not that of *Mesohippus*, but that of living, far larger descendants of *Mesohippus* (1:1.34).

The driving forces.—To put the significance of this comparison in its proper light, one should recall how neoneurologists have discovered the two major factors correlated with neocortex size, viz., general evolution and body size. The first has been demonstrated by comparing the brains of living reptiles, mammals of the lower orders, and mammals of the higher orders; the second by observing differences of forebrain structure in different living members of mammalian families. On such heterogeneous material rests the thesis that the extent of the neopallium and the degree of its fissuration in any given mammal are dependent on the place the species occupies in the hierarchy of living mammals, and on the size of the animal. (*See*, e.g., Kappers, Huber, and Crosby, 1936, p. 1516–1519.)

This thesis is well grounded; it is valid as far as Recent times are concerned. Horsebrain evolution confirms the importance of both factors. However, the Lower Eocene equid brain shows that the evolutionary level of a brain was not at all times determined by the order to which the mammal belongs. The evolution of the brain in the Equidae, furthermore, has revealed that the extent of the neocortex—that is, the evolutionary level of a brain—is not determined solely by the two properties of the body, size and specialization.

Mesohippus bairdii and *Ovis aries* are of similar size, and both are specialized ungulates. By their teeth, their feet—as far as we know, by their bodies—they are assigned to similar levels of evolutionary development. Their brains are of similar size, but the neocortex was considerably smaller in *Mesohippus*, as well as the taller *Miohippus*, than it is in sheep.

Consequently, there is a third determinant upon which depends the extent of the neocortex; it appears that this factor is time.

Certain remarks of some authors implicite contain the statement that the evolution of the forebrain is a process distinct from the evolution of body characters. The term neëncephalon (for the episphaerium or neocortex) was created by L. Edinger (1908, p. VI) for the brain portion which, in contrast to the rest of the brain (palaeencephalon; American spelling: paleëncephalon), evolves "durchaus unabhängig von der Körpergrösse." In the transition from reptiles to mammals Simpson (1927, p. 259) recognized a "factor of the brain and mental advances" as related to, but distinct from, the evolution of the mechanical advantages of the structure of the higher group. Conditions in several stages of the evolution of the Equidae have suggested a special relation between time and, in contrast to the rest of the body, the brain.

More than the one actual evolutionary series of mammalian brains now at hand must be known before we can hope to understand the force which can drive mammalian cerebra to neocortex expansion, and its relations to progress in body size, to progressive specialization of body characters, and to time.

Living animals of course contribute important data. Living animals of different classes show that no neocortex existed before Reptilia evolved from Amphibia, and that the origin of birds on the one hand, and of mammals on the other hand, was accompanied by great steps in neocortex evolution. Fossil data fail to show corresponding progress in body size in these transitions. The living orders of mammals show that not every kind of body specialization is paralleled by cortex specialization. But why have mammals as specialized as the bats a poorly developed brain? Is it because the specialization of their body was, in the main, concluded in the Eocene? It is the time element in brain evolution on which attention should be focused by paleoneurologists.

It is difficult to understand the tempi of brain evolutions. There was almost no progress in the sirenian brains from the Middle Eocene to Recent times (in spite of size increase), whereas the human brain is the product of rapid evolution. Regarding these tempi we can, however, attempt to correlate—or to exclude the possibility of correlating—brain evolution with either increase of body size or progress of specialization, or both.

The most promising line of attack on the problem of the time element is perhaps a study of the period or periods in which, during the evolution of one phyletic series, great progress was made or stagnation occurred in brain evolution—the period in the history of the group, and perhaps the period in earth history. Is it of general significance that in the earliest history of the Equidae (as in the earliest history of birds and mammals in general) the forebrain retained characters which among living animals characterize reptiles? Is brain evolution generally less progressive than the evolution of other systems in the earliest, otherwise morphologically most incisive phase of specialization of a group? Is it significant that in the Equidae independence of brain evolution from either general evolutionary progress or body size, or both, was found only in the Eocene and Oligocene? Is it significant that the Lower Eocene brains of the condylarth *Phenacodus*, the much smaller perissodactyl *Eohippus*, and those of *Coryphodon* and *Notostylops* are remarkably similar? What does it mean that the forebrains of several Oligocene artiodactyls and of *Mesohippus* and *Miohippus* differ from the forebrains of living ungulates by the same characteristic features? Are these cases, within restricted groups, of Dacqué's "Zeitsignatur" thesis (1935, p. 226–251, and other publications of Dacqué) according to which certain organs at certain times of earth history are subject to a "style" as characteristic of the period as building styles are in the history of man? The frontal lobe of the equid neocortex gained more conspicuously than the rest of the brain, inside a neurocranium whose outer shape remained unchanged, in the latest phases of evolution; will a disciple of Dacqué point to the fact that this was in the period in which originated the human brain, one of whose chief characteristics is the voluminous frontal lobe? Is the frontal lobe the seat of ultimate progress in every mammalian brain evolution? Is it significant that, in the evolution of the Equidae, a cerebrum with all main characters of that of the modern horse was first achieved when, in the Upper Miocene, the head size was reached which is today that of the newborn horse?

The horse series is notable in general for marked evolutionary progress in size and in specialization. The series likewise shows marked structural changes in the brain which consist mainly in the expansion of the neëncephalon. Independence of brain evolution from progress in body size or specialization, or both, is shown in this phyletic series by the following facts:

(1) The evolutionary level of the Lower Eocene brain was below that of any Recent placental mammal. All other parts we know of *Eohippus* show that it was an equid ungulate. The brain by no feature indicates that it will develop into the brain of *Equus*. Brain evolution was lagging behind skeleton evolution.

(2) Skeleton evolution and body size progressed only negligibly from the Lower to the Middle Eocene. In the brain, evolution advanced to a form superior to that which has ever been attained in the lower orders of placental mammals. The forebrain overlapped the midbrain, and new sulci developed in the neocortex. Brain evolution had been more progressive than skeleton and size evolution.

(3) From the Middle to the Upper Oligocene, progress of skeleton specialization was almost imperceptible, but the Equidae became much taller. Shoulder heights of mounted skeletons are: 450–515 mm. in *Mesohippus*, but 640 mm. in *Miohippus*. Our one *Miohippus* brain is that of a young individual; thus it does not reveal the brain size of adult *Miohippus* individuals, and the specimen is little larger than *Mesohippus* brains; but the characters presumably present in the adult *Miohippus* brain were fully developed in this specimen. Whereas in closely related living mammals the taller forms have a richer neocortex fissuration, the *Miohippus* brain at hand shows extremely little progress beyond the *Mesohippus* brain. Brain evolution appears to have been at a standstill like skeleton specialization, notwithstanding increase in body size.

FISSURATION

Sulci and evolution.—According to the degree of fissuration, the placental mammals are currently grouped into lissencephalic and gyrencephalic orders. This distinction is justified in general, as concerns the living placentals; for example, the rodents have few or no sulci, the ungulates are throughout gyrencephalic. It is also generally true that lower mammals are lissencephalic and that larger mammals have more sulci than small ones. But neither "lower and higher mammals," nor orders with only small and orders with large representatives, coincide with those two groups based on neocortex anatomy. The Sirenia are large, specialized subungulates; they are as lissencephalic as the Insectivora which are small and unspecialized. The Anthropoidea, gyrencephalic, contain one family whose neocortex is smooth except for the fossa Sylvii—the Hapalidae, monkeys much smaller than any others.

Paleoneurology does away with this impracticable distinction. For the paleoneurologist, there are no gyrencephalic orders. Early Tertiary skulls, small and large, with primate, carnivore, ungulate, or other characters, all contained lissencephalic brains.

It follows that brain sulci made their appearance independently within each order.

Turner, in his comprehensive study of the brain sulci of living mammals, concluded from the existence of smooth pallia in primates that "the brain follows apparently in each order its own plan of evolution" (1890–1891, p. 151). The idea does not seem to have been taken up by others. My first survey of fossil brains gave me a similar conception, from the paleontologist's viewpoint; I incidentally mentioned in the anatomical chapter that "augenscheinlich" gyrification developed independently in the different orders of mammals (1929, p. 81). There exists now, I believe, ample evidence of this fact. Nobody doubts that the masticatory surface of the teeth expanded independently within each order by enlargement of, and additions to, early-specialized cusps or ridges. Similarly, in a later stage of their history in the higher orders, the neopallium enlarged by expanding over the brain surface and by progressively folding into more and more sulci.

Thus it is questionable whether similar-looking sulci in different mammalian orders can logically be regarded as homologues. Homology seems justifiable in the case of sulci (such as the Sylvian and lateralis systems) whose presence is apparently connected with the mechanism of brain development. It may be correct to regard the corono-ansate sulci of ungulates and carnivores as the same formation; but from the viewpoint of phylogeny the common view that the corono-ansate is the "forerunner" of the sulcus centralis of primates is untenable. Certain other generally accepted conceptions must also be rejected—for example, the idea that a system "begins" in carnivores as one sulcus and in primates "separates" into two sulci.

The main sulci.—There is no indication of a Sylvian fossa on the endocranial cast of *Eohippus*. If developed at all, it must have been in an initial stage in the Lower Eocene Equidae, as it was in the Middle Eocene. In the brain of *Orohippus*, the Sylvian fossa was represented by a tiny semicircular depression in the ventral rim of the neocortex.

Three of the many sulci of the horse brain had come into existence in *Eohippus* as short, straight, shallow, widely separated furrows on a lissencephalic forebrain. In the posterior region the longest of the three, the lateral sulcus, may not have been developed on both hemispheres. This region is not known in *Orohippus*. In the middle region there is dorsally a 4.5 mm.-long suprasylvian sulcus both in *Eohippus* and *Orohippus;* the pars media thus was the first to develop, and it remained the only part as long as no proper Sylvian fossa existed. Anteriorly the *Eohippus* brain had its only nonlongitudinal sulcus. This sulcus begins at some distance from the fissura magna cerebri and runs obliquely laterad to the frontal pole which it encircles just as the dorsal part of the presylvian sulcus does in the later Equidae. There is no indication in *Eohippus* I that the presylvian sulcus continued on the lateral surface of the brain; it did in *Eohippus* II, but as this fragment consists only of the anterior part of the forebrain no more is disclosed of the lateral course of the presylvian sulcus than the bend from the dorsal to the lateral surface. The *Orohippus* II fragment, consisting of the circumsylvian region, shows that in this phase the term presylvian was the appropriate name for this sulcus; the part disclosed in *Orohippus* II descends across the lateral side of the neocortex, running baso-posteriorly to the region anterior to the Sylvian groove.

Although only a restricted area is known of the *Orohippus* brain, progress over *Eohippus*—at least over *Eohippus validus*—is revealed not only in the more definite beginning of the Sylvian fossa and the extension of the presylvian sulcus, but also in a new sulcus developed as a straight short longitudinal furrow—the sulcus posticus. Its presence in *Orohippus* strongly suggests that further sulci had come into existence in addition to the three developed in the Lower Eocene. The neocortex area disclosed in *Orohippus osbornianus* suffices to show that gyrencephaly had been achieved by the Equidae in the Middle Eocene.

The whole complement of the major sulci of the horse brain existed in *Mesohippus*. Only two sulci developed later than the Middle Oligocene. These youngest sulci are both so inconspicuous in *Equus* that authors usually do not mention them as separate elements. The evolutionary history of the horse brain, however, establishes these sulci, which in the horse are connected with their neighbors, as originally separate formations. As short, unbranched, and straight furrows the intra-orbital sulcus first appears in *Miohippus*, the sulcus interlateralis dorsalis in *Parahippus*.

Mesohippus possessed a long Sylvian fossa, with a usually bifurcated processus acuminis. There existed short pieces of the ectosylvian sulcus which later, as a more or less complete arch, delimited the gyrus arcuatus primus around the fossa Sylvii. The gyrus arcuatus secundus was the first developed in evolution; *Mesohippus* had the four main parts of the ungulate suprasylvian sulcus. Pars anterior, pars media, and ramus ventralis formed a circumsylvian arch. Pars media and pars posterior sulci suprasylvii constituted one of the longitudinal furrows which characterize the posterior two thirds of the *Mesohippus* cerebrum; the others are a short sulcus posticus on the lateral surface, the ectolateral, lateral, and endolateral sulci on the dorsal surface. The anterior third of the dorsal side is characterized by transverse fissuration. It was crossed by the cruciate and ansate sulci and the transverse part of the presylvian sulcus. The presylvian and diagonal sulci descended obliquely across the anterior region of the lateral brain surface.

In the *Mesohippus* stage these sulci were strikingly different from their homologues in the brains of later Tertiary and living Equidae. They were more or less straight, generally unconnected, and had few, mostly very short branches.

The "ramus ventralis" of the suprasylvian sulcus would be a long branch, if it had to be regarded as a ramus; however, it is an important part of the quadripartite sulcus, as it forms the posterior leg of the circumsylvian arch. The sulcus ansatus had, varying individually, a short posterior and one or two anterior longitudinal offshoots. The medial one of the latter—the sulcus coronalis of the horse brain—was not yet a constant feature in the *Mesohippus* brain but was developed in some individuals.

In some *Mesohippus* brains the sulcus coronalis gained contact with the presylvian sulcus; occasionally, the endolateral or the ectolateral ended anteriorly in the lateral sulcus, or the ectolateral in the suprasylvian sulcus. Otherwise sulci hardly ever connected. Not only were the few branchlets which one or the other sulcus occasionally developed too short to cross the surface of a gyrus, but some of the sulci themselves did not extend as far over the surface as they did in later forms. The diagonal sulcus apparently did not reach the dorsal surface. The lateral sulcus is in living ungulates ("without exception"—Kappers, Huber, and Crosby, 1936, p. 1531) associated with the ansate; in *Mesohippus*, the lateral ends well behind the cruciate sulcus.

The one *Miohippus* brain at hand shows very little progress in fissuration over the *Mesohippus* stage. A tiny sulcus intraorbitalis appeared, and there was some undulation in the course or certain long sulci. The neocortex of living ungulates of *Miohippus* size has a larger surface not only in that it extends farther down on the lateral brain surface than it did in *Miohippus*, but also in that the fissuration is more complicated.

In the *Parahippus* stage, the full set of the sulci of *Equus* was developed. In our material only one cerebral hemisphere, of a young individual, yields satisfactory evidence of the fissuration; but in this specimen there is ample evidence of great progress in fissuration over *Miohippus*. The lateral, as a deep sulcus, still ended posteriorly to the cruciate, but a very shallow anterior continuation seems to have almost joined the latter sulcus. The diagonal sulcus was continued unto the dorsal brain surface. The intra-orbital joined the presylvian sulcus. Branches of lateral and ectolateral united to connect the two sulci across the intermediate gyrus.

Our endocasts of *Merychippus* contemporary with *Parahippus* do not show any progress. In our material, the earliest modern neocortex of the horse series is found in the Upper Miocene *Merychippus*.

That character of the Upper Miocene *Merychippus* endocasts (in particular the natural endocast IV) which so distinguishes the *Merychippus* brain from those of its ancestors that the epithet "modern" is called for is the subdivision of the neocortex surface by a network of sulci. For example, in this stage the sulcus lateralis joins the sulcus cruciatus; a pre-existing anterior longitudinal branch of the cruciate now continues the lateralis line forward to the ansate sulcus; here the line is taken over by the coronal sulcus, and the coronal is continuous with the presylvian sulcus in both our Upper Miocene specimens. The surface appears divided into numerous areas delimited by more or less transverse or vertical branches of longitudinal sulci, more or less longitudinal branches of transverse sulci, and connections of oblique sulci.

The network pattern.—The further evolution of fissuration consists (1) in the expansion of these more or less circumscribed areas, corresponding to the size increase of the cerebrum, and, (2) in their being subdivided by more projections from the main sulci, and the development of accessory sulci—that is, a greater infolding of the "two-dimensional" cell layers covering the white matter which expands in three-dimensional fashion. The condition produced by the latter process is recognized generally as one which distinguishes the brains of large mammals from those of smaller congeners. In the phylogeny of the Equidae one sees this process occurring parallel to the evolution of greater body size.

In the course of this process one ostensibly new sulcus appears on the brain surface. This is the sulcus orbitalis of Elliot Smith's description of the horse brain (1902, p. 313). It crosses the median part of the anterior facies of the frontal lobe, baso-anteriorly from, and parallel to, the transverse leg of the presylvian sulcus (*see* pl. 4, fig. 2). This sulcus of the anterior facies of the hemisphere is a continuation either of a sulcus branch or of an independent sulcus (fig. 21 B) of the medial cortical wall. As is the case with the other two sulci which were not yet developed in *Mesohippus*, the classical descriptions of the horse brain do not name the sulcus in the anterior convexity; however, it is mentioned both by Ellenberger (1892, p. 286) and by Flatau and Jacobsohn (1899, p. 413), as a branch of the sulcus splenialis which crosses from the medial to the frontal pallium surface.

The splenial sulcus was or course developed in *Mesohippus*, but no anterior branch crossed the borders of the medial brain facies. The low anterior facies of the *Mesohippus* frontal lobe was divided into two gyri only, by the transverse leg of the presylvian sulcus. Unfortunately, details of the anterior slope of the hemispheres are not well represented in any of our specimens between *Miohippus* and *Equus;* thus we do not know at which stage the branch in question crossed the anterior edge of the medial brain wall and became the orbital sulcus. As the frontal slope is low in our two *Parahippus* brains, it seems improbable to me that this sulcus had appeared in *Parahippus*. I rather believe that its first appearance on the outer brain surface was in the *Merychippus* stage.

The extension of this sulcus, originally confined to the medial brain surface, to form another transverse division on the frontal lobe, appears to be correlated with the increasing height of the anterior facies of the frontal lobe.

In those *Mesohippus* endocasts in which this region is well preserved, the transverse gyrus which adjoins the olfactory bulbs and is posteriorly delimited by the presylvian sulcus has diameters of 6 mm. (specimens I and VII) and 7 mm. (specimen VI). In the pony endocast, whose olfactory bulbs are closely appressed to the cerebrum, the gyrus in the corresponding place also has a diameter of 7 mm.; its upper limit, however, is the orbital sulcus. Above this transverse gyrus follows the oblique gyrus limited by the presylvian sulcus; its diameter ranges between 7 and 10 mm. In the large *Equus* endocasts the position of the olfactory bulbs is somewhat detached so that more of the frontal facies of the cerebrum is visible than in the pony. Two transverse gyri are seen in *E. occidentalis* and in *E. caballus* II, like two tiers placed one above the other. The lower tiers are 16 mm. high, and the upper tier has a diameter varying around 16 mm. These broad gyri, however, are not smooth but are sculptured by various grooves. The details of the fissuration represented by this indistinct endocast sculpture were studied in the *Equus caballus* II brain. In this warped specimen the diameter of each tier is 19 mm. They are subdivided by various more or less short sulci so that each consists of three distinct subgyri of 6 or 7 mm. diameter. Thus the surface of the frontal area between the presylvian sulcus and the insertion of the olfactory bulb, which was one smooth gyrus in *Mesohippus*, is subdivided in the horse into subgyri whose diameter is generally the same as that of the one gyrus in *Mesohippus*.

These seemingly insignificant details of frontal lobe fissuration would not be reported had not a similar phenomenon been observed in the other regions of the neopallium. A survey of the well-moulded specimens in our material suggests that there was a tendency, from *Mesohippus* to *Equus*, to maintain a constant typical diameter of the surface ridges. Table 8 shows the general similarity of gyrus breadth in small and large Equidae. For example, the gyrus between the lateral and ectolateral sulci is about 5 mm. broad in *Mesohippus* (except No. I, in which it is slightly narrower). The average distance between the lateral and ectolateral sulci is 10 mm. in the young *Pliohippus* I, but the gyrus is mostly divided, by the sulcus interlateralis dorsalis, into two areas of 5 mm. breadth. **Wherever in the *Equus* brain, with the expansion of the meshes in the net of sulci, diameters twice as large as those of *Mesohippus* gyri are reached, an accessory or branch sulcus subdivides the area.**

TABLE 8.—*Diameters of gyri of good endocranial casts and of the* Equus caballus *II brain*

The extremes (column I) are uncommon; the majority of sulci have distances from each other typical for each brain (column II).

	I	II
Meso. I–V	4–8	5–6
Meso. VI	4–8	6
Para. II (young)	5–9	7
Mery. IV	7–11	8–9
Plio. I (young)	5–9	7
Neohipp.	5–11	8
Hipp. III	5–11	6–7
Pony	5–11	6–7
Eq. niobr.	5–11	7–8
Eq. occid.	7–13	7–8
Eq. cab. brain	5–12	7–8

The areas of similar breadth are not completely separated by the sulci in *Mesohippus*, and several are much longer than broad. They appear practically circumscribed in the *Merychippus* IV endocast. The secondary sulci in *Equus* create surface sections with the typical diameters, but these sections again are continuous with each other to a great extent.

It is not for the paleoneurologist to comment upon the trend to establish similar surface ridges in all these Equidae. We are ignorant, *e.g.*, of modifications of nerve fibers radiating into the expanding, and subdividing surface areas. Our observations on endocranial casts may or may not have a neurological significance. As far as observable, the phenomenon rather pertains to the physical side of morphology. It bears out in a surprisingly exact manner the idea of Baillarger's law, viz., that folding into sulci compensates between the expansion, as the square, of the gray matter area, and the expansion of the white matter as the cube. With the restricted knowledge we have of brain evolution, the pallium expansion down the lateral convexity appears to be a significant advance in the evolution of the brain structure, whereas the increasing fissuration probably can be ascribed merely to the retention in large brains of the balance in volume between gray and white matter.

"PRONATION"

Findings in living mammals.—Besides greater complication, another general difference is reported to exist between the sulci of small and large brains, and between primitive and highly developed brains. Certain sulci shift mediad in the transition.

Krueg first (1878, p. 317, p. 340), and later other authors have asserted that dorso-medial sulci and cytoarchitectonic areas shift mediad in the evolution from small to large brains. When the cortex expands, it "spills" (Krueg) from the dorsal surface down the median brain wall.

Krueg's particular observations concerned ungulates (1878) and subungulates (1880). He remarked that in small artiodactyls such as *Moschus* and *Tragulus*, and in *Hyrax*, the splenial sulcus is so high on the medial forebrain wall as to be visible in dorsal views, whereas it is in lower regions of the median surface in roe and deer, giraffe, camel, horse (*see* our fig. 21 B), and elephant. Krueg called this (supposed) inward rotation of sulci of the medio-dorsal area "Pronation der Hemisphäre." In his general remarks on the phenomenon (1878, p. 340) he regards it as universally occurring "mit dem Grösserwerden des Gehirns"; he believed that pallia expand in all directions from a fixed point, probably from the insula. Krueg found later that pronation does not occur in carnivores (1880, p. 650, 666–667).

The occurrence of pronation in ungulates was so generally accepted that Garrod (1885, p. 16), comparing the brain of a hippopotamus with those of a camel and a giraffe, noted as an exception "the much less pronation" in the larger hippopotamus brain. According to Haller (1934, p. 226–227), the forces which drive the splenial sulcus from the dorsal surface in small ungulates to the medial cortical wall in large ungulates are: (1) elaboration of the Sylvian system whose apex advances mediad toward the dorso-medial rim of the pallium, (2) enlargement of the posterior areas of the marginal (= lateralis) system.

As "supination" Krueg described "dass bei den Gehirnen kleiner Tiere die Furchen der Median-seite mehr auf die Oberseite hinaufrücken" (1878, p. 317). It is necessary in passing to mention this term and what it implies—viz., the possibility of the evolution of small brains from large brains —because this implication appears to be taken for an established evolutionary fact. Thus Kappers, Huber, and Crosby, when demonstrating the intimate connection between the topography of the sulci and of the cytoarchitectonic areas, speak of "the marked shifting of the sulcus splenialis to the dorso-lateral side of the brain" in *Tragulus* (1936, p. 1637); "the way in which supination of the sulcus splenialis is effected" is through a relative increase of the visuo-sensory area on the convexity of the brain in the smaller animals of an order. Possibly "supination" occurs in those relatively rare cases of evolution when dwarf forms develop from large mammals, but this remains to be demonstrated. *Tragulus* is a more primitive artiodactyl than *Cervus*. A difference between *Cervus* and *Tragulus* does not prove that the pallium can roll outward in brain evolution.

Brodmann's (1906) study of the area striata seemingly enlarged the scope of pronation as a phenomenon of mammalian brain evolution. His statements do not refer to similar brains of different size, but to the brains of mammals which he supposes to be ascending steps of the evolutionary ladder. The area striata is the visuo-sensory region which in mammals generally caps the occipital pole of the cerebral hemisphere. The limits of this area, and the share of the whole neocortex it occupies, are not only different in the different orders, but they vary within such small groups as human races. In the Ungulata the medial border of the area is the sulcus splenialis; the lateral border is, in *Equus*, the sulcus interlateralis dorsalis. Thus the area striata constitutes a major part of the region in which Krueg observed the inward shift of the pallium.

Brodmann investigated the extent of this area on the medial and dorsal brain surfaces, respectively. He observed that, in general, the lower a group stands in the mammalian system, the smaller is the medial surface area and the larger the lateral. His conclusion was that the area striata "in der Säugereihe aufsteigend sich von der lateralen Fläche mehr und mehr auf die mediale Fläche zurückzieht" (1906, p. 394). The stages quoted by Brodmann as attesting this evolutionary trend are, however, *Macropus, Spermophilus*, and *Tragulus* → Carnivora → Prosimia → apes → European man. I hope that the wording of Brodmann's explanation of the shift of the area excuses quoting this, too, literally: "Dass die Area im allgemeinen mehr dorsalwärts rückt, je weiter man in der Mammalierreihe absteigt . . . hängt offenbar mit dem zunehmenden Grössenwachstum des Rhinencephalon . . . zusammen" (1906, p. 394).

We need not point out that Brodmann's arrangement of his data does not convincingly prove the occurrence of a mediad shift of the area striata in general mammalian brain evolution. On the other hand, it is of importance for the testing of "pronation" to review the actual findings of Brodmann and of Alouf's (1929) study of the area striata, for they do show that in certain primitive brains the area is dorsal and that in the highest developed brain, that of a European man, the area is medial with only a small extension onto the convexity of the hemispheres.

The conditions shown in Brodmann's figures and those of Alouf (marked "A" below) are, arranged in convenient groups, the following:

The area striata is entirely dorsal, not reaching the medial edge of the hemisphere, in *Mus* (A), *Sciurus* (A), and *Lepus* (A); mostly dorsal, with a small medial field, in *Erinaceus* (A) and *Tragulus*. About one third is on the medial surface in *Macropus, Vespertilio* (A), *Semnopithecus*, and *Cercopithecus;* the medial field is slightly smaller than the dorsal field in *Spermophilus* and *Sus*. Dorsal (or lateral) and medial portions are approximately equal in *Equus* (A), *Capra, Cercoleptes, Lagothrix*, and *Simia*. The medial field is slightly larger than the outside field in *Mustela, Felis domestica Nycticebus, Lemur catta* (A), and *Hapale;* the medial field constitutes two thirds of the area in *Pteropus, Canis* (A), *Lemur macaco*, and a Javanese man. The area striata is almost entirely an area of the medial brain wall in the brain of the European man studied by Brodmann.

Findings in the Equidae.—Sulci and cell areas have changed in relative size and position in the course of equid evolution. Shifts of the fissura prima and the lobus anterior cerebelli, the rhinal fissure, and the motor association area have been observed, or strongly suggested by form changes. In each of these cases the change appeared as the consequence of an evolutionary trend of a certain brain region— trends long known to exist in mammals in general. No similar cause has been advanced which explains the shifting of the medial areas of the cerebral convexity.

Such a shift did occur in the evolution of the horse brain, but not in the mode postulated on the basis of observations in living mammals. In the Equidae, the shift did not take place during all the periods of increasing brain size. No shift is observed in the evolution from the primitive to a more highly developed cerebrum; it became manifest only in late stages of equid evolution.

One can reasonably assume that the area striata was involved in this process. A change in position or extent of this area cannot, however, be accurately traced in endocast material; one obstacle is that this does not contain the medial cerebral wall.

Although the medial wall of the cerebrum and its splenial sulcus cannot be directly studied in any of the stages preceding *Equus*, our material indirectly reveals certain changes in their general topography. These will be discussed below. Direct tests of the pronation phenomenon are possible in three regions of the dorsal cerebral convexity. In the middle region of the hemispheres, the pars media sulci suprasylvii is well discernible in practically all our endocranial casts; the same is true, posteriorly, of the lateralis system, and anteriorly of the corono-ansate sulcus.

If with the size increase of the cerebrum in ungulates homologous parts generally (Krueg, 1878, p. 340), and the apices of the Sylvian system in particular (Haller,

Table 9.—*Inter–suprasylvian and cerebral breadth*

I: The shortest transverse distance between the suprasylvian sulci (pars media).
II: The ratio of I (= 1) to the breadth of the neocortex measured across the same transverse plane as the closest approach of the suprasylvian sulci. This neocortex breadth is identical with cerebral breadth in this region except in *Eohippus* in which the rhinencephalon projects laterally below the neocortex, and the ratio of I to the cerebral breadth is 1 : 1.66.
III: The ratio of I to the greatest cerebral (temporal lobe) breadth.

	. I	II	III
Eo.	12	1.50	1.92
Meso. I	33	1.24	1.42
II	34	1.24	1.41
III	35	1.17	1.40
IV	34	1.41	1.44
V	33	1.42	1.58
VI	36	1.42	1.47
Mio.	35	1.54	1.83
Para. II	(38)	1.42	1.58
Mer. III	42	1.71	1.83
Plio. I	43	1.21	1.86
II	35	1.31	2.46
Neoh.	35	1.97	1.97
Hipp. III	49	1.31	1.86
Pony	64	1.44	1.52
Eq. cab. I	66	1.56	1.59
II	66	1.61	1.69
Eq. occ.	73	1.57	1.75

1934), moved toward the dorso-median rim, the dorsal area between the two suprasylvian sulci should have gradually decreased in relative breadth in the evolution of the Equidae.

Column I of table 9 shows the absolute increase of the narrowest distance between the partes mediae of the suprasylvian sulci. From *Eohippus validus* to *Equus occidentalis*, this inter-suprasylvian pallium region has enlarged to sixfold its former breadth. From *Mesohippus* to *Equus caballus*, it has about doubled; averages compare as 1:1.94, while greatest cerebral breadths compare as 1:2.17.

Concerning relative breadth of the region in question, two general facts which were frequently encountered in the present study once again show up in columns II and III of table 9. The first is the conspicuous difference between the brains of *Eohippus* and *Mesohippus;* the second, that variability is an innate character of fissuration. This variability is apparent even in the case of a sulcus as important as the suprasylvian, and even in a brain as simply fissured as that of *Mesohippus*. Variations encountered in so small a number as six *Mesohippus* brains include, on the one hand, an intersylvian area relatively broader than in any of the other brains, and, on the other hand, ratios occurring in *Equus* (pony). In view of this variability it is obvious that conditions in single specimens (unfortunately, the usual material of comparative brain anatomists) have no general significance.   With single specimens from our series one could show that the proportions of inter-suprasylvian breadth to the two cerebral breadths never changed in the Equidae.   Perhaps the average of the ratios found in our six *Mesohippus* and four *Equus*, respectively, are valid data.   These averages indicate some slight narrowing of the space between the two Sylvian systems.   The averages of ratio II are 1.32 in *Mesohippus* and 1.54 in *Equus;* those of ratio III are 1.45 and 1.64, respectively.   However, relatively narrower inter-suprasylvian areas than in *Equus* have occurred ever since the *Miohippus* stage and existed in *Eohippus*.   Thus the measurements of the material at hand fail to show the postulated trend of the Sylvian system to expand mediad and to narrow the medio-dorsal field above this system.   The relative position of the pars media sulci suprasylvii appears to have been essentially stable in the evolution of large brains from small brains in the phylogeny of the Equidae.

The position of this sulcus in the architecture of the brain surface shows an interesting detail.   In the Eocene specimens, the pars media is the only existing part of the suprasylvian sulcus.   Its course is along the summit of the rounded vault of the *Eohippus* cerebrum.   It is so far dorsal in our *Orohippus* fragment that the area between the right and left sulci must have been very narrow.   The reverse of pronation occurred in the evolution to the *Mesohippus* stage ("supination" with increase of brain size!).   While the area lateral to the pars media sulci suprasylvii had greatly expanded, so had the area medial to it; the sulcus is in a lateral position on the dorsal side of the boxlike cerebrum of *Mesohippus*.   With considerable variations mediad and laterad, this position is maintained up to *Equus*.

The pars posterior sulci suprasylvii does show a change in position.   It is on the lateral cerebral convexity, at the upper border, in *Mesohippus, Miohippus,* and *Parahippus*.   It is on the dorsal surface, near the lateral border, from *Merychippus* onward.   These statements are, of course, vague descriptions, as there really is no such thing as a border between lateral and dorsal aspects of the cerebral convexity; the difference thus defined indeed is very slight.   One can say that the posterad course of the pars posterior sulci suprasylvii was slightly more downward in the earlier than in the later equid brains.   Consequently, one sulcus has become more medial in the course of evolution.   However, this occurred laterally in that posterior brain region in which mediad shift of the medial sulci was supposed to be caused not only by pronation of the whole hemisphere, but by expansion of the lateralis region—viz., of an area medial to the sulcus which did shift mediad.   Again, therefore, the evolutionary story of the Equidae is not in accord with the postulates of neoneurology.

In the area of the lateralis system only the sulcus lateralis existed in our *Eohippus*, and it appears to have been well developed only on one of the two hemispheres. It is on the median slope of the cerebral vault.   This sulcus is found in a more lateral position in *Mesohippus* ("supination"!).   In this and later stages, the posterior medio-dorsal area of the hemispheres is practically flat.   The course of the lateral sulcus, from *Mesohippus* to *Equus*, generally marks the transition from the horizontal portion to the gentle slope which continues into the lateral brain surface.

While remaining in this architecturally similar position, the lateral sulci have not moved away from each other as much as did the lateral outlines of the hemispheres. I have measured the distance between the two lateral sulci in the adult brains in a transverse plane which seemed, to the eye, to correspond in the various specimens; it is distant about one-fifth of the cerebrum length from the posterior pole, in a region where the laterals usually form straight longitudinal lines and are closest to each other. This inter-lateral distance is ±24 mm. in *Mesohippus*, 30 mm. in *Miohippus*, 20 mm. in *Merychippus* II, and 30 mm. in *Pliohippus* II, *Equus occidentalis*, and the *Equus caballus* II brain. It is true that the laterals diverge posterior to the region in which the above distances were taken, and that shortest inter-lateral distances somewhat greater than 30 mm. apparently occur in other *Equus* brains; nevertheless our data show that, in contrast to pre-Oligocene and Oligocene times, this medio-dorsal, posterior forebrain area has not broadened in correspondence with the cerebral breadth increase during later times. Consequently, this area has become relatively narrower. This phenomenon becomes really striking in the *Pliohippus-Equus* step of evolution. The lateral sulci are in the *Pliohippus* II specimen at the same distance from each other as they are in the much larger *Equus* specimens.

In the area between the two lateral sulci measurable data for exact comparisons are even fewer in our material than in the case of the laterals themselves; the median region is blurred in many endocasts, particularly of the later stages. However, the data we have suffice to show that a median shift of the endolateral sulcus did take place. As the endolateral was not developed in *Eohippus*, *Mesohippus* is the oldest stage in which its formation could be studied. The breadth of the gyrus medial to the endolateral sulcus varies in *Mesohippus*, but it is generally broader than the gyrus between the endolateral and lateral sulci. The two gyri seem to be of equal breadth in *Merychippus* II, and the *Mesohippus* condition is reversed in later stages. The distance between the two endolaterals varies between 13 and 17 mm. in *Mesohippus*. It is 18 mm. in *Miohippus* and 20 mm. in the small, Middle Miocene *Merychippus* II. In *Pliohippus* II, the left endolateral is about 10 mm. from the midline, the right one is about 7 mm. from the midline. (A sulcus fragment on each of the *Hipparion* III hemispheres is possibly a remnant of the endolateral sulcus. These furrows are both 10 mm. from the midline of the cerebrum.) Thus it appears that the dorsal field between the two endolateral sulci had not gained in breadth during the great enlargement of the brain from the largest *Mesohippus* to *Pliohippus*. After the *Pliohippus* stage this field became absolutely narrower. The distance between the two endolaterals is 10 mm. in the *Equus caballus* II brain. In *Equus*, the endolateral has come to deserve its two other names, sulcus endomarginalis and sulcus confinis. Here, then, in the latest stage of the evolution of the horse brain, an originally median gyrus of the dorsal convexity has become a dorsal gyrus of the median brain wall (fig. 21 B).

A corresponding mediad shift appears to have occurred in anterior cerebral regions. The sulcus whose course reveals these changes is the ansate between its emergence from the medial brain wall and its juncture with the coronate sulcus. In *Mesohippus* this is a generally transverse furrow about 6 mm. long; it thus crosses up to one-third of the breadth of the hemisphere. This sulcus is 9 mm. long in the young *Miohippus* and *Parahippus* II brains. But it is not longer than that in the

Middle Miocene *Merychippus* I, and it has become an oblique sulcus; the corono-ansate junctures are more anterior than the junctures of the ansate sulci with the median longitudinal fissure, and they are about 15 mm. apart.   Each ansate seems to have been only 8 mm. long in both our Upper Miocene *Merychippus* brains.   It is not measurable in the later stages, and not reproduced at all in *Equus* endocranial casts.   In *Equus* brains the sulcus between the fissura magna and the root of the coronalis is so short, relatively, that it is not even given a name of its own in horse-brain descriptions.   It is no more than the dorsal prolongation of a mainly median sulcus, visible on the outside in an oblique length of 9 or 10 mm.   What we described as a dorsal sulcus running laterad from the fissura magna in *Mesohippus* etc.—the ansate—is described in the large brains of the living perissodactyls ("Bügel a" of ass, horse and rhinoceros; Krueg, 1878, p. 328) as a sulcus running upward and forward on the medial brain side, ending on the dorsal surface at the coronal sulcus.

Discussion.—We may summarize the data concerning "pronation" as follows: Pallial areas which are medio-dorsal in very small ungulates are in the medial wall of the cerebral hemispheres in large ungulates.   The area striata is a dorsal field in small rodents and in the hedgehog, and it is an almost entirely medial field in man. These conditions in the brains of living mammals gave rise to the thesis that in the evolution from small to large, and from primitive to higher-organized brains, the sulci and areas of the dorsal convexity are shifted toward and onto the medial wall.

The facts of brain evolution in the Equidae have disproved the validity of this generalization.

In the early phases of the evolution of the horse brain there was, on the contrary, a laterad expansion of medio-dorsal areas.   The relative breadth of the middle region of the dorsal convexity remained practically the same from *Eohippus* to *Equus*. On the other hand, our phyletic series of equid brains has shown that after the Oligocene anterior and posterior medio-dorsal areas do not expand transversely as much as the whole cerebrum; consequently the expansion of these areas must have been in part down the medial brain wall.   The longitudinal lateral sulcus is relatively, and the endolateral even absolutely, nearest to the medial edge of the hemispheres in the latest stage of horse evolution, and the transverse ansate sulcus is relatively shortest in this phase.   These signs of a mediad shift of dorsal regions became particularly manifest during the Pliocene—that is, in the stage in which brain evolution consisted mainly in increase of size and height of the cerebral hemispheres.

Consequently, the signs of the so-called "pronation of the hemispheres" can occur in, but are not generally features of, mammalian brain evolution.

As one follows, in the Equidae, the evolutionary development of a low and primitive cerebrum into a large, high type of structure, it becomes apparent that it is unnecessary to appeal to any special phenomena (such as pronation, or expansion differences between different pallial regions) to account for the changes in the position of the medio-dorsal areas.

The proponents of the pronation theory have not given attention to two facts which, in my opinion, sufficiently account for the disappearance from the dorsal brain surface of medial areas when brains become larger and, in particular, higher: (1) The primitive (reptilian) neocortex is a latero-dorsal band between paleocortex

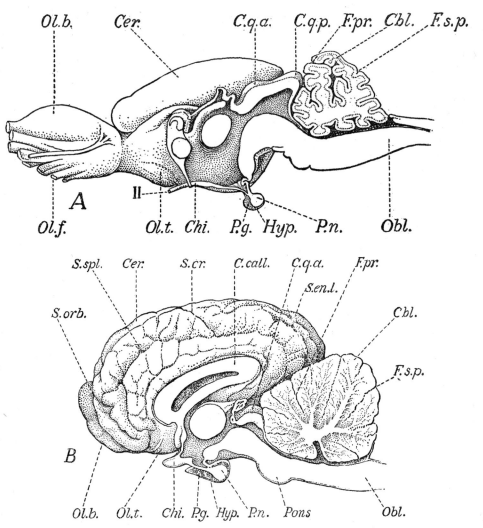

FIGURE 21.—*Medial side of right half of brain of Didelphis and Equus*

(A) *Didelphis virginiana* Kerr, living marsupial with a brain form similar to that of *Eohippus*. (After Loo.) × 2.7.
(B) *Equus caballus* L. (After Sisson.) About × ⁴⁄₅.

and archicortex. In mammalian evolution, the neocortex expands from this region over the whole dorsal convexity, laterad and mediad, pressing the paleocortex basad in one direction, the archicortex in the other direction. (2) The medial "edge" of the dorsal surface is a conspicuous line for the eye but has no significance whatever in the structure of the cerebrum. The share of the medial wall neocortex in the whole neocortex must be greater in highly developed high brains than in more primitive and lower brains.

In our series of endocasts the expansion of the neocortex is seen only in its progress down the lateral part of the hemisphere wall. Incidentally, the outward direction of this expansion shows that the thesis of inward rotation of the cortex in ungulate evolution can certainly not be applied to the whole area mediad from the insula.

The medial part of the hemisphere can, in our material, be directly examined only in the brain of the modern horse. It contains a large portion of the neocortex (fig. 21 B). Neocortex covers the entire height of the medial facies anteriorly and posteriorly. In our *Equus caballus* II brain the medial neocortex is 52 mm. high at the anterior end of the corpus callosum; this is four-fifths of the entire height of the brain in that region. The lowest region of the medial neocortex is that above the corpus callosum; we may recall here that it is the middle region of the cerebrum in which the dorsal convexity shows no distinct signs of mediad shifting in horse brain evolution. Above the posterior curve of the corpus callosum, medial neocortex height is 32 mm. in our horse brain—that is, not quite half the total height of the hemisphere in this transverse plane (70 mm.).

This region is from 36 to 43 mm. high in *Mesohippus*. On the lateral brain wall, only half of this height was occupied by neocortex, whereas in *Equus* almost the entire lateral wall is neocortex. On the medial wall, too, neocortex is more extensive in a highly developed than in a primitive brain (*compare*, for example, figures A and B in fig. 21); the archicortex (Ammon's horn) is more compressed, more coiled. Perhaps one may assume that neocortex formed a relatively smaller part of the medial, as of the lateral, brain surface in *Mesohippus* than it does in *Equus*. Certainly medial cortex is a larger part of the whole cortex in the high brain of *Equus* than it was in the lower ancestral brains.

If one could draw the neocortex of fossil and living Equidae, not in the customary way which shows lateral, dorsal, and median areas separately, but spread out in one plane, one would, I expect, see the following situation. The middle region of these maps might correspond, topographically, to the reptilian neopallium. Expansion would be great laterally, but corresponding, if less, medially. The line representing the dorso-medial edge of the hemisphere would be in different positions in the different maps. It would gradually become more distant from the medial border in the post-Oligocene maps—that is, after the equid type of cerebrum form had been generally established in *Mesohippus*. In particular, the edge would show a perceptible (relative) shift toward the middle of the map when, in the latest phases of the evolution of the horse brain, the cerebrum gained more in height than in breadth. A relatively larger region than in the maps of ancestral brains would be medial wall area in the neocortex map of *Equus*.

The "spilling," in this phase of cerebral height increase, of originally medio-dorsal pallium areas and sulci over the medial rim of the dorsal convexity is only a dorsally visible sign of the presence of a relatively more extensive medial facies.

In these imaginary maps the relative positions of the chief sulci would possibly be found basically the same from *Mesohippus* to *Equus;* on the other hand it is possible that more cytoarchitectonic areas than the frontal lobe cortex changed in relative size, and that sulci shifted correspondingly.

To summarize our findings in the Equidae: "Pronation" does not occur in the evolution of this family. The signs on which this theory is based are absent in the Eocene-Oligocene stages in which, on the contrary, expansion of the dorso-median area of the cerebrum took place on the dorsal side. In later stages, dorso-median areas do become median areas. This is not, however, an inward rolling of the hemisphere but is the consequence of the expansion of the whole neocortex which involves the medial wall of the hemispheres.

Our deduction from the conditions in the Equidae presumably explains why in the tiny brains of very small living artiodactyls the dorsal edge of the low medial wall contains a sulcus which in large artiodactyls runs in the spacious medial wall. This difference is not necessarily the sign of an evolutionary process; *e.g.*, it is not necessarily related to special changes of any particular cell area in the ungulate brain.

It is beyond the scope of this paper to speculate on the differences between the brains of the other living mammals which according to Brodmann testify to a mediad pallial shift in mammalian evolution. The more medial position of the area striata in man than in apes suggests that in this case the greater height of the human brain may be a factor. However, another factor determining the position of the visuo-sensory area is the relative size of this field on the one hand, and of the adjoining areas on the other. The relative proportions of these areas are, naturally, very variable in different mammals.

RHINENCEPHALON

CONCEPTIONS OF RHINENCEPHALON SIZE AND EVOLUTION

Before reporting on the changes of the olfactory surfaces in our series of endocranial casts, it may be well to consider critically the current conception of rhinencephalon size, in particular of its evolutionary significance.

Turner proposed to arrange the Mammalia in three groups as macrosmatic, microsmatic, and anosmatic according to "the development of the olfactory apparatus," "the organs of smell" (1890–1891, p. 106). Although contained in a paper on brain anatomy, this, the original definition of the grades of "osmatism," included—as I understand it—the olfactory organ as well. It had no evolutionary implications. Among Turner's examples of macrosmatic (living) mammals, the Ungulata are named in the first place.

Whereas comparative physiology (*e.g.*, v. Frisch, 1926, p. 209) classifies the horses, along with mice, etc., as macrosmatic, it seems to me that comparative neurologists have formed a different conception of macrosmatism. It is, tacitly, in its relation to the adjacent neëncephalon that the mammalian rhinencephalon, and in particulr the bulbi, are currently described as large or small; it is from this viewpoint that brains, and genera or groups, are termed macrosmatic or microsmatic. Haller's (1934, p. 178) definition may be quoted as typical for such apparently absolute statements: "Bulbus und Lobus sind bei den Säugern ganz verschieden entwickelt, man unterscheidet daher makroosmatische und mikroosmatische." Ungulates are, according to Haller, intermediate forms. The macrosmatic mammals are the small ones which live with their noses near the ground, "also Edentaten, Marsupialier, Nagetiere, Musteliden" (p. 178).

The series of Equidae discussed in this paper is one example showing that Haller's criteria for macrosmatism, body size plus mode of living, cannot be generally accepted. If macrosmatism were a matter of muzzle-ground relations, it should have increased from the small *Eohippus* to the tall *Equus*. Certainly the muzzle of a standing *Eohippus* was considerably nearer the ground than is that of *Equus;* but it is obvious that in the taller Equidae there had to be not less contact with the food-giving soil, but increasingly more than in little *Eohippus*. *Eohippus*, living in wooded areas, may have partly fed on leaves; its descendants are grazing, and need more food just because they are bigger. Yet the brain of *Equus* is not more macrosmatic than was that of *Eohippus*. Haller's specific ecological theory of macrosmatism breaks down in the case of the Equidae. Actually, his examples of mammals with macrosmatic brains are groups with low cerebral hemispheres.

This method of judging the degree of development of olfactory bulbs and lobes by their relative size—*i.e.*, as they are seen against the neëncephalon in living mammals—has given the macrosmatism/microsmatism distinction an evolutionary tinge. For example, Kappers, Huber, and Crosby write that the olfactory bulbs are large in many *lower* mammals; among these, however, they quote the ungulates (1936, p. 1402).

Olfactory bulbs of relatively very large size, attached to high cerebral hemispheres, exist in living mammals only in special cases: animals with trunks—tapir and elephant. This may be a retention of primitive conditions, or it may be a specialization, as is the trunk itself; the evolution of these particular brains is not yet known. The only specialization of mammalian olfactory bulbs known as an evolutionary process is reduction; its results are the microsmatism of the higher primates and the Mystacoceti, and the anosmatism of the Odontoceti.

This special trend is probably one of the facts which suggested that reduction is the only possible evolutionary trend in the rhinencephalon; another fact is that the non-olfactory parts of the forebrain are the higher developed the higher a group is classified between reptile and man. There seems to be almost universal acceptance of the anthropocentric conception that large olfactory centers in a mammalian brain are the mark of a low evolutionary status. The concentrated precipitation of this idea is found in text books. "While still prominent in primitive edentates, the archipallial olfactory part of the brain becomes reduced among the higher mammals, until in man it is very small" (Walter, 1939, p. 719; in Walter's terminology the archipallium is the whole "original olfactory part of the pallium"—p. 706—that is, palaeopallium + archipallium). In their summary of the characters and trends which distinguish mammalian brains from those of the other vertebrates, Neal and Rand state: "The olfactory lobe degenerates" (1936, p. 495).

It is not for the paleoneurologist to discuss physiology, but we may ask, incidentally, whether there exists any group of animals in which the olfactory sense is as keen as it is in the majority of mammals?

On the other hand, the task devolves upon paleoneurology to trace, as exactly as possible, rhinencephalon evolution in mammalian phylogenies.

CEREBRAL OLFACTORY REGIONS

The investigation of the archicortex, relay station of secondary and tertiary olfactory fibers, is impossible in fossil brains. The mammalian archicortex is the hippocampus, a formation in the medial wall of the cerebrum. Comparisons of primitive and highly developed brains of living mammals have shown that with the development of the neopallial regions the hippocampal cell layers expand by coiling up, and are pushed backward, downward, and outward. It can be reasonably assumed that this process took place in the phyletic series of Equidae; but no replica of the hippocampus is present in their endocranial casts.

The majority of the fibers of the olfactory bulb cells end in the paleopallium, the piriform lobe cortex. The study of this secondary olfactory center suffers only a slight handicap by the nature of our material. The paleocortex is chiefly on the external surface of the brain; but it also extends up the medial side of the hemispheres. Endocasts thus exhibit its major part but do not reveal how great a portion this was of the whole paleocortex of a fossil mammal.

It has been shown in preceding chapters that the prepiriform olfactory areas and the piriform lobe with the paleopallium constituted the basal half of the cerebral hemispheres in the Eocene and Oligocene Equidae, and that their share of the cerebral surface becomes gradually restricted topographically until today they form only a part of the lower surface of the equid cerebrum.

While thus decreasing relatively, the olfactory surface of the cerebrum became absolutely much larger. The posterior extremity of the piriform lobe is 30 mm. from the anterior end of the rhinal fissure in *Eohippus*, 83 mm. in *Equus caballus* I, 89 mm. in *Equus caballus* II and *Equus occidentalis*. The maximum breadth across the olfactory regions of the cerebral hemispheres is 23 mm. in the *Eohippus* specimen and 90 mm. in the *Equus* endocasts. The piriform lobe is not completely revealed in *Eohippus*. In *Mesohippus* V the length of the piriform lobe is 32 mm., and its breadth is 15 mm. The corresponding measurements on the external surface of the *Equus caballus* II brain are only 52 and 27 mm., respectively. Cerebral lengths and breadths of these two specimens compare as 1:2; but the ratios of piriform lengths and breadths are 1:1.6 and 1:1.8, respectively.

These figures illustrate what had already been obvious in visual comparison—viz., that the paleopallium gradually became a lesser portion of the cerebral surface in the Equidae. That decrease in relative size occurred which is considered characteristic of the "passing from lower to higher mammals" (*e.g.*, Kappers, Huber, and Crosby, 1936, p. 1423).

In the Equidae, this "reduction" of the paleopallium surely cannot be regarded as "degeneration," even if only the external surface is taken into account. However, the gradual restriction of the piriform lobe to the lower regions of the cerebral surface does not tell the whole story. The paleopallium expanded more than is revealed by the two surface diameters of the piriform lobe. Folds have developed in the lower lip of the rhinal fissure from *Merychippus* onward, and the olfactory cortex profited, expanding on the medial brain wall, from the increase in cerebral height.

The piriform lobe cortex is not only related to the olfactory system, but its size "is influenced also by the number of somatic impulses which come forward to interrelate with those of the olfactory center" (Kappers, Huber, and Crosby, 1936, p. 1423). The primary centers of smell, the bulbi, are exclusively olfactory; they are displayed in their entirety in fossil brains.

THE OLFACTORY BULBS—POSITION AND SHAPE

The olfactory bulbs were quite anterior to the cerebral hemispheres in *Eohippus* (fig. 2, fig. 3 A). They usually still protrude anteriorly in *Equus* but are overlapped by the frontal lobes either partly (pl. 3) or completely (pony, pl. 4). They extended upward as much as did the frontal regions of the cerebrum in *Eohippus*. The roof of the ethmoidal chambers remained the unpneumatized skull roof up to the Oligocene (fig. 22 A, B). With the progress of cerebral height increase, the olfactory bulbs gradually became confined to an area adjoining only the lower regions of the anterior side of the cerebrum (fig. 22 C). Their posterior surfaces either remain close to the frontal poles of the cerebral hemispheres—in the pony and in *Pliohippus* I (in which they were described, from Tilney's viewpoint of an anatomist of modern brains, as "retroverted"—1931, p. 483)—, or the main body of the olfactory bulb is somewhat detached (*Pliohippus* II, *Equus occidentalis*, *Equus caballus* I). The latter condition seems associated with osteological rather than neurological developments. Such a position of the olfactory bulbs is related to a greater longitudinal diameter of the transverse, pneumatized septum which dorsally separates the cerebral and ethmoidal chambers. The osteological evolution of this region of the head will be discussed in another paper.

The position of the cribriform plate is only partly revealed by impressions of the lateral attachments in the endocranial casts of *Eohippus* II (upper section only) and *Mesohippus*. Its main portion appears to have been almost perpendicular, and the baso-posterior slant of its lower region not very pronounced. In the Middle Miocene the lamina cribrosa had begun to occupy a different, more basal location in the skull, but its inclination shows little progress, in *Merychippus* I, over the *Mesohippus* stage. It is in the later stages that there develops the oblique position of the cribrous lamina whose occurrence in most living mammals is rightly regarded as a secondary condition (Matthes, 1934, p. 928). This slant is attributed either to large cerebral hemispheres pushing forward, or to large olfactory organs pushing backward under the brain. In the Equidae both factors were involved. The slant of this wall between brain and nose varies considerably. The lamina is almost perpendicular in the young *Pliohippus* I, but there is a short basal, subhorizontal posterior continuation. A stronger slant was established in *Pliohippus* II and *Neohipparion*. In the two domestic horse skulls at hand there still exists, above an oblique or horizontal basal facies, an anterior facies of the olfactory bulbs with very little slope. On the other hand, under the high frontal lobes of the pony, the lamina cribrosa may be said to form anteriorly the lower, oblique wall of the brain chamber.

The olfactory bulbs of *Eohippus* and of *Mesohippus* were of a similar shape. They can be described as subglobular, in particular in contrast to the shape of the bulbi in later stages; these are oblong. During the increasing overlapping of the bulbi by the cerebrum, their diameter of greatest expansion—their axis—became an increasingly oblique one.

Subglobular olfactory bulbs which lie in front of the cerebrum obviously exhibit the primitive condition in the mammalian brain. This condition, which in the Equidae is maintained at least up to *Mesohippus*, today exists in, for example, the insectivores (fig. 4, A, B). In our comparison of the *Mesohippus* brain with the

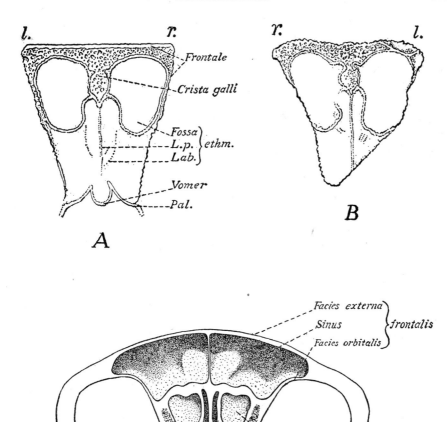

l.   *r.*   *r.*   *l.*

Frontale

Crista galli

Fossa⎫
L.p. ⎬ethm.
Lab. ⎭

Vomer

Pal.

A   B

Facies externa⎫
Sinus   ⎬frontalis
Facies orbitalis⎭

Vomer
Sphenopalatine sinus
Palatine

Fossa
Lam. perp. ⎫ethmoidalis
Labyrinthus⎭

C

FIGURE 22.—*Transverse skull sections near anterior extremity of brain chamber*

(A, B) *Mesohippus* sp. (specimen no. II). The proximal side of the section (B) crossed the orbit 16 mm. posterior to its anterior rim, just anterior to its summit, and crossed the right jaw between the two hindmost molars which in this young specimen are M^1 and M^2. The section is slightly oblique; the olfactory bulb chambers (fossae ethmoidales) are sectioned, left, 3 mm. anterior to their dorso-posterior extremity, right, at 4 mm. which is the plane of their greatest lateral extent. Dorso-medially, the olfactory bulbs extend about 7 mm. farther anterad. About 1½ mm. were destroyed by the saw between the proximal and the distal section (A). Fossilization had destroyed and removed almost all the delicate bone material of the ethmoidal labyrinth. The lateral surfaces of the cast, from which the bone was mostly removed, are moulded by the insertion of turbinals from top to bottom. Small spongiosa cells, and some larger ones on the left side in the proximal section, form a narrow layer in the frontal bone; there was no frontal sinus in *Mesohippus*. × 1½.

(C) *Equus caballus.* Posterior view of skull sectioned across the postorbital bars. (After Baum.) × ¾.

brains of living ungulates of *Mesohippus* size it has been shown that the bulbi of the modern forms are in a more ventral position.   The evolutionary development of the cerebral hemispheres leaves no doubt that the ventral position of the bulbi of, *e.g.*,

the sheep ("their cephalic extremities turn slightly dorsad in front of the lobi fron-
tales," Burkholder, 1904, p. 33) is a progressive feature of the brain as a whole; but
the basal position as such has no bearing on the size of the bulbi.

The evolutionary expansion of the cerebrum, encroaching upon the endocranial
space originally occupied by the olfactory bulbs, not only presses these downward,
but it also tends to flatten the ethmoidal chambers and their contents, the bulbi.
But this, too, does not in itself reduce the size of the bulbi, or diminish the extent
of the surface by which the olfactory fila enter the bulbus. These differences in the
appearance of the olfactory bulbs are due primarily to differences of the associated
cerebra rather than to a real dissimilarity of the bulbi themselves.

THE RELATIVE SIZE OF THE OLFACTORY BULBS

The olfactory bulbs of *Eohippus* are as broad, as high, and half as long as the
terminal segment of my little finger; the olfactory bulbs of *Equus occidentalis* are
almost the size of my whole thumb.

To find the meaning of this great increase in volume of the bulbi in the Equidae,
it has been attempted to demonstrate their relative evolution in the manner most
nearly exact—viz., by the ratios of bulb diameters to the diameters of other brain
portions (table 10).

When reading table 10 one must realize that the customary diameters impart, in the case of the
olfactory bulbs, an idea of shape and size even less accurate than is the case with other brain portions.

Breadth is the only diameter which has the same significance in all stages of the evolutionary
series.

Height, the elevation of the dorsal tip above the ventral surface of the bulbi, connects in one
measurement the horizontal levels of a ventral and a dorsal point between which may lie half the
longitudinal extent of the bulbs, or very little of it. Besides being thus restricted in significance
by the variations in bulbous shape, the measurement of perpendicular height is handicapped in accuracy by the fact that the orientation of the endocasts is, to a certain extent, arbitrary. The dorsal
surface of the cerebrum is essentially horizontal, but it is never flat. This technical limitation of
accuracy, as well as impediments due to morphology, naturally exist also with regard to measuring
the horizontal length of the olfactory bulbs.

Length was measured in most specimens to the dorsal contact of the casts of ethmoidal and
cerebral chambers. The horizontal plane defined by this incisure between the olfactory bulbs and
the cerebral hemispheres lies at a variable level on the bulbs not only in every evolutionary stage,
but in the later stages also in every individual. In the majority of our specimens the bulbi extend
upward in front of the cerebrum. In our two *Pliohippus* specimens and in our *Neohipparion* specimen, the dorsal surface of the casts of the ethmoidal chambers is almost horizontal, even showing
a slight anterad slope. In the pony the bulbi are so closely applied to the lower side of the cerebrum
that their dorsal surface slopes steeply. In these cases, the level of the incisure described above is
coincident with the highest point of the bulbi; it is, consequently, a level on which the bulbi have no
horizontal length at all. Length was measured in mid-height of the bulbi in these specimens. In
any case, except in the earliest Equidae horizontal length is not really the length of the olfactory
bulbs in the way cerebral length is the length of the cerebral hemispheres, due to the change in position of the bulbi. As the posterior parts of the bulbi became increasingly overlapped by the cerebrum, the bulbi changed from organs whose longest diameter was approximately horizontal to organs
standing obliquely in the skull.

All this explains the incoherence of the figures in column III of table 10.

The longest diameter or axis was the diameter of the olfactory bulbs which increased most in the
evolution of the Equidae. The ratios of the olfactory bulb axis to cerebral length are given in col-

umn IV of table 10.   The earliest form in our series of endocasts in which it was possible to measure
the axis (from the lowest point of the bulbi to the highest point) is the last form with a simple cerebrum, *Merychippus* I.   The endocasts of the older forms unfortunately do not completely reveal
the lower side of the bulbs; however, enough is seen of the subglobular form and forward position
of the bulbs to suggest that surely in *Eohippus*, and perhaps in *Mesohippus*, the axis can have surpassed but little the perpendicular height or horizontal length measurements.

TABLE 10.—*Olfactory bulbs*

Ratios of the diameters of one olfactory bulb (= 1) to the diameters of one cerebral hemisphere (columns I–IV) and
one-half of the medulla oblongata (V–VI).   I, V: height; II, VI: breadth; III: length; IV: longest = oblique diameter
(axis) of bulb to length of cerebral hemisphere.

	I	II	III	IV	V	VI
Eoh.	(1.5)	1.3	2.5		0.6	0.5
Meso. III	(II: 2.0)	2.0	4.7			0.7
IV			5.7			
VI		2.0	4.8			
Par. I		2.3	5.6			
Mery. I	1.8	2.4	10.0	2.9		
III			7.9		0.9	
Plio. I	1.9	3.2	7.2	3.7		
II	1.9	3.3	9.4	3.2		
Neoh.	2.5	2.6	3.9	2.6	1.0	1.0
Eq. occ.	2.8	2.3	7.6	2.7	0.9	0.7
Eq. cab. I	2.8	2.2	8.6	3.2	1.3	0.8
II	2.8	1.9	6.4	2.4	1.1	0.8
Pony	3.0	2.3	20.0	2.7	1.3	0.8

Notwithstanding the limitations in accuracy and completeness of the data, the
ratios of the olfactory bulb diameters to the diameters of other brain parts do show,
in my opinion, that during their great increase in absolute size the bulbi of the Equidae decreased much less in relative size than is postulated by the neoneurological
conception of rhinencephalon evolution reviewed above.

Our first comparison of the bulbi is with the cerebrum: the customary comparison
of brain anatomy (table 10, columns I–IV).

First of all these ratios show, once again, that the composition of the brain of
Eohippus, a brain of subplacental type, differs from that developed in the descendants
of this form.   Even though we do not surely know the maximum height of the olfactory bulbs of *Eohippus*, the height positively known is as much as two-thirds of
the greatest (posterior) height of the cerebral hemispheres.   Each bulbus was almost
as broad as a cerebral hemisphere.   The horizontal length was as much as two-fifths
of the length of the cerebrum.

After the Eocene, the proportion of olfactory bulb breadth to cerebral hemisphere
breadth (column II) did not change.   The ratio varies, but there is no discernible
trend in this variation.   Ratios like that of the two Mesohippi occur in the modern
horses.   In breadth, the expansion of the olfactory bulbs corresponded to that of the
cerebral hemispheres.

The axis of the olfactory bulbs has increased in a fashion parallel to the expansion
in length of the cerebral hemispheres.   Column IV, an incomplete record, indicates

that, during the great size increase of the cerebrum from Middle Miocene to Recent times, the olfactory bulbs expanded correspondingly in one more diameter, besides breadth. If, as I presume, length was the greatest diameter of the bulbi in *Eohippus*, the *Eohippus* ratio of column III can be repeated in column IV. This would establish a similar proportion between the longest diameters of bulbus and cerebrum from *Eohippus* to *Equus*.

On the other hand, relative height (column I) and relative length (column III) have decreased considerably from *Eohippus* to *Equus*. The decline of the height and breadth ratios is the expression of two different processes. (1) Perpendicular height and horizontal length of the bulbi became relatively less with the changes in position and shape which resulted in the oblique position of the bulbi. (2) The considerable decline of the height and breadth ratios shows that the bulbi did not expand at the same rate as did the cerebrum. With the relative decrease in height and breadth must be contrasted, however, the parallelism in increase of breadth and greatest diameter of the two brain portions; in these features are expressed the progressive evolution of the bulbs. Obviously, the decrease in relative size does not characterize the evolution of the bulbi themselves; bulbus evolution in the Equidae consisted in great absolute enlargement. The relative size decrease of the olfactory bulbs is one more expression of the cerebral expansion, the dominating feature in the evolution of the equid brain.

The change in position of the bulbi illustrated by the two declining ratios, length and height, is the shift from a location prominent in every view of the brain to a position less dominant in the brain picture. It is therefore understandable that those brains which all authors agree to call macrosmatic have low cerebra, with the bulbi in an anterior position. It is true that most of these brains belong to mammals of the lower orders. However, the tracing of the fate of the bulbi in the Equidae strongly suggests that *Equus* is as macrosmatic, neuro-physiologically, as were its ancestors which still had the morphologically macrosmatic brain type. This assumption is supported by the fact that the olfactory organ has enormously increased in size in the evolution of the Equidae. Perhaps one can say that the expansion of the olfactory bulbs was, together with the elongation of the muzzle, proportionate to body size. As the horse's nose is so much higher above the ground than that of its small ancestors, demands upon the olfactory sense surely have not decreased.

In judging the olfactory bulbs by their changing relations to the cerebral hemispheres, we have followed the customary method of comparison. However, this method yokes together two brain portions whose modes of evolution are essentially different.

The evolution of the brain in the Equidae testifies to the existence of an evolutionary force, known before, which drives solely toward expansion and differentiation of the neocortex, thereby enlarging the cerebrum. While the bulbi adjoin, and are intimately connected with the cerebral hemispheres, they are only the primary olfactory center. No general tendency rules the evolution of a sensory center. Its size is correlated only with the acuteness of the sense. In contrast to the cerebrum as a whole, sensory centers are adaptive; they can either enlarge, or become reduced, or even lost. The olfactory bulbs of man, cetaceans, pterosaurs, and birds became not only relatively, but absolutely, smaller during evolution. A cerebrum becomes, of course, smaller when a dwarf form is developed; but reduction of the cerebral hemispheres in relative size or importance appears unimaginable.

As a matter of fact, there is discernible in fossil brains no particular region whose evolution, compared with that of the olfactory bulbs, would be interesting. We cannot follow the evolution of the optic and acoustic centers. To round off the picture of the steady size increase of the olfactory bulbs we have, however, compared their height and breadth diameters with those of the most conservative brain portion, the medulla oblongata (table 10, columns V and VI).

In the relations between olfactory bulb and oblongata diameters we find, once again, *Eohippus* different from his descendants. The olfactory bulbs of *Eohippus* were twice as broad, and almost twice as high, as the slender oblongata of this little animal. In the incomplete record of the later forms, we find the perpendicular height ratio varying from just below to slightly above 1:1. The oblique axis of the bulbus consequently was always greater than oblongata height. The breadth ratio appears not to have changed from *Mesohippus* to *Equus*. The breadth of each olfactory bulb never dropped below half the oblongata breadth.

Height and breadth of the medulla oblongata increase in correlation with the increase in body size. Our bulbus:oblongata ratios indicate that from the *Mesohippus* stage onward expansion was comparable in the oblongata and in the bulbi, a sensory center not generally dependent on body size.

It follows that the olfactory bulbs of the Equidae, while being shifted from an anterior into an antero-basal position, have greatly increased in absolute size. The degree of bulbus expansion appears to have corresponded to the enlargement of the medulla oblongata, and suggests a direct relation to the increase in body size. The bulbi have not enlarged as much as the cerebrum. This is particularly true of the Eocene period; the olfactory bulbs were relatively much larger in *Eohippus* than in *Mesohippus*. But in the evolution of the horse brain the decrease in relative size of the olfactory bulbs and of the cerebral olfactory surfaces was not so considerable as to warrant the current conception that progressive brain evolution in mammals generally means reduction of all olfactory centers.

ONTOGENY AND PHYLOGENY

THE BRAIN IN HORSE ONTOGENY

Our study of the brain in horse phylogeny should not close, I believe, without a comparison of the evolutionary with the ontogenetic development of the brain in horses. Such a comparison is of limited interest and value at the present time when the evolution of the brain has been studied only in the Equidae, and when neither this evolutionary story nor the ontogenetic development of the horse brain have been studied in a really satisfactory number of specimens. Another objection to the value of such a comparison might arise from the fact that the development of the nonfunctioning brain is largely a typically embryonic process. This, however, is true in the ungulates only of a relatively shorter period of intra-uterine life than in other mammals. All ungulates have the morphological pattern of the brain, including the convolutional pattern of the cortex, finished at the time of birth (Riese, 1945, p. 148). The brain of the horse attains all the form characters of the adult brain, except the size, well before birth (Anthony and Grzybowski, 1930, p. 160). The prenatal completion of brain development in the Ungulata is, of course, correlated with their advanced behavior at birth. Should it be found that Anthony and Grzybowski's observation of finished brain development before birth is not the rule in ungulates, a proportionate relation with the size of the new-born seems possible. For example, among births in the Chicago Zoo, reported in 'Life" (Oct. 9, 1944), a rhinoceros weighed 45 pounds, but a zebra weighed 100 pounds.

The subject of our comparison with brain evolution is, therefore, intra-uterine brain development—of course only in the period after the decrease of the embryonic flexures. Incidentally, no record seems to exist of the growth after birth either of the brain or of the neurocranium proper in horses. It is well known, however, that the neurocranium gains less in size than the facial cranium. Dr. Ernst Schwarz (whom I consulted concerning the *Miohippus* in its second year) tells me that after a horse has reached the age of 2 years there is but negligible growth of the whole skull although the teeth, and the closure of the sutures, are not complete before the age of 5 years. Thus the brain must have attained its adult size before the horse is 2 years old, whereas total body size will still increase by one fifth to one fourth, and body weight by at least one third.

SIMILARITIES

Some general situations and trends observed in phylogeny are re-enacted in ontogeny. The embryonic cerebrum is at first relatively short, and it gradually overlaps midbrain and cerebellum. On its originally smooth surface the sulci develop successively; their first appearances are in the form of short, straight, unbranched, shallow furrows—the sulcus type of *Eohippus* and *Orohippus*. Increasing complication of the sulci is, of course, in ontogeny as in phylogeny, due to the greater surface expansion of gray cortex matter than of white fiber matter.

In the mammalian brain evolution described in this paper, we have seen that progress takes place in two regions, viz., in the median lobe and hemispheres of the cerebellum, and in the cerebral hemispheres, particularly the neocortex. Certain quantitative data of ontogeny apparently mirror the difference in evolutionary behavior between these characteristically mammalian brain portions on the one hand and the brain stem portions on the other hand. Only in human ontogeny have such details been studied. In man, the brain stem shows a more rapid growth up to the end of the fifth fetal month than later on; during that early period cerebellum and cerebrum grow slowly, and they increase in volume rapidly from the sixth month to birth (Dunn, 1921, p. 488).

Dunn did not measure separately the different parts of cerebellum and cerebrum. In the evolution of the horse it has been observed that the anterior lobe of the vermis cerebelli does not expand as much as do the median lobe and its lateral appendages, the cerebellar hemispheres. A parallel to this difference in the evolutionary trends of the regions anterior and posterior to the fissura prima cerebelli is reported in Kuithan's description of cerebellar development in sheep. After an initial period of uniform growth of the cerebellum "fängt bei 11 cm. langen Schafembryonen der hinter der Primärfurche gelegene Teil an, sich in drei Längszonen stärker zu verdicken" (Kuithan, 1895, p. 28). The median (and posterior?) and lateral lobes from then on enlarge at a greater rate than the anterior lobe. The resulting forward shift of the primary fissure, a conspicuous feature in the evolution of the equid

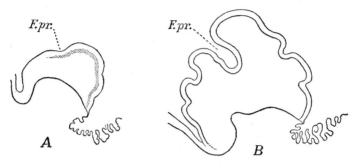

FIGURE 23.—*Ontogeny of sheep cerebellum*
(A) 50 mm. embryo. (B) 90 mm. embryo. (After Kuithan.) × 20.

cerebellum, is not mentioned either by Kuithan or in Bradley's (1903) study of the development of the ungulate cerebellum. This shift is, however, plainly shown in Kuithan's figures 13 and 14 (our fig. 23, A and B); the fissura prima is farther anterior on the vermis surface in the 90 mm. sheep embryo than in the 50 mm. sheep embryo.

DISSIMILARITIES

Sizes.—Anthony and Grzybowski have given a detailed description of the intra-uterine morphogenesis of the horse cerebrum from the first appearance of the rhinal fissure to the establishment of the adult sulcal pattern. Only a few of the illustrations of their paper show the entire brain.

A study of the data of Anthony and Grzybowski reveals considerable discrepancies between the ontogenetic progress of skull length, cerebral length, and fissuration, respectively. Even if allowance is made for distortion of the embryo brains through preservation, it is obvious that variation between individuals in the developmental tempo of the (nonfunctioning) cerebrum far surpasses the variability observed in the phyletic series of adult brains.

Anthony and Grzybowski's embryonic stages I–XII are successive stages not of intra-uterine age but of progress in fissuration. The age of the feti was not known except of that representing stage VI ("6 mois environ," p. 148). The head length of this specimen is 117 mm., but Robb's 5–6 months old horse fetus skull is 163 mm. long (1935, p. 48). Cerebrum length is 29 mm. in Anthony and Grzybowski's 6-month embryo, but 31 mm. in Bradley's 4-month-old and 46 mm. in Bradley's 5-month-old horse feti (1899, fig. 2). Dissimilarity in developmental tempi is striking in Anthony and Grzybowski's stages IV to X. These stages of increasing fissuration have head lengths (p. 147–148) of 80, 95, 117, 113, 95, 146 and 154 mm., respectively; cerebrum lengths (measured by me in their figures 3–10) are 22, 28, 29, 36, 33, 35 and 47 mm., respectively.

The ratios of cerebrum length (= 1) to skull length in these embryos are interesting for several reasons. The 10 embryonic stages of which Anthony and Grzybowski record both cerebral and head lengths, arranged according to increasing head length

TABLE 11.—Eohippus, Mesohippus, *and horse embryos of similar head lengths*

Latin numbers: embryonic stages of Anthony and Grzybowski (1930); the other embryos are those of Bradley (1899). Head length on the one hand and brain measurements on the other hand are those of different individuals in the fossil forms. The *Mesolippus* measurements are averages of five to seven specimens.

	Head length	Cerebrum		
		length	height	breadth
VII	113	36	24	40
VI	117	29		27
IX	146	35	24	39
4 months		31	22	30
5 months		46	30	
Eohippus	(135)	27	24	23
XI	180	74	43	
XII		71		80
Mesohippus	181	59	39	50

(from I: 47 mm., to XI: 180 mm.), have the following ratios: 3.1, 3.2, 3.6;—3.7 and 2.9 in two heads of the same length, 95 mm., the last of the embryo stages with heads smaller than existed in adult fossil Equidae;—3.1, 4.0, 3.3, and 2.4 in the sequence of embryos with skull sizes of Eocene and Oligocene horse ancestors.

These figures show graphically the independent variations of cerebral and skull growth in ontogeny. A comparison of these ontogenetic with the phylogenetic length ratios (table 6) illustrates the greatest difference between the development of the brain in the individual and in evolution: the cerebrum is precocious in ontogeny. Cerebral development is completed long before that of the skull, whereas in phylogeny we found cerebral evolution lagging behind skull evolution in the early history of the Equidae. In correspondence, the cerebral hemispheres are larger in horse embryos than they were in adult horse ancestors of similar head sizes (*see* table 11). In the evolution of these short-snouted early Equidae the cerebrum gained in length more than the skull, and the highest length ratio of cerebrum to skull ever attained in adult Equidae existed in *Mesohippus*. This ratio, 1:3.1, is found in embryos much smaller than *Mesohippus*—for example in the youngest of Anthony and Grzybowski's embryos, in a 47 mm.-long head.

Shapes.—In the phyletic series of adult brains, an originally slender cerebrum gradually becomes subcubic. When the rhinal fissure begins to form in the horse embryo, the cerebrum has the shape which in an adult mammal would represent a high stage of evolution: "très subsphérique" (Anthony and Grzybowski, p. 149);

"ses bords postérieur et antérieur sont . . . à peu près perpendiculaires par rapport à l'axe longitudinal" (p. 148).   This is, of course, an embryonic condition.   According to Anthony and Grzybowski (p. 163), the telencephalic height index, $\frac{height \times 100}{length}$, decreases constantly in the ontogeny of the horse, from 82.8 in stage I, or at least from 83.9 in stage IV, to 55.7 in stage XII embryo and 55.0 in one brain of an adult horse.   When variability is taken into account, this development does not appear to be quite so striking as it seems in Anthony and Grzybowski's single representatives of different stages.   For example, our two adult *Equus caballus* specimens have telencephalic height indices of 67.9 and 66.7, respectively, figures closer to that of Anthony and Grzybowski's embryonic stage VIII rather than their adult specimen. In our material, the variability of this index in fully developed brains is also shown in *Mesohippus*.   Specimens II, IV, VI, and III were brains of individuals with successive ages between 2 years and old age; their telencephalic height indices are 71.7, 65.1, 68.3, and 71.7, respectively.   It is generally true, however, that during intra-uterine ontogeny the telencephalic height index drops.   In our phyletic series of equid brains the index drops, too, but it rises again in the latest phases.   However, the shapes of the embryonic and the adult ancestral cerebra are so different that it does not seem profitable to compare the two series of indices.

A morphological detail illustrates different trends in the ontogeny of the telencephalon on the one hand and its phylogeny on the other.   In ontogeny the change in the topographical relation of the olfactory bulbs to the cerebral hemispheres is just the opposite of that observed in phylogeny.   In evolution, as the frontal lobe of the cerebrum becomes gradually higher, the bulbi become relatively lower.   In embryonic development the bulbi grow upward from the base of the cerebrum.   In Anthony and Grzybowski's youngest embryo, they are a 2 mm.-high formation at the lower anterior pole of the 12 mm.-high cerebrum.   In their stage IX, the perpendicular height of the bulbus is 5 mm., against 35 mm. cerebral height.   Stage XI is a horse embryo of *Mesohippus* skull length.   Whereas in *Mesohippus* the olfactory bulbs extend upward almost to the full height of the cerebrum, in the embryo they rise but 15 mm. high along a 43 mm.-high cerebrum.

These relations furnish another illustration of the fact that the cerebrum is much larger in an embryo than it was in an ancestral head of corresponding size.   In phylogeny, the cerebrum expanded more than the olfactory bulbs after the *Mesohippus* stage; in ontogeny, a large cerebrum exists before the head size of *Mesohippus* is reached, but the bulbi are still small in this stage.   Forster (1927, summarized p. 130) found that, whereas the bulbi and cribriform plates in monkeys and apes become relatively smaller during ontogeny, a progressive relative enlargement during the entire development of the individual is characteristic of macrosmatic mammals.

Fissuration.—The expansion of the neocortex area over the cerebral convexity, a characteristic feature of progress in phylogeny, is not re-enacted in the ontogeny of the horse brain.   To judge from Anthony and Grzybowski's figures, the rhinal fissure develops in the embryo in its final position, in the lower regions of the cerebrum.   It is bent (as in *Orohippus*), whereas in *Eohippus* it is straight.   The rhinal fissure is the only furrow present in Anthony and Grzybowski's stage I; the neo-pallium is smooth.

A comparison of the succession in the appearance of neopallial sulci in pig, sheep, ox (Ziehen, 1906, p. 339–342), and horse (Anthony and Grzybowski, 1930) suggests a general similarity of the ontogenetic sequence in these ungulates, with differences such as a later appearance of the presylvian sulcus in the ox than in the other forms. However, each report is based on a very small number of embryo brains. One hesi-tates to regard the one cerebrum representing each stage of those series as a typical specimen. Similarly, the following comparison of the ontogenetic and phylogenetic succession in the Equidae of the first appearance of the sulci may have to be revised if more horse embryos are studied.

In the embryogenesis of the horse, the sulci (given Arabic numerals below) make their appearance as follows in Anthony and Grzybowski's embryonic stages (Latin numerals): I. 1: rhinalis. II. 2: Sylvia (Anthony and Grzybowski's "ectosyl-via"). III. 3: suprasylvia media. IV. 4: praesylvia, 5: intra-orbitalis ("orbi-taire"). V. 6: ectosylvia ("sillons entre la suprasylvia et l'ectosylvia"), 7: diag-onalis. VI. 8: lateralis, 9: ectolateralis. VII. 10: endolateralis, 11: cruciatus, 12: suprasylvia posterior ("postsylvia"), 13: posticus ("oblique"). No new sulcus appears in stage VIII. In stage IX operculization is observed in the Sylvian region, 14: "la première ébauche de la pseudosylvia" (the fissure one cannot distinguish from the Sylvia in endocasts), and sulcus 15: the coronal is formed. The sulcus interlateralis dorsalis is not mentioned by Anthony and Grzybowski; their illustra-tions show that it first appears in stage X, as sulcus no. 16. The ansate (sulcus 17) is neither mentioned by nor shown in their figures; Ziehen (1906, p. 341) mentions it in the sheep ("Bügel a") as developing later than the coronal.

In stage I of phylogeny, *Eohippus*, the sulci 1, 3, 4, and 8 were in existence, and perhaps no. 2. The sulci 3 and 8 were developed in a form similar to that in which they first appear in the embryo, viz., as straight, relatively short, shallow furrows. Fewer sulci were developed in *Eohippus* than are present in embryos of similar head size.

Of stage II, *Orohippus*, we do not know the whole neopallium, —hardly more than the circumsylvian area. The restricted region represented in our material shows no. 2, the Sylvia, as a small groove, and, as a newly acquired sulcus, no. 13.

We have no knowledge at all of stage III, *Epihippus*.

In stage IV of the phyletic series, *Mesohippus*, all the main sulci are present in the neopallium. There had developed, at some time between the beginning of the Middle Eocene and the beginning of the Oligocene, the sulci which develop in ontog-eny as numbers 6, 7, 9, 10, 11, 12, 15, and 17.

The fifth sulcus of ontogeny first appears in phylogeny in stage V, *Miohippus*.

In stage VI, *Parahippus*, no. 16 is added.

Undulation of the sulcus lines, multiple ramification, and accessory sulci are prac-tically absent in *Mesohippus*. These features begin to appear in ontogeny in stage IX, a cerebrum smaller than that of *Mesohippus*. In a general way, however, the sulci of *Mesohippus*—and of the similar *Miohippus*—are comparable to the sulci of Anthony and Grzybowski's fissuration stage X in some respects and to those of stage XI in other respects. The anterior, transverse sulci are farther developed (longer) in *Mesohippus* and *Miohippus* than in the embryo X, and agree with XI; but in XI the longitudinal sulci are in a higher stage of development than they were in the Oligocene Equidae. It follows that the main sulci of *Mesohippus* were in a stage intermediate between the stages achieved in the smaller cerebrum (47 mm. long) of a smaller embryo head (154 mm. long) and the larger cerebrum (74 mm.) of an embryo head with a *Mesohippus* head length (180 mm.). Thus the brains of horse embryos are not only larger, but they are more highly developed also with regard to fissuration than were the brains of adult horse ancestors with corresponding head sizes. In the fissuration of stage XI of horse embryogenesis, "L'aspect de l'adulte commence a s'établir" (Anthony and Grzybowski, p. 160) which is far from true of *Mesohippus* or *Miohippus*.

General similarity to the fissuration of the brain of the adult living horse developed in phylogeny in the Upper Miocene *Merychippus*. These are the ancestors whose skull corresponded, in size and proportions, to that of the domestic horse at birth. One might say that in the majority of important characters brain phylogeny caught up with ontogeny in this size stage.

This agrees, incidentally, with Reeve and Murray's (1942) modification of Robb's (1935) thesis of complete parallelism in ontogeny and phylogeny of the development of certain skull features. Reeve and Murray found that the modus of gain of the face over the cranium in phylogeny differed from that of ontogeny up to the *Merychippus* stage; it shifted to the modus of horse ontogeny within the genus *Merychippus*. The matter is mentioned here in order to accentuate a fact not remarked upon by those authors, but found significant in our neurological study of the Equidae. To compare Eocene, Oligocene, and early Miocene equid skulls with similar-sized heads in the horse ontogenic series is comparing adults with embryos.

SUMMARY

The brain of the horse develops more rapidly than the skull in ontogeny; its structure is fully developed before birth, and its adult size is attained at the latest in a 2-year-old. In phylogeny, brain evolution was relatively slow in the stages whose sizes correspond to those of horse embryos; in the adult Eocene and Oligocene horse ancestors the cerebrum was smaller and less fissured than it is in corresponding intra-uterine stages of the horse. The individual sulci do not seem to appear in the same order in ontogeny as they did in phylogeny. At their first appearances they are similarly short and straight in ontogeny and in phylogeny, but complication begins in smaller heads in individual development than in evolution. From birth to adult age no considerable change seems to occur in the horse's brain, except in size. From the Upper Miocene *Merychippus* to *Equus*, brain evolution continued to progress in other features as well as size; but the major characteristics of the modern horse brain were already achieved in this ancestor, which had reached the size of newborn modern horses.

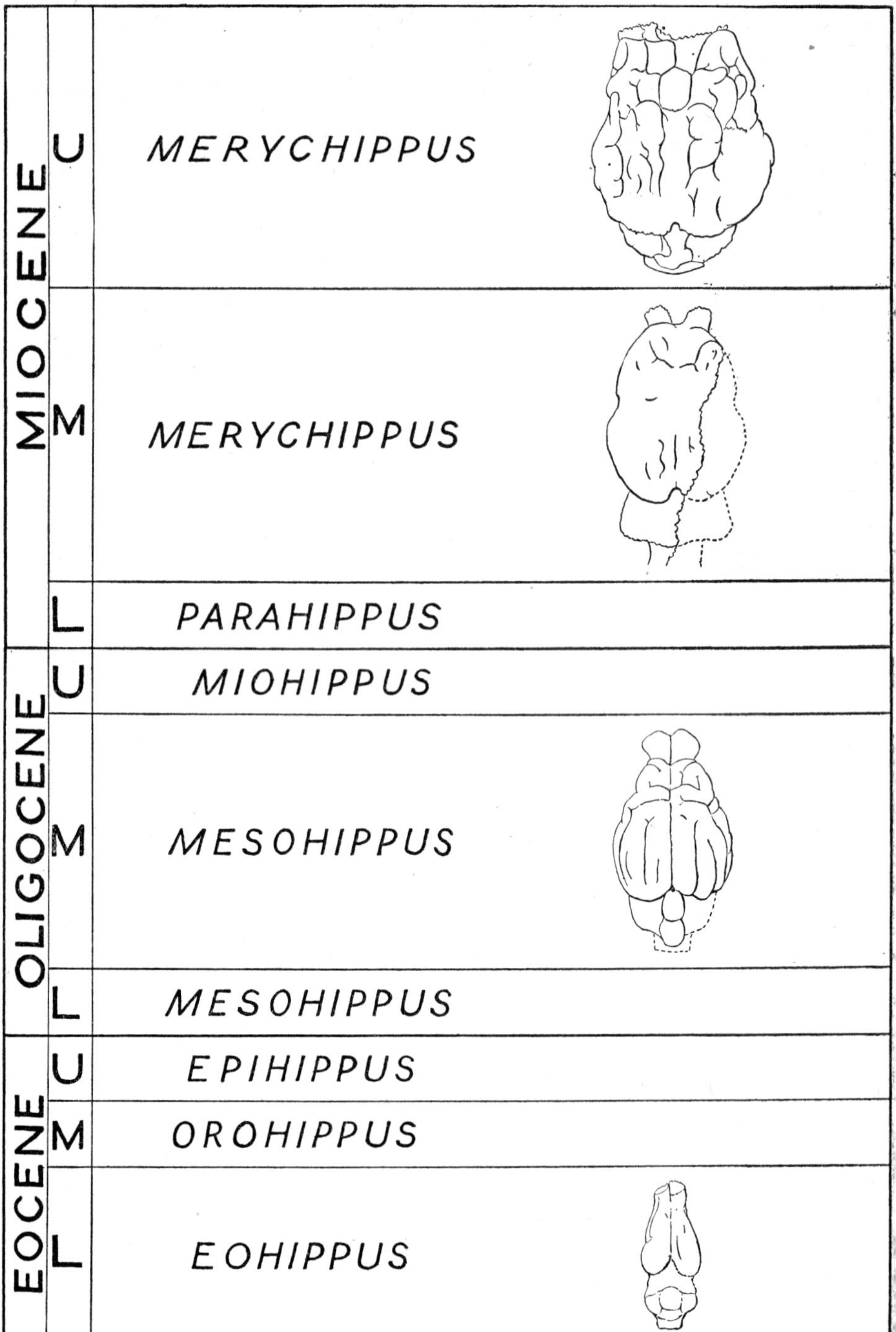

FIGURE 24A.—*Endocranial casts of fossil and living Equidae*

This chart shows the specimens *Eohippus* I, *Mesohippus* III, *Merychippus* I and III, *Pliohippus* II, *Equus occidentalis*, *Equus caballus* I and pony, in one-third natural size. The material of the forms not represented is either incomplete (*Orohippus*, see figs. 6, 7; *Miohippus*, see fig. 12; *Parahippus*, see fig. 13) or non-existent (*Epihippus*).

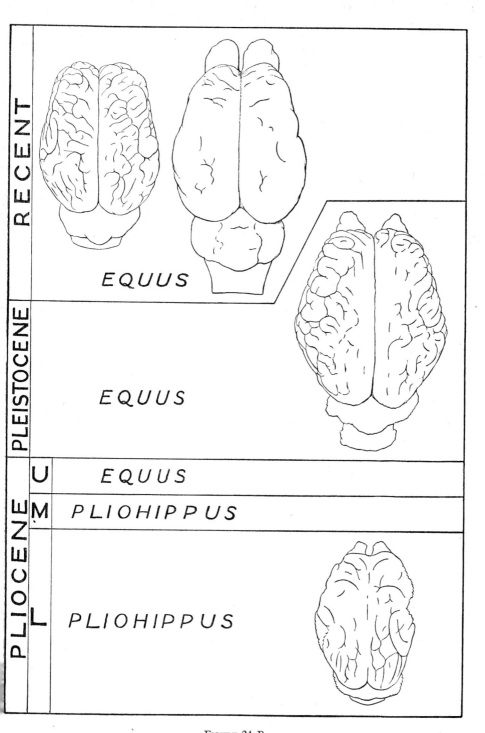

FIGURE 24 B

SUMMARY

FACTS

We have followed the evolution of the brain through the 55,000,000 years of the history of the Equidae, from the miniature Lower Eocene "dawn-horse" to the extant horse. On the basis of endocranial casts from almost every stage of the horse ancestry, the actual course of a progressive development of the brain in an evolutionary series has been observed for the first time.

While the Equidae developed from cat size to horse stature, the brain became progressively a smaller part of the body. However, until sheep size was attained (Middle Oligocene), the ratios of total brain length and breadth to skull length, body length, and body height changed hardly at all. During the development of the powerful muzzle (Miocene) the brain became a smaller portion of the head and appears to have remained so since, whereas its relation to body volume continued to decline.

During the whole course of this evolutionary development, each division of the brain increased in absolute size. There were, however, considerable differences in the rate of enlargement of the brain parts.

The medulla oblongata expanded steadily. Its enlargement seems to have closely corresponded to the increase in body size.

The midbrain is shown, in the endocast material, only in *Eohippus*. It was overlapped by the adjoining brain portions in the Middle Eocene. From *Eohippus* to *Equus*, midbrain breadth enlarged by seven-tenths, height increased by half, and length was apparently doubled.

The diencephalon proper is the one division of the brain not revealed in our material; but the outline of the basally attached pituitary body was seen in *Mesohippus* and *Parahippus*. The relation of this growth-promoting gland to the development of large body size is clearly demonstrated in its spectacular expansion from *Mesohippus* to *Equus*. Pituitary length doubled, as did cerebrum length; but pituitary breadth in *Equus* is four to five times that of *Mesohippus*.

The brain portions whose evolutionary history is told in detail by the series of endocranial casts are cerebellum, cerebrum, and bulbi olfactorii.

The cerebellum of *Eohippus* was a structure whose vermis reached as far dorsad and whose flocculi extended as far laterad in the skull as did the cerebrum. During the evolution of the Equidae the cerebellum did not expand as much as the cerebrum. Its dorsal vault gradually became lower than that of the cerebral hemispheres. Its breadth, even in the Oligocene, was only five-sevenths of the cerebral breadth. This proportion was generally maintained in the later forms.

Within the cerebellum, a more vigorous development took place in the exclusively mammalian portions—paramedian lobes and paraflocculi (neocerebellum)—than in the portions inherited from the reptiles—flocculi and vermis (paleocerebellum).

The flocculus reaffirms its paleocerebellar character in the evolution of the Equidae. Its increase in volume from *Eohippus* to *Equus* was very small, apparently less than that of any other part of the brain. There is no sign of any evolutionary development of this ancient portion of the cerebellar hemispheres.

In the vermis cerebelli, the lobus anterior is commonly the smallest of the three lobes in living mammals. It was the largest vermis lobe in *Eohippus*, being two-thirds of the vermis in length. While its cortex had expanded, through lobulation, in *Orohippus*, the absolute size of the anterior lobe had not changed; but, as a result of expansion of the median lobe, the anterior lobe had become a relatively smaller portion of the vermis. This trend continues in the history of the Equidae until in *Equus* the anterior lobe, much larger—in particular, much higher—than that of *Eohippus*, is reduced in relative length to one-third of the vermis, or less.

Little change can be observed in the lobus posterior which is, however, never completely visible in endocranial casts. It increased in absolute size and always formed the greater part of the posterior facies of the vermis, which always was perpendicular to the dorsal surface of the medulla oblongata.

The median vermis lobe, on the contrary, strikingly demonstrates its association with the progressive neocerebellum. Several stages in a vigorous evolution of the lobus medius are displayed in the endocast series. The lobus medius is, in particular, one of the parts which show that great advance in brain evolution took place between the Lower Eocene and Middle Eocene equid genera, whose skeletons differ so little. The profile of anterior and median lobes was a low curve in *Eohippus;* in *Orohippus*, the median lobe had swollen to form a high vault behind the anterior lobe. No infolding of the vermis cortex was observed in *Eohippus* except the fissura prima between anterior and median lobes. In *Orohippus*, anterior and posterior lobes had each become subdivided into three sublobules. The median lobe, however, was differentiated into anterior lobulus simplex with two sublobules and posterior lobulus complicatus with at least four sublobules. Vermis lobulation had ceased to be expressed in the endocasts in the *Mesohippus* stage; obviously, in this phase of horse evolution the furrows had become so densely spaced that, as is the case in *Equus*, they failed to imprint the endocranium. The progressing expansion of the median lobe cerebellar cortex is, however, expressed in the endocasts by significant changes in the outline of the lobe. The right and left lateral margins of the anterior and posterior lobes are symmetrical up to the *Equus* stage; but those of the median lobe in the Miocene have bent outward and become indented in irregular fashion. The increasing sinuosity of the median lobe outlines is the sign, on the endocasts, of the development of the S-shaped cluster of lobules which the median vermis lobe forms in the modern horse brain.

While thus convoluting and expanding its cortex by infolding, the lobus medius did not become a larger portion of the cerebellum. It was through vigorous expansion of the neocerebellar portions, following on that of the median lobe in the evolution of the Equidae, that cerebellar breadth increased by almost half from *Orohippus* to *Mesohippus*. It was mainly due to expansion of the neocerebellum that from *Mesohippus* to *Equus* a similar proportion of cerebellum and cerebrum was maintained—a similarity which, as far as we know, was one of breadth alone.

The progressive evolution of the cerebrum overshadowed the evolutionary changes of all the other divisions of the brain in the history of the Equidae.

In the Early Eocene, the cerebrum was a small and slender region between midbrain and olfactory bulbs, neither higher nor broader than the cerebellum. It overlapped the midbrain in the Middle Eocene, has increasingly overlapped the cerebellum at least since the early Oligocene, and the posterior part of the olfactory bulbs since the Miocene, until in a living form such as the Shetland pony the greater part of the cerebellum and the entire olfactory bulbs have come to lie under the cerebrum.

The 27 mm.-long cerebral hemispheres of *Eohippus* constituted two-fifths of the brain length. Approximately doubled in absolute length, they were about two-thirds of the whole brain length in *Mesohippus*. The relative length of the 136 mm.-long cerebrum of the Pleistocene *Equus occidentalis* is five-sevenths, that of the 122 mm.-long pony cerebrum five-sixths. Of the two shorter diameters of the cerebrum, breadth increased proportionately to length. In height, the cerebrum seems to have gained proportionately less than length and breadth in the Eocene, Oligocene, and Miocene, but relatively more than the other two diameters from the end of the Miocene to Recent time. Greatest cerebral breadths and heights were those in the temporal lobe region from *Eohippus* to *Equus*. The differences in diameters between this posterior area and the anterior region of the cerebrum became gradually less, as the frontal lobe area expanded at a greater rate than the other lobes. This special trend in the frontal area gradually transformed the outline of the hemispheres from an anteriorly tapering oval almost to a quadrangle. The profile of the anterior cerebral regions, a gentle slope in *Eohippus*, gradually changed—particularly during the latest stages—to a high vault.

Neocortex capped somewhat less than half the cerebral hemispheres in *Eohippus*— a situation found, among living mammals, only in the lowest groups of the marsupial and placental hierarchies. This primitive condition is little changed in the Oligocene Equidae. One still finds the neocortex extending over only the upper half of the cerebrum, although spreading somewhat farther basad in the frontal lobe—whereas in extant ungulates of *Mesohippus* or *Miohippus* size the rhinal fissure, limiting the neocortex, is in the lower half of the cerebral convexity. In the Equidae, the rhinal fissure had come to lie on the lower brain surface in the Miocene. It continued its downward shift. In the Pliocene, Pleistocene, and Recent Equidae the neocortex has so expanded as to envelop much of the basal surface of the cerebral hemispheres.

While the endocranial cast series thus shows the neocortex gradually taking over a larger portion of the cerebral convexity, the condition of the medial surface of the hemispheres cannot be seen in endocasts. However, certain changes in the mediodorsal region of the endocast cerebra show that during the evolution of the equid brain originally dorsal areas shifted to the median wall. The signs thus interpreted are found posteriorly and anteriorly. The postero-dorsal median area did not broaden proportionately to the cerebral breadth increase in this region. When, in the late stages of equid history, the cerebrum became very high, a longitudinal median sulcus disappeared from the postero-dorsal surface; it is found in *Equus* brains as a dorsal sulcus of the median surface. Likewise, anteriorly, the transverse dorsal continuation of a sulcus of the median surface became relatively shorter. Thus dorsal areas were added to the original median area during the evolution of the horse brain. This fact suggests that the medial neocortex, too, not only increased in absolute size with the median wall but gradually came to occupy a relatively larger area of the median surface of the hemispheres.

Besides extending its share of the cerebral surfaces, the neocortical surface increased progressively through infolding. This enlargement was of greater dimensions than is indicated in the endocast series by the successive appearance of more and more sulci. The result of this process is the fissuration of the horse brain. This is comparable in its complication to the human brain fissuration, and in man two-thirds of the neocortical surface are concealed in sulci.

The brain of *Eohippus* was lissencephalic. There were only three sulci in the neocortex, and they were straight and short: a longitudinal one in the posterior region, another in the middle region, and a transverse one anteriorly. In the small area known of the *Orohippus* cerebrum, the Sylvian fossa was found in an initial stage, one sulcus is developed which had not been present in *Eohippus,* and at least the anterior one of the *Eohippus* sulci apparently had become longer. The distribution of the sulci in this small area shows that gyrencephaly was achieved in the Middle Eocene phase of equid brain evolution. In *Mesohippus* all major sulci of the horse brain had come into existence. However, the pattern of fissuration is, in dorsal view, strikingly different from the modern equid pattern. The sulci are straight—transverse in the anterior third, longitudinal in the posterior two thirds of the dorsal surface. They lack connecting branches, and some of them do not have the extent they reached in later stages. The one *Miohippus* brain in our material shows very little advance over the condition of *Mesohippus.* Some sulci are slightly undulating, and one accessory sulcus had appeared, as a short, straight furrow on the lateral surface. This sulcus is not recognizable as a separate element in the later equid brains, having become connected with other elements of fissuration. The progress of fissuration in the *Parahippus* stage consists in particular in the achievement of connections between main sulci; furthermore, a dorsal accessory sulcus was newly developed. Middle Miocene *Merychippus* brains do not seem to have progressed beyond the *Parahippus* stage of fissuration.

Our Upper Miocene *Merychippus* material discloses that within the genus *Merychippus* considerable further progress was made in neocortex fissuration. Vigorous infolding of the surface produced a network of sulci comparable to that which characterizes the cerebrum of the horse. More accessory sulci appeared, the sulci developed additional branches, and some sulci had increased in length. Thus three longitudinal sulci, separate elements in the preceding stages, appear in this stage as a single long furrow. A sulcus which is not represented at all on the endocasts of the earlier Equidae, because it was a sulcus of the median wall only, has extended onto the anterior convexity. *Merychippus* was the first of the Equidae in which the increasingly vaulted frontal lobe had a definite anterior facies; this facies was subdivided by the seemingly new sulcus.

A continuation of this process of subdivision of the enlarging gyri, by sulcus branches and by accessory sulci, constitutes the post-Miocene progress of neocortex evolution as far as this is observable in endocranial casts. Thus balance was maintained between the expansion of the cortical gray matter, as the square, and that of the white matter, as the cube—a principle well known from comparisons of small and large extant cerebra. During this process, the average absolute breadth of the gyri remained similar in the Equidae. Typical gyrus breadth of the *Equus caballus* brain differs from that of *Mesohippus* only by $1\frac{1}{2}$ mm.

Concomitant with the building up of the cerebrum, and in particular of the frontal lobes as a large and high formation, the olfactory bulbs gradually came to be located in lower brain regions. Until the Middle Miocene, the bulbi were anterior to the cerebrum; up to the Middle Oligocene, they were globular structures almost as high as the cerebral hemispheres. In the Early Eocene, the bulbi also were almost as broad as the hemispheres. This earliest stage of equid evolution had relatively the largest olfactory bulbs of the whole series. A major reduction in relative bulbus size occurred during the Eocene. From the beginning of the Oligocene onward, however, the height and breadth diameters of the bulbi increased proportionately with the similar diameters of the medulla oblongata. Bulbus expansion kept step even with cerebral expansion in two diameters. The breadth increase of the bulbi was proportionate to that of the cerebrum, and their longest diameter (an oblique axis) increased in proportion with cerebrum length. On the other hand, height and horizontal length of the bulbi have decreased relatively if comparison is made with the corresponding diameters of the cerebrum. Likewise, the olfactory surfaces of the cerebrum have decreased in relative size, if compared with the neocortex. Absolutely, all olfactory surfaces of the forebrain have enormously increased from *Eohippus* to *Equus*.

CONCLUSIONS

The data summarized above are derived from material of a sort not previously assembled for study, a phylogenetic series of progressive brain development. Its general significance becomes apparent when this historical evidence is held against current beliefs as to brain evolution. These are based on the study of material from which our material differs in two major respects: (1) Neoneurological material comes from a cross section of the Mammalia, the mammals living at one time; our material covers 55,000,000 years. (2) Ours is not a series arranged by human judgment, but a phyletic series from consecutive geological periods; it represents the progressive evolution of one brain.

One paleoneurological theory of evolution must be briefly discussed. Although the outcome of a typical nineteenth century ideology, it has found its way into so many kinds of literature that to test it with the evidence of our study seems necessary. A synthesis of genetically unconnected paleontological and zoological data, Marsh's "general law of brain growth in the extinct mammals" (1886, p. 58 ff.) contains a major truth, corroborated by our material: "This increase was confined mainly to the cerebral hemispheres, or higher portion of the brain" (p. 58). But other paragraphs of Marsh's "law" are invalidated by the data of the present paper.

(1) Marsh has shown "the comparative size of the brain" by figures of endocasts in skulls so selected as to create the impression that brains became increasingly larger proportionate to bodies in "the extinct mammals throughout Tertiary times." While this was a possible course of evolution, it did not occur in, for example, the Equidae.

(2) Marsh contends that "The brain of a mammal belonging to a vigorous race, fitted for a long survival, is larger than the average brain, of that period, in the same group. The brain of a mammal of a declining race is smaller than the average of its cotemporaries of the same group" (p. 59). Knowing that to Marsh a large brain was one with a high ràtio to body volume, and considering the examples he gave (for vigorous race, the small Middle Eocene rhinocerid *Colonoceras;* for declining race, one of the giants among living ungulates, the hippopotamus), it is easy to disentangle from Marsh's wording two valid facts which must have induced his idea. The first is recorded by Marsh himself below the above quotation: "The brain of small animals is proportionately larger in bulk than that of large animals." In Marsh's opinion this circumstance "in a general comparison of brain growth of mammals . . . can have only a limited effect, which would not change, essentially, the general results." However, the second fact is that we know of no case in which there is a development of large forms at the beginning of an evolutionary series. "Small animals" are rather characteristic of this "vigorous" stage. The evolutionary development of a large body is necessarily accompanied by a decrease of the brain:body ratio, in progressive as well as declining evolution.

In the present investigation we happen to have studied, for reasons of pure comparative anatomy, brains of early Equidae ("vigorous race") together with contemporary brains belonging to groups approaching extinction: *Eohippus* with *Coryphodon*, and *Mesohippus* with *Merycoidodon*. In both cases the structure of the contemporary brains was similar. The latter is a case of two genera of similar body size; the size of the brain was similar in the "declining race" and in the equid form "fitted for long survival."

(3) "In tracing the different groups of mammals, each from the early Tertiary to the present time, it was found that in every series where the material was sufficient to make a fair comparison, the brain-growth had been constant, and followed the same law" (Marsh, 1886, p. 58). The validity of this contention was restricted by data known prior to the present study. Various living mammals have brains in every respect similar to those of their early Tertiary ancestors; the neurological history of mammals as different as Chiroptera and Sirenia demonstrates that, while progressive brain evolution was a widespread phenomenon, it was by no means a universal occurrence in the Mammalia. The horse series rather definitely suggests that "brain-growth" was not necessarily constant in every phase of progressive brain evolution.

In comparing the results of this study with the currently accepted ideas of brain evolution one must, to achieve proper perspective, overcome one's reverence for a century of comparative neurology of mammals, one's awe of data which great scientists have collected, checked, and rechecked with methods unavailable to paleoneurologists, on unlimited amounts of material.

Neoneurological material is derived from a period of animal history whose fauna impresses every brain anatomist with the fact that man is the crown of creation, the ultimate in brain evolution. Below man in the hierarchy of extant animals are the higher mammals; below these are the lower mammals, more primitive in a number of features among which is, quite definitely, the brain. But man's brain has not evolved from that of any of the living higher mammals, nor have any brains of these higher mammals evolved from any brains of the living lower mammals. The extant brains represent the present stage of different evolutionary developments. No living genus is descended from another living genus.

However, comparative neurology generally seems to assume that such evolution took place; that the highest-developed brains have passed, in evolution, through forms represented in other living vertebrates. With very rare exceptions, there is in the neoneurological literature no allusion to the fact that the evolutionary stages from living shark to living man do not illustrate a historical process. At best, it is assumed that the structurally progressive sequence, into which the brains of the hundreds of extant mammalian genera can be arranged, can reveal all possible modes of brain evolution in mammals. The current conception of brain evolution is, therefore, not based on facts but is a working hypothesis.

Our phyletic series of fossil brains, above all, testifies to the fact that under this working hypothesis the major trends of progressive mammalian brain evolution have been correctly derived from comparisons of extant brains. The reasons for this general agreement between neoneurology and paleoneurology appear, to me, obvious when the data of general paleontology are examined. The living lower mammals are the extant representatives of groups whose general organization has changed little since their initial differentiation from the common mammalian stock; the living higher mammals are the products of progressive Tertiary evolution.

Our material shows, however, that in actual, phylogenetic brain evolution there were phases different from the stages of brain evolution existing in living mammals. Consequently, whereas current conceptions of neurological evolution contain the general truths, modification is called for regarding details. The nature of our material suggests that its differences from the evolutionary levels of extant brains are due to a factor not recognizable in the living world; brain evolution seems to have depended on time.

We have mentioned above that the brain did not undergo a definitely progressive development in all mammalian phylogenies. The variety of brains developed in the higher mammals is evidence that there were numerous types of neurological progress during the Tertiary. The phyletic series we have described is one case of one type of progressive brain evolution. It is merely this one case, then, from whose data we derive affirmation, extension, or restriction to current neuro-evolutionary concepts in the features listed below.

I. The following processes, assumed to have occurred in the passage from lower to higher stages of mammalian evolution, have occurred as assumed in the evolution of the horse brain.

(1) When body size increases in evolution, the brain:body ratio decreases. The history of the Equidae may be regarded as a final refutation of the idea that a high ratio of brain volume to body volume is a sign of a high evolutionary level ("brain power" of Marsh and numerous other authors; this criterion of evolution is applicable only to the Anthropoidea, and perhaps only for the brief period in which man has evolved).

(2) Progressive brain evolution (while changing microscopic structures not known in extinct genera) morphologically affects two particular portions of the brain— those termed by L. Edinger neocerebellum and neëncephalon. In the cerebellum of the Equidae, the two neocerebellar lateral lobes have expanded more than the other, paleocerebellar divisions. The neëncephalon is the neocortex; its expansion, involving great enlargement of the cerebral hemispheres, is the dominant feature in the evolution of the horse brain.

(3) The evolutionary course of increasing neocortical dominance in the brain has no relation to body size. The Equidae afford particularly good proof of this theorem, since their osteological and odontological evolution is correlated with their increasing body size. Neocortex expansion, however, progressed in the Early and Middle Eocene times, when no increase in body size occurred; and it appears to have been at a standstill during Middle and Late Oligocene times, while body size continued to gain.

II. In the following features the facts of the fossil record do not fully agree with evolutionary conceptions deduced from conditions in living mammals.

(1) As the evolution of the neocortex consists in the increasing superposition of nonolfactory over olfactory formations, the latter decrease in relative size during progressive brain evolution. Regression of the olfactory brain regions, relative or even absolute, and diminishing importance of the olfactory sense are currently regarded as a universal feature of mammalian evolution. However, in the history of the Equidae a considerable decrease in relative size took place only in the earliest stages, and only with regard to the olfactory bulbs. During their great increase in absolute size from *Eohippus* to *Equus* the bulbi and the cerebral olfactory surfaces decreased so little in relative size that *Equus* appears as macrosmatic as, at least, its post-Eocene ancestors. The relative regression of the olfactory surfaces in mammalian brain evolution must be seen as an expression of the neocortical trend rather than as a trend affecting the olfactory centers. The relative size of the bulbi is not necessarily a criterion of the evolutionary level of a brain.

(2) Among the living mammals with gyrencephalic brains, the larger representatives of each group have more sulci and more-complicated sulci than their smaller congeners. This relation between fissuration and body size is very obvious also in horse evolution. It is particularly well illustrated by changes during the *Merychippus* stage. The smaller, Middle Miocene *Merychippus* had relatively simple sulci. When in the Late Miocene the size of the new-born modern horse had been reached, the fissuration of the *Merychippus* neocortex became more complicated— in fact, similar to that of the horse. However, other stages of brain evolution in the Equidae show that (1) fissuration can increase without increase in body size (this occurred in the transition from *Eohippus* to *Orohippus*); (2) not every increase in body size is accompanied by sulcus complication (in our material, there is very little difference between the fissuration of *Mesohippus* and that of its taller descendant, *Miohippus*).

(3) Among the living mammals, cortex regions which lie medially on the dorsal surface in small ungulates are found dorsally on the medial surface in large ungulates; and a cytoarchitectonic area which is dorsal in lower mammals is median in man.

From these differences it has been concluded that a mediad shift of dorsal cortex is an evolutionary phenomenon of mamals in general, and its meaning has been variously interpreted. In the evolution of the horse brain such a shift has indeed occurred. The endolateral sulcus, which in *Mesohippus* was dorsal, has in *Equus* become a sulcus of the medial wall of the cerebral hemisphere. Posterior as well as anterior medio-dorsal areas have become relatively narrower. However, this process started after the Oligocene, and its rate increased when the cerebrum gained relatively more in height than in the other diameters. During the Eocene and Oligocene, on the contrary, the medio-dorsal area broadened considerably. It follows that a gain of the medial wall cortex at the expense of dorsal areas does not invariably occur in the evolution of larger and higher-developed brains. As the mediad shift of medio-dorsal cortex became particularly manifest in those phases of horse-brain evolution in which the height of the cerebrum and thus the extent of the median wall increased considerably, the phenomenon appears to signify nothing but the presence of a successively larger median facies of the hemispheres. Concomitant with the development of a high cerebrum, the share of median wall cortex in the whole cortex increased.

III. The following trends and conditions, observed in tracing the evolution of the horse brain from the Early Eocene to the Present, have not been found in comparative studies of extant brains.

(1) The fissura prima cerebelli gradually shifted from the posterior region of the dorsal surface to the anterior facies of the vermis. Thus in the evolution of the Equidae the anterior lobe gradually became a smaller portion of the vermis, whereas among living mammals the relative size of the anterior lobe is not distinctive of the evolutionary stage of the brain.

(2) The median vermis lobe showed conspicuous expansion earlier than the lateral lobes of the cerebellum.

(3) The pituitary gland enlarged considerably more than any part of the paleoencephalon. This phenomenon of paleoendocrinology was known to occur in the phylogenetic development of giant reptiles and birds but had not previously been observed in the evolution of large mammals.

(4) The frontal lobe gained more in size than the other regions of the cerebrum. A relatively small or large frontal lobe is, therefore, not—as conditions in living mammals have suggested—characteristic of an order; and the phylogenetic trend to frontal lobe enlargement is not peculiar to the anthropoids.

Frontal lobe cortex includes an agranular (motor association) and a granular (higher association) area. Cytoarchitectonic comparisons of a few lower and a few higher mammals and man have shown that both areas contribute to the so-called "phylogenetic increase in the frontal part of the brain" (Kappers, Huber, and Crosby, 1936, p. 1608), but that this is climaxed by the extraordinary relative extent of the area granularis in man. The distribution of the two areas in the horse is not known. It has been mapped (Rose, 1942) in one other ungulate, the sheep. Rose's description of the "phylogeny" of the granular area may be inserted here as an example of what we have referred to as neoneurological conceptions of evolution (italics mine). "In rodents, insectivores, chiroptera and marsupials no granular frontal cortex has been found so far.   It seems to *appear for the first time* in the ungulates (sheep) as a tiny field, which though *enlarging* in carnivores still remains undifferentiated *until it comes* to the lemurs.   In the lemurs its differentiation *becomes* more clearly marked until it reaches its highest development in primates and particularly in man" (p. 31).

In a really phyletic series, which must include fossil brains, one naturally cannot distinguish the shares of the agranular and granular areas in frontal lobe enlargement. The paleoneurological record of the only previously known phyletic enlargement of the frontal lobe, that during the brief evolution of the Hominidae, consists in no more than that frontal lobe surface is 21–25 per cent of the total endocast surface in stone age men, and 28–31 per cent in living races (Weil, 1929, p. 90).   Our interpretation of such facts rests, of course, on the data provided by neoneurology.   In the case of the Equidae, the similarity of the *Eohippus* cerebrum to that of the lowest living mammals, on the one hand, and the spectacular changes in form and relative size of the frontal lobe from *Eohippus* to *Equus*, on the other hand, suggest the acquisition of the granular area within the evolutionary history of the family.   The presumed acquisition and apparent enlargement of the granular area may mean—to speculate further—acquisition of new, presumably mental faculties by the Equidae during their Tertiary history.   Thus the Equidae possibly are a case of the gradually improving mentality which the anthropocentric Marshs of the Old and New Worlds believed to have been universal throughout animal history, and to play a decisive role in survival.

(5) Increasing dominance of the cerebrum characterizes the vertebrate grades fish—amphibian—reptile—bird—mammal—man.   In the Mammalia it is intimately connected with the trend to neocortical predominance which is currently regarded as a process occurring in the transition from lower to higher mammals.   The process has been verified as a truly evolutionary one in our phyletic series of brains.   However, in the brains of this one family of higher mammals it runs the full course of the stages which are regarded as characteristic of differently classified living Mammalia. Three morphological manifestations of the trend can be distinguished throughout the series of endocranial casts from successive periods: (1) the increase in relative size of the cerebrum, with the most conspicuous step between Early and Middle Eocene; (2) the expansion of the neocortex over the cerebral surface which forces the rhinal fissure downward, a shift hardly perceptible in the series of early genera, in full swing at the beginning of the Miocene; (3) the expansion of the neocortex by infolding with the most remarkable advances between Early and Middle Eocene and between Middle and Late Miocene.

Thus there have existed within one family at different times brain forms as different as those which at the present time are peculiar to a lowly marsupial and to a highly specialized ungulate.

Judged by their living representatives, the ungulate group of mammals has been classified as one of the gyrencephalic orders; extant hoofed mammals have convoluted cerebral hemispheres.   If the early history of the Equidae is taken into consideration, this generalization breaks down, and the little neurological evidence we possess from the early history of other gyrencephalic groups suggests that further investigation will enlarge the scope of this statement.   An ungulate with skull and feet specialized in a way easily recognizable as leading to the horse had, in the Early Eocene, a lissencephalic brain. This equid ungulate had only three short sulci on the cerebrum which, furthermore, did not extend over the midbrain roof. *Eohippus* in fact had a brain which among living mammals is not found in any placental, but whose chief features are characteristic of the brain of the opossum, *Didelphis marsupialis*.

(6) The brains of *Eohippus* and *Didelphis* differ only in minor details, morphologically (differences of internal structure remain, of course, unknown). One appears as much as the other an intermediate between reptilian and typically mammalian brains.

However, in the evolution from this type of brain in *Eohippus* to the brain of the horse, the early stages were not like those suggested by the conditions in living mammals.

Among living mammals the evolutionary level of the brain is correlated with the general evolutionary stage of the group and, within the group, with body size. The cases of opossum and horse illustrate these correlations. *Didelphis* is a very primitive marsupial; the brains of the larger and more specialized kangaroos are far advanced over the stage represented by the opossum brain. *Equus* is a highly specialized, large ungulate; while all living ungulates have brains which are far more highly developed than those of the lower mammals, gyrencephaly, at least, is less developed in the smaller forms. These correlations give standards of comparison valid in the mammals now living; they may possibly be found applicable also to contemporary mammals of other times than the Present.

On the other hand, this scale of standards cannot be applied to the mammals as a whole, Jurassic to Recent. When equid brains of different Tertiary periods are compared, this phyletic series is found to differ from the extant steps of progressiveness in several respects: (1) As has been said above (II, 2), during the Eocene and Oligocene progress of fissuration was not always correlated with gains in body size. (2) During the great advance in brain evolution from *Eohippus* to *Orohippus* there was no concomitant advance in the other parts of the body we know—that is, no osteological or odontological differentiation or size increase. (3) The brain forms of Eocene and Oligocene Equidae are not such as exist today in ungulates of corresponding specialization and size, but are more primitive. The similarity of the *Eohippus* brain to that of a primitive extant marsupial has been mentioned (III, 6). What we know of the brain of *Orohippus* recalls, of living mammals, a tiny subungulate, the hyrax brain. The brains of *Mesohippus* and *Miohippus* are generally comparable to the brains of living artiodactyls of similar size; but their olfactory bulbs were as prominent, and their rhinal fissures were in positions as high as those which in living mammals are characteristic of, for example, the insectivores.

These disagreements with the evolutionary levels represented in extant mammalian brains are not found only in our restricted material of the Equidae. They were observed also in other ungulates contemporary with the early Equidae. Oligocene artiodactyls of *Mesohippus* size differ from their living congeners in the same primitive features of the brain as does *Mesohippus;* their neopallium was smaller, and their olfactory bulbs were not surmounted by the cerebrum to the degree observed in living artiodactyls. In the Early Eocene, ungulates as different as *Eohippus,* *Phenacodus*, and *Coryphodon* had similar brains. Reptilian characters were far more definite in these early placental brains than they are in any placental mammal of the Present.

The ungulates which departed markedly from the standards applicable to Recent forms all lived in the earlier parts of the Tertiary. Time, therefore, appears to be the factor which, besides general evolution and body size, was influential in brain formation.

(7) The reptilian features of Lower Eocene ungulate brains enlarge the significance of the following previous findings in the early history of the higher tetrapods. The only Mesozoic brains of warm-blooded vertebrates known are those of one Upper Jurassic and two Upper Cretaceous birds, and of two Upper Jurassic mammals. While none of these is a complete specimen, enough is preserved in each case to show beyond doubt that if these brains are judged by Recent standards they were reptilian rather than avian or mammalian. The main difference between these endocranial casts and reptilian endocasts is that they are shaped like the brains had been shaped, whereas the reptilian endocranium is generally much more voluminous than the brain. It thus was obvious that during the earliest, Mesozoic history of the warm-blooded classes, when skulls etc. had been, for countless millions of years, avian and mammalian, the brain lagged behind in evolution. The present evidence shows that this discrepancy between osteological and neurological differentiation continued, at least in some of the ungulates, during many millions of years in the Tertiary.

(8) The skull sizes of the Eocene and Oligocene Equidae correspond to those of horse embryos up to birth. In contrast to the relatively slow evolution of the brain in those early phases of equid phylogeny, the brain is a precocious organ in intrauterine ontogeny. One of the differences illustrating the dissimilarity of ontogeny and phylogeny is the fact that the cerebrum is larger and its fissuration is more advanced in horse embryos than in horse ancestors with correspondingly large skulls.

BIBLIOGRAPHY

Abel, O. (1926) *Die Geschichte der Pferde auf dem Boden Nordamerikas*, p. 395–437 *in* Amerikafahrt. Jena (G. Fischer),

———— (1928) *Das biologische Trägheitsgesetz*, Biologia generalis, vol. 4, p.1–102.

Albrecht, P. (1884) *Sur la fossette vermienne du crane des mammifères*, Soc. d'anthrop. de Bruxelles, Bull., 1884, p. 136–151.

Alouf, I. (1929) *Die vergleichende Cytoarchitektonik der Area striata*, Jour. für Psychol. Neurol., vol. 38, p. 5–41.

Anthony, R., and de Grzybowski, J. (1930) *Le néopallium des Equidés: étude du développement et de ses plissements*, Jour. Anat., vol. 64, p. 147–169.

Ärnbäck-Christie-Linde, A. (1900) *Zur Anatomie des Gehirnes niederer Säugetiere*, Anat. Anzeiger, vol. 18, p. 8–16.

Baum, H. (1894) *Die Nasenhöhle und ihre Nebenhöhlen (Stirn- und Kieferhöhle) beim Pferde*, Arch. wiss. prakt. Thierheilkunde, vol. 20, p. 89–170.

Beddard, F.E. (1909) *Contributions to the anatomy of certain Ungulata, including* Tapirus, Hyrax, *and* Antilocapra, Zool. Soc. London, Proc. 1909 (I), p. 160–197.

Black, D. (1915) *A study of the endocranial casts of* Ocapia, Giraffa *and* Samotherium, *with special reference to the convolutional pattern in the family of Giraffidae*, Jour. Comp. Neurol., vol. 25, p. 329–360.

———— (1920–1921) *Studies on endocranial anatomy. II. The endocranial anatomy of* Oreodon, Jour. Comp. Neurol., vol. 32, p. 271–327.

Bolk, L. (1906) *Das Cerebellum der Säugetiere*, Jena & Haarlem, 338 pages. Also in: Petrus Camper vol. 3 (1904–1905), p. 1–136, 485–598; vol. 4 (1906), p. 115–194.

Bonin, G. von (1937) *Brain-weight and body-weight of mammals*, Jour. gen. Psychol., vol. 16, 379–389.

Bradley, O. C. (1899) *The convolutions of the cerebrum of the horse*, Jour. Anat. Physiol., vol. 33, p. 215–227.

———— (1903) *On the development and homology of the mammalian cerebellar fissures, Part II*, Jour. Anat. Physiol., vol. 37, p. 221–240.

———— (1904) *The mammalian cerebellum: its lobes and fissures*, Jour. Anat. Physiol., vol., 38, p. 448–475.

Brême, G. (1903) *Über die durch die Pacchionische Granulationen verursachten Eindrücke der Schädelknochen*, Zeitschr. Morph. Anthr., vol. 5, p. 415–437.

Brodmann, K. (1906) *Beiträge zur histologischen Lokalisation der Grosshirnrinde. Fünfte Mitteilung. Über den allgemeinen Bau des Cortex pallii unter den Mammaliern und zwei homologe Rindenfelder im besonderen. Zugleich ein Beitrag zur Furchenlehre*, Jour. für. Psychol. Neurol., vol. 6, p. 275–400.

Brydon, R. (1890) *Shetland ponies*, Jour. Royal Agric. Soc. England, ser. 3, vol. 1, p. 207–210.

Burkholder, J. F. (1904) *The anatomy of the brain*, Chicago (Engelhard & Co.).

Chubb, S. H. *The horse under domestication*, pp. 38–69 *in:* Evolution of the horse, Am. Mus., Guide Leaflet Ser., no. 36, 7th ed.

Ciurlo, L. (1932) *La fossa subarcuata del temporale nei mammiferi. Ricerche morfologiche ed embriologiche*, Arch. ital. di Otol., Rinol. e Laringol., vol. 43, p. 707–737.

Clark, W. E. Le Gros (1932) *The brain of the Insectivora*, Zool. Soc. London, Proc. 1932, II, p. 975–1013.

Colbert, E. H. (Manuscript) *A list of measurements of the skeletons of Equidae mounted in the American Museum of Natural History.*

Cook, H. T. and Gregory, J. T. (1941) Mesogaulus praecursor, *a new rodent from the Miocene of Nebraska*, Jour. Paleont., vol. 15, p. 549–552.

Cope, E. D. (1884) *The Vertebrata of the Tertiary formations of the west. Book I*, U. S. Geol. Survey Territories, Report, vol. 3, p. 1–1009.

———— **and Matthew, W. D.** (1915) *Hitherto unpublished plates of Tertiary Mammalia and Permian Vertebrata*, Am. Mus. Nat. Hist., Monograph ser., no. 2.

Cornevin, C. (1889) *Examen comparé de la capacité crânienne dans les diverses races des espèces domestiques*, Jour. de méd. vét. et de zootechnie, ser. 3, vol. 14, p. 8–13.

Cuvier, G. (1882) *Recherches sur les ossemens fossiles*, Nouv. éd., tome troisième, Paris (G. Dufour).

Dacqué, E. (1935) *Organische Morphologie und Palaeontologie*, Berlin (Bornträger).

dal Piaz, G. (1905) *Sugli avanzi di Cyrtodelphis sulcatus dell' Arenaria di Belluno*, Palaeontogr. ital., vol. 11, p. 253–279.

Denker, A. (1899) *Zur vergleichenden Anatomie des Gehörorgans der Säugetiere*, Anat. Hefte II (Erg. Anat. Entwgesch.), vol. 9, p. 297–325.

Dietrich, W. O. (1936) *Die Huftiere aus dem Obereozän von Mähringen auf der Ulmer Alb*, Palaeontographica 83, A, p. 163–209.

Dräseke, J. (1903) *Das Gehirn der Chiropteren*, Monatsschr. für. Psychiatrie Neurol., vol. 13, p. 448–463.

Dubois, E. (1923) *Phylogenetic and ontogenetic increase of the volume of the brain in Vertebrata*, Kon. Akad. Wetensch. Amsterdam, Proc., vol. 25, p. 230–255.

Dunn, H. L. (1921) *The growth of the central nervous system in the human fetus as expressed by graphic analysis and empirical formulae*, Jour. Comp. Neurol., vol. 33, p. 405–491.

Economo, C. v. (1929a) *Wie sollen wir Elitegehirne verarbeiten?* Zeitschr. f. d. ges. Neurol. u. Psychiatrie, vol. 121, p. 323–409.

———— (1929b) *Der Zellaufbau der Grosshirnrinde und die progressive Cerebration*, Ergeb. Physiol., vol. 29, p. 83–128.

Edinger, L. (1908) *Vorlesungen über den Bau der nervösen Zentralorgane des Menschen und der Tiere*, Zweiter Band. Vergleichende Anatomie des Gehirns. 7. Aufl. Leipzig (F. C. W. Vogel).

———— (1910) *Über die Einteilung des Cerebellums*, Anat. Anzeiger, vol. 35, p. 319–323.

Edinger, T. (1928) *Über einige fossile Gehirne*, Palaeont. Zeitschr., vol. 9, p. 379–402.

———— (1929) *Die fossilen Gehirne*, Berlin (J. Springer), and Erg. Anat. Entwgesch., vol. 28, p. 1–249.

———— (1933a) *Die Foramina parietalia der Säugetiere*, Zeitschr. Anat. Entwgesch., vol. 102, p. 266–289.

———— (1933b) *Über Gehirne tertiärer Sirenia Ägyptens und Mitteleuropas sowie der rezenten Seekühe*, Bayer. Akad. d. Wiss., Abh., Neue Folge, vol. 20, p. 1–36.

———— (1937) *Palaeoneurologie*, Fortschr. Paläont., vol. I, p. 235–251.

———— (1941) *Phylogeny of the equid brain*, Geol. Soc. Am., Bull., vol. 52, p. 1966.

———— (1942) *The pituitary body in giant animals, fossil and living*, Quart. Rev. Biol., vol. 17, p. 31–45.

Ellenberger, W. (1892) *Die Furchen der Grosshirnoberfläche des Pferdes, der Wiederkäuer und des Schweines*, Arch. f. wiss. u. prakt. Thierheilkunde, vol. 18, p. 267–291.

Ewart, J. C. (1904) *The multiple origin of horses and ponies*, Highland and Agric. Soc. Scotland, Trans., ser. 5, vol. 16, p. 230–268.

Fiske, E. W. (1913) *An elementary study of the brain, based on the dissection of the brain of the sheep*, New York (Macmillan.)

Flatau, E. and Jacobsohn, L. (1899) *Handbuch der Anatomie und vergleichenden Anatomie des Centralnervensystems der Säugetiere*, I. Berlin (S. Karger).

Flower, W. H. (1891) *The horse. A study in natural history.* London (Kegan Paul, Trench, Trübner & Co.).

Forster, A. (1927) *La lame criblée de l'ethmoïde. Etude morphologique*, Archives d'Anat. Histol. Embryol., vol. 7, p. 79–131.

Frisch, K. V. (1926) *Vergleichende Physiologie des Geruchs- und Geschmackssinnes*, Handb. d. norm. u. pathol. Physiol., vol. 11, p. 203–239.

Frye, J. C. and Hibbard, C. W. (1941) *Pliocene and Pleistocene stratigraphy and paleontology of the Meade basin, southwestern Kansas*, State Geol. Surv. Kansas, Bull., vol. 38, p. 389–424.

Garrod, A. H. (1885) *On the brain and other parts of the Hippopotamus* (H. amphibius), Zool. Soc. London, Trans., vol. 11, p. 11–17.

Gervais, P. (1872) *Mémoire sur les formes cérébrales propres a différents groupes de mammifères*, Jour. Zoologie, vol. 1, p. 425–469.

Gidley, T. W. (1900) *A new species of Pleistocene horse from the Staked Plains of Texas*, Am. Mus. Nat. Hist., Bull., vol. 13, p. 111–116.

———— (1901) *Tooth characters and revision of the North American species of the genus* Equus, Am. Mus. Nat. Hist., Bull., vol. 14, p. 91–141.

———— (1903) *A new three-toed horse,* Am. Mus. Nat. Hist., Bull., vol. 19, p. 465–476.

Granger, W. (1908) *A revision of the American Eocene horses,* Am. Mus. Nat. Hist., Bull., vol. 24, p. 221–264.

Haller von Hallerstein, V. (1934) *Äussere Gliederung des Zentralnervensystems,* Handb. d. vergl. Anat. d. Wirbelt., vol. 2, I, p. 1–318.

Hay, O. P. (1913) *Notes on some fossil horses, with descriptions of four new species,* U. S. Nat. Mus., Proc., vol. 44, p. 569–594.

Hilzheimer, M. (1926) *Natürliche Rassengeschichte der Haussäugetiere,* Berlin and Leipzig (de Gruyter).

Hofmann, M. (1900) *Zur vergleichenden Anatomie der Gehirn- und Rückenmarksarterien der Vertebraten,* Zeitschr. Morphol. Anthropol., vol. 2, p. 247–322.

———— (1901) *Zur vergleichenden Anatomie der Gehirn- und Rückenmarksvenen der Vertebraten,* Zeitschr. Morphol. Anthropol., vol. 3, p. 239–299.

Holl, M. (1900) *Über die Insel des Ungulatengehirnes,* Arch. f. Anat. u. Physiol., Anat. Abt. (Arch. Anat. Entwgesch.) 1900, p. 295–334.

Hürzeler, J. (1936) *Osteologie und Odontologie der Caenotheriden,* Abh. Schweiz. Paläont. Ges., vol. 58, p. 1–112.

Kappers, C. U. A. (1928) *The influence of the cephalization coefficient and body size upon the form of the forebrain in mammals,* Kon. Akad. Wetensch. Amsterdam, Proc., vol. 31, p. 65–80.

———— (1936) *The endocranial casts of the Ehringsdorf and Home soloensis skulls,* Jour. of Anat., vol. 71, p. 61–76.

————, Huber, G. C., and Crosby, E. C. (1936) *The comparative anatomy of the nervous system of vertebrates, including man.* I, II, New York (Macmillan).

Köppel, A. (1898) *Vergleichende Bestimmungen des Innenvolumens der Rückgrat- und Schädelhöhle bei Menschen und Thieren,* Archiv f. Anthropologie, vol. 25, p. 171–184.

Kohlbrugge, J. H. F. (1902) *Die Grosshirnfurchen von Tragulus javanicus, Cervulus muntjac und Sus babirussa,* Monatsschr. f. Psychiatrie u. Neurol., vol. 11, p. 344–358.

Koller, R. (1922) *Zur vergleichenden Anatomie der Hypophysenumgebung,* Zeitschr. Anat. Entwgesch., vol. 65, p. 183–203.

Krueg, J. (1878) *Über die Furchung der Grosshirnrinde der Ungulaten,* Zeitschr. wissensch. Zool., vol. 31, p. 297–345.

———— (1880) *Über die Furchen auf der Grosshirnrinde der zonoplacentalen Säugethiere,* Zeitschr. wissensch. Zool., vol. 33, p. 595–672.

Kubacska, A. (1932) *Paläobiologische Untersuchungen aus Ungarn. C. Schädelfragment, Nasen- und Hirnhöhle-Steinkerne eines plistozänen Equiden aus Gyügy,* Geologica hungarica, ser. palaeont. vol. 10, p. 57–65.

Kuithan, W. (1895) *Die Entwicklung des Kleinhirns bei Säugetieren,* Münchener mediz. Abh., VII. Reihe, Heft 6, p. 1–40.

Landacre, F. L. (1930) *The major and minor sulci of the brain of the sheep,* Ohio Jour. Sci., vol. 30, p. 36–51.

Lange, S. J. de. (1911) *Das Vorderhirn der Reptilien,* Folia neurobiol., vol. 5, p. 548–597.

Lartet, E. (1868) *De quelques cas de progression organique vérifiables dans la succession des temps géologiques sur des mammifères de même famille et de même genre,* Acad. Sci. Paris, Compte Rendu, vol. 66, p. 1119–1122.

Le Double, A.-F. (1902) *La fossette cérébelleuse moyenne est-elle un stigmate anatomique caractéristique du criminel-né?* Bibliographie anatomique, vol. 11, p. 56–78.

Legge, F. and Lanzilloti-Buonsanti, A. (1884) *Contribuzioni allo studio delle circonvoluzioni cerebrali del cavallo,* Clinica veterinaria, vol. 7 (not seen).

Loo, Y. T. (1930) *The forebrain of the opossum,* Didelphis virginiana. *Part I. Gross anatomy,* Jour. comp. neurol., vol. 51, p. 13–64.

Loomis, F. B. (1926) *The evolution of the horse,* Boston (Marshall Jones).

Lothringer, S. (1886) *Untersuchungen an der Hypophyse einiger Säugethiere und des Menschen,* Arch. f. mikrosk. Anat., vol. 28, p. 257–292.

Marcou, J. (1896) *Life, letters and works of Louis Agassiz,* New York (Macmillan and Co.).

Marsh, O. C. (1884) *Dinocerata*, U.S. Geol. Surv., Mon., vol. 10, p. 1-XVIII, 1-237.

Matthes, E. (1934) *Geruchsorgan*, Handb. d. vergl. Anat. d. Wirbelt. 2. Bd., 2. Hälfte, p. 879-948.

Matthew, W. D. (1924) *Third contribution to the Snake Creek fauna*, Am. Mus. Nat. Hist., Bull., vol. 50, p. 59-210.

———— (1926) *The evolution of the horse. A record and its interpretation*, Quart. Rev. Biol., vol. 1, p. 139-185.

———— *Evolution of the horse in nature*, pp. 8-37 *in:* Evolution of the Horse, Am. Mus., Guide Leaflet Ser., no. 36, 7th ed.

———— **and Gidley, J. W.** (1906) *New or little known mammals from the Miocene of South Dakota*, Am. Mus. Nat. Hist., Bull., vol. 22, p. 135-153.

McGrew, P. O. (1938) *The Burge fauna, a Lower Pliocene mammalian assemblage from Nebraska*, Univ. Calif. Publ., Bull., Dept. Geol. Sci., vol. 24, no. 11, p. 309-328.

Megaw, B. R. S. (1943) *The Manx pony: A descendant of the British prehistoric horse*, Manx Mus., Jour., vol. 5, p. 100-103.

Merriam, J. C. (1913) *Preliminary report on the horses of Rancho la Brea*, Univ. Calif. Publ., Bull. Dept. Geol. Sci., vol. 1 (no. 21), p. 397-418.

Mobilio, C. (1914) *Il mantello cerebrale degli equidi. Difference tra l'* equus caballus, eq. asinus, eq. mulus *et* hinnus, Arch. ital. Anat. Embriol., vol. 13, p. 114-271.

———— (1915) *Encefalo e sue parti e capacità cranica in rapporto al peso del corpo e fra loro negli Equidi*, Monitore zool. ital. vol. 26, p. 273-304.

Moodie, R. L. (1922) *On the endocranial anatomy of some Oligocene and Pleistocene mammals*, Jour. comp. Neur., vol. 34, p. 342-379.

Mortimer, H. (1938) *The influence of the anterior pituitary on cranial form and structure*, in: *The pituitary gland*, Assoc. Res. in Nerv. and Ment. Disease, Research Pub., vol. 17, p. 222-238.

Neal, H. V. and Rand, H. W. (1936) *Comparative anatomy*, Philadelphia (Blakiston).

Osborn, H. F. (1890) *Preliminary account of the fossil mammals from the White River and Loup Fork formations, contained in the Museum of Comparative Zoology. Perissodactyla*, Harvard Univ., Mus. Comp. Zool., Bull., vol. 20, p. 87-100.

———— (1918) *Equidae of the Oligocene, Miocene and Pliocene of North America, Iconographic type revision*, Am. Mus. Nat. Hist., Mem., New Series, vol. 2, p. 1-330.

———— (1929) *The titanotheres of ancient Wyoming, Dakota and Nebraska*, U. S. Geol. Surv., Mon., 55, vol. II.

Palmer, R. W. (1913) *The brain and brain-case of a fossil ungulate of the genus* Anoplotherium, Zool. Soc. London, Proc. 1913 (II), p. 878-893.

Putnam, T. J. and Davidoff, L. M. (1938) *Acromegaly*, In: *The pituitary gland*, Assoc. Res. in Nerv. and Mental Disease, Res. Pub., vol. 17, p. 714-724.

Reeve, E. C. R. and Murray, P. D. F. (1942) *Evolution in the horse's skull*, Nature, vol. 150, p. 402-403.

Riese, W. (1943) *The cellular structure of the marsupialian cortex*, Le naturaliste Canadien, vol. 70, p. 139-144.

———— (1945) *Structure and function of the brain of the opossum (Didelphis virginiana) at the time of birth*, Jour. Mammal., vol. 26, p. 148-153.

Robb, R. C. (1935) *A study of mutations in evolution. I. Evolution in the equine skull. II. Ontogeny in the equine skull*, Jour. Genetics, vol. 31, p. 39-52.

Rogner, V. (1883) *Über das Variieren der Grosshirnfurchen bei Lepus, Ovis und Sus*, Zeitschr. wiss. Zool., vol. 39, p. 596-614.

Romer, A. S. (1933) *Vertebrate paleontology*, Chicago (Univ. Chicago Press).

Rose, J. E. (1942) *A cytoarchitectural study of the sheep cortex*, Jour. comp. Neurol., vol. 76, p. 1-55.

Saito, J. (1923) *Untersuchungen über die Hypophysengewichte von Pferden*, Biochem. Zeitschr., vol. 142, p. 308-311.

Scharrer, E. (1936) *Das Zentralnervensystem*, Bronn's Klassen und Ordnungen des Tierreichs, 6.Bd., V.Abt., Säugetiere; 3.Buch, Teil I, 1. Liefrg., p. 1-169.

Schlaikjer, E. M. (1935) *Contributions to the stratigraphy and palaeontology of the Goshen Hole Area, Wyoming. IV. New vertebrates and the stratigraphy of the Oligocene and early Miocene*, Harvard Univ., Mus. Comp. Zool., Bull., vol. 76, p. 95-189.

———— (1937) *A study of* Parahippus wyomingensis *and a discussion of the phylogeny of the genus,* Harvard Univ., Mus. Comp. Zool., Bull., vol. 80, p. 253–280.

Schotterer, A. (1931) *Über grundsätzliche Eigentümlichkeiten im Skelettbau der Zwergpferde,* Zeitschr. für Säugetierk., vol. 6, p. 85–132.

Schultz, J. R. (1938) *A late Quaternary mammal fauna from the tar seeps of Mc Kittrick, California,* Carnegie Inst. Washington, Pub. no. 487, p. 111–215.

Scott, W. B. (1891) *On the osteology of* Mesohippus *and* Leptomeryx, *with observations on the modes and factors of evolution in the Mammalia,* Jour. Morphol., vol. 5, p. 301–406.

———— (1894) *The Mammalia of the Deep River beds,* Am. Philos. Soc., Trans., vol. 18, p. 55–185.

———— (1937) *A history of land mammals in the western hemisphere,* New York (Macmillan).

———— (1941) *The mammalian fauna of the White River Oligocene. V. Perissodactyla,* Am. Philos. Soc., Trans., New Ser., vol. 28, p. 747–980.

Seton, E. Th. (1928) *Lives of game animals,* vol. IV, Garden City, N. Y. (Doubleday, Doran & Co.).

Simionescu, I. (1934) *Sur quelques cerveaux fossiles du Néogène de Roumanie,* Soc. Romậne de Géol., Bull., vol. 2, p. 162–172.

Simpson, G. G. (1927) *Mesozoic Mammalia. IX. The brain of Jurassic mammals,* Am. Jour. Sci., ser. 5, vol. 14, p. 259–268.

———— (1932a) *Skulls and brains of some mammals from the* Notostylops *beds of Patagonia,* Amer. Mus. Nat. Hist., Novitates, no. 578, p. 1–11.

———— (1932b) *Mounted skeletons of* Eohippus, Merychippus *and* Hesperosiren, Amer. Mus. Novitates, No. 587, p. 1–7.

———— (1933) *Braincasts of* Phenacodus, Notostylops, *and* Rhyphodon, Am. Mus. Nov., no. 622, p. 1–19.

Sisson, S. (1917) *The anatomy of the domestic animals,* 2nd ed. (3d ed., revised by T. D. Grossmann, 1938) Philadelphia and London (W. B. Saunders).

Smith, G. E. (1902) *Descriptive and illustrated catalogue of the physiological series of comparative anatomy, contained in the Museum of the Royal College of Surgeons of England,* 2d ed., vol. 2.

Stirton, R. A. (1940) *Phylogeny of North American Equidae,* Univ. Calif. Pub., Dept. Geol. Sci. Bull., vol. 25, p. 165–198.

Thorpe, M. R. (1937) *The Merycoidodontidae, an extinct group of ruminant mammals,* Peabody Mus. Nat. Hist., Mem., vol. 3, pt. 4, XXI and 309 pp.

Tilney, F. (1931) *Fossil brains of some early Tertiary mammals of North America,* Neurol. Inst. New York, Bull., vol. 1, p. 430–505.

Trautmann (1909) *Die makroskopischen Verhältnisse der Hypophyse einiger Säuger,* Arch. f. wiss. u. prakt. Tierheilk., vol. 35, p. 614–637.

Turner, W. (1890–1891) *The convolutions of the brain: a study in comparative anatomy,* Jour. Anat. Physiol., vol. 25, p. 105–153.

Voris, H. C. and Hoerr, N. L. (1932) *The hindbrain of the opossum,* Didelphis virginiana, Jour. Comp. Neurol., vol. 54, p. 277–355.

Walter, H. E. (1939) *Biology of the vertebrates,* New York (Macmillan).

Weber, M. (1928) *Die Säugetiere,* Band II. Jena (G. Fischer).

Weil, A. (1929) *Measurements of cerebral and cerebellar surfaces. Comparative studies of the surfaces of endocranial casts of man, prehistoric men, and anthropoid apes,* Amer. Jour. phys. Anthropol., vol. 13, p. 69–90.

Weinberg, R. (1903) *Fossile Hirnformen. I.* Anchilophus Desmaresti, Zeitschr. wiss. Zool., vol. 74, p. 491–500.

Wells, L. H. (1939) *The endo-cranial cast in recent and fossil Hyraces (Procaviidae),* S. African Jour. Sci., vol. 36, p. 365–373.

Wood, H. E. (1934) *Revision of the Hyrachyidae,* Am. Mus. Nat. Hist., Bull., vol. 67, p. 181–295.

Zannini, P. (1922) *Der Canalis craniopharyngeus beim Pferde,* Anat. Anz., vol. 55, p. 441–456.

Ziehen, T. (1906) *Die Morphogenie des Centralnervensystems der Säugetiere.* O. Hertwig's Handb. vergl. u. exper. Entwickelungslehre d. Wirbelt., 2.Bd., 3.Teil, p. 273–394.

Zinram, K. (1931) *Eine neue Methode zur Darstellung von Hohlräumen in Knochen,* Anat. Anz., vol. 71, p. 401–419.

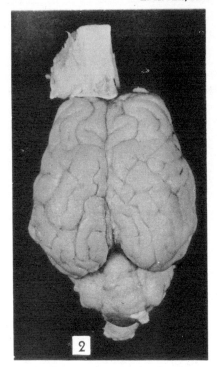
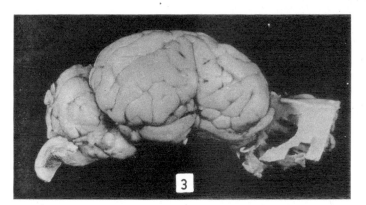
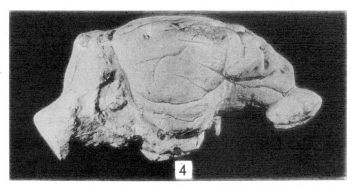

1. *Mesohippus bairdii*, endocranial cast (specimen no. VI); 2, 3, *Ovis aries*, brain, with parts of left frontal and ethmoidal bones in situ. Dorsal views. 4. *Cephalophus nataliensis*, endocranial cast. Right side views. × about $\frac{4}{5}$ (p. 58).

MESOHIPPUS, OVIS, AND *CEPHALOPHUS*

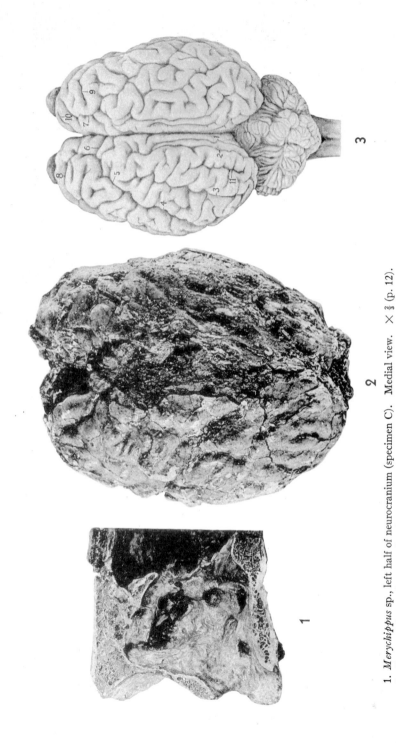

1. *Merychippus* sp., left half of neurocranium (specimen C). Medial view. $\times \frac{2}{3}$ (p. 12).
2. *Equus niobrarensis*, natural endocast of cranium roof. Dorsal view. $\times \frac{2}{3}$ (p. 98).
3. *Equus caballus*, brain in dorsal view, after Sisson; Sisson's figure, "about $\frac{5}{7}$ nat. size," reduced to $\frac{2}{3}$: approximately $\frac{1}{2}$ natural size; lettering 5–11 are added. *1*, Sulcus endolateralis; *2*, S. lateralis; *3*, S. ectolateralis; *4*, S. suprasylvius; *5*, S. cruciatus; *6*, S. ansatus; *7*, S. coronalis; *8*, S. praesylvius; *9*, S. diagonalis; *10*, S. orbitalis; *11*, S. interlateralis dorsalis.

1

2

Plaster endocranial cast.   1. Dorsal, 2. left side views.   × about $\frac{2}{3}$ (p. 99).

EQUUS OCCIDENTALIS

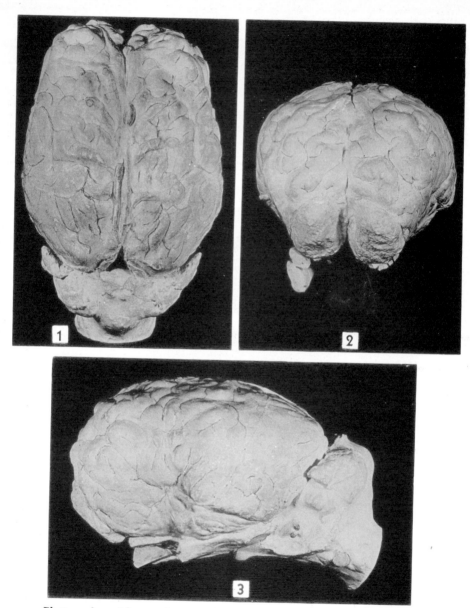

Plaster endocranial cast.   1. Dorsal, 2. anterior, 3. left side views.   × ⁴⁄₇ (p. 100).

SHETLAND PONY

INDEX

175